D1163682

TREATMENT OF

Experimental Data

ARCHIE G. WORTHING
UNIVERSITY OF PITTSBURGH

JOSEPH GEFFNER
WEIRTON STEEL COMPANY

FIRST EDITION
SECOND PRINTING

NEW YORK: JOHN WILEY & SONS, INC.
LONDON: CHAPMAN & HALL, LIMITED

ᴜGᴇ

IN THE REPRINTING OF THIS BOOK, THE RECOMMENDATIONS OF THE WAR PRODUCTION BOARD HAVE BEEN OBSERVED FOR THE CONSERVATION OF PAPER AND OTHER IMPORTANT WAR MATERIALS.   THE CONTENT REMAINS COMPLETE AND UNABRIDGED.

PREFACE

This book is in part a consequence of a long series of irritations on the part of the senior author. During the course of years he encountered too often tables of unsmoothed values, tables without descriptive legends or with inadequate legends, graphs with poorly chosen coordinate scales, graphs without accompanying descriptive legends and occasionally without indication as to what the coordinates themselves represented, references to the significance of a so-called knee of a curve when the location of the knee was a function of the chosen coordinate scales, lack of understanding of how to determine, to express, and to apply precision indexes, blind faith in a least squares computation regardless of the assumptions and limitations, and many other faults which may be remedied with reasonable effort. For several years, this author has offered a course for graduate students entitled *Treatment of Experimental Data* in which such matters among others have been discussed. The present textbook is an outgrowth of that course.

This book has been written with the physicist, the chemist, and the engineer in mind. The authors feel that, for a very large percentage of them, the book has a worth-while message. Although obviously the discussions are necessarily rather mathematical, considerable effort has been made to keep physical situations in mind throughout.

We have generally steered away from the statistical treatment of quantum mechanics on the one hand and of business and educational theory on the other hand. We do, however, include a chapter on correlation.

As determinants shorten and simplify many treatments, they have been used in discussions wherever convenient. Recognizing, however, that many users of this text may need to have their memories refreshed with regard to methods of use, *A Brief Discussion of Determinant Methods* has been included as Appendix 1. In the discussion there given, particular attention has been paid to the processes of setting up, simplifying, and evaluating and to their application in solving simultaneous equations and in determining the equations of curves. The convenience obtained and the time saved by the use of determinants should be better known.

The text, despite much care, probably contains many errors. Some of them undoubtedly reflect lack of knowledge on the part of the authors,

iii

others have crept in by various paths. Whatever their origins, it is hoped that those who discover them will be kind enough to notify the authors.

A. G. WORTHING
JOSEPH GEFFNER

PITTSBURGH, PA.
May 1943

CONTENTS

SYMBOLS FREQUENTLY USED IN DISCUSSIONS OF METHOD TOGETHER WITH THEIR MEANINGS

[Symbols concerned with Fourier Series expansions are defined at appropriate places in Chapter V]

a, $a_{\overline{X}}$, $a_{\overline{Y}}$, etc.	Average deviations for a single reading and for the means $\overline{X}$, $\overline{Y}$, etc.
f	Frequency of occurrence of a particular value in a series of readings.
h, $h_{\overline{X}}$, $h_{\overline{Y}}$, etc.	Modulus of precision for a single reading and for the means $\overline{X}$, $\overline{Y}$, etc.
k_1, k_2, etc.	Least squares factors entering Cox and Matuschak Tables.
m	Order number of an item in a series of n items.
n	Number of items in a series under consideration.
p, $p_{\overline{X}}$, $p_{\overline{Y}}$, etc.	Probable error for single reading and for the means $\overline{X}$, $\overline{Y}$, etc.
P_x, P_{hx}, $P_{x/\sigma}$, $P_{x/p}$	Probability of occurrence of a deviation between $-x$ and $+x$, $-hx$ and $+hx$, $-x/\sigma$ and $+x/\sigma$, $-x/p$ and $+x/p$.
ΔP_x	Probability of occurrence of a deviation between x and $x + \Delta x$.
P_y	Probable error with respect to a line of regression of Y on X.
Q_1, $Q_2 \cdots Q_k$	Values obtained by adjusting means $\overline{X}_1$, $\overline{X}_2$, $\cdots \overline{X}_k$ of quantities interrelated by certain known or assumed laws.
r	Correlation coefficient.
S_y	Standard error of estimate of Y of the regression line of Y on X.
U, $\overline{U}$, u	$f(X, Y, Z)$, $f(\overline{X}, \overline{Y}, \overline{Z})$, $f(x, y, z)$.
w, $w_{\overline{X}}$, $w_{\overline{Y}}$, etc.	Weight assigned to a single reading and to the means $\overline{X}$, $\overline{Y}$, etc.
X, X_1, X_2, etc.	Individual measurements of a quantity.
$\overline{X}$	Arithmetic mean of X_1, $X_2 \cdots X_n$.
$\overline{\overline{X}}$	A grand mean, an arithmetic mean of $\overline{X}_1$, $\overline{X}_2 \cdots \overline{X}_n$.
$\overline{X}'$	An assumed, rounded off approximation to $\overline{X}$.
$\overline{X}''$	A pseudo mean for X_1, $X_2 \cdots X_n$ whose value depends on the method of taking the mean.
x, x_1, x_2, etc.	Deviations of X, X_1, X_2, etc., from $\overline{X}$. Or independent measurements of a quantity for cases where the deviation from the mean is not of concern.
Y, Y_1, Y_2, etc. $\left.\begin{array}{l}\\ \\\end{array}\right\}$ $\overline{Y}$, y, y_1, y_2, etc.	Quantities similar to corresponding X and x quantities.
Z, Z_1, Z_2, etc. $\left.\begin{array}{l}\\ \\\end{array}\right\}$ $\overline{Z}$, z, z_1, z_2, etc.	Quantities similar to corresponding X and x quantities.
Z	Special function of correlation coefficient r introduced by Fisher because of the skew distribution of the latter quantity.
Δ	The correction to an assumed $\overline{X}'$ to yield $\overline{X}$; or the correction applied to a measured $\overline{X}$ to yield the adjusted mean, Q; or an operator indicating a finite increment.
ρ	Index of correlation for nonlinear correlation.
σ, $\sigma_{\overline{X}}$, $\sigma_{\overline{Y}}$, etc.	Standard deviation for a single reading and for the means $\overline{X}$, $\overline{Y}$, etc.

CHAPTER I

REPRESENTATION OF DATA BY TABLES

1. Introduction. All of us, whether we realize it or not, are continually making measurements. Such actions as noting the time of day, weighing oneself, and feeling the temperature of a tub of water with one's hand or foot are typical commonplace observations. Usually the results of such observations are easily obtained, of little consequence, and soon forgotten. However, measurements made by a tailor in fitting a suit of clothes, a physician in diagnosing a disease, or a physicist in measuring the speed of light are of greater significance. Here the accuracy of the measurements is a matter of concern; and it is often necessary that the measurements be analyzed to obtain the desired final result. It is usually important that the results be preserved, at least temporarily; and it is desirable to present them in a form convenient for use and readily understood by others. It is with such problems that this book is concerned.

All data, unless scattered, are encountered and dealt with in the form of tables, graphs, or equations. It is appropriate, therefore, that we begin with a discussion of these three devices for representing data, pointing out the advantages and disadvantages of each, describing the rules for their proper usage, and illustrating the applications for which each is best suited. Since original data are usually first tabulated, then graphed, and finally perhaps expressed as equations, we consider first the methods and principles of tabular representation.

All measurements involve at least two variables, one assumed independent and the other dependent. In the simplest measurements, the independent variable is ignored. Thus, recognizing the fact that apples, on standing, lose weight by evaporation of water through the skins, we may consider the weight of a bag of apples as a function of the time elapsed since picking. Generally, though, the observation that a bag of apples weighs 5 pounds contains all the information desired; it adds nothing to specify the time, the independent variable. More often, we are interested in both dependent and independent variables, and frequently in the relationship between them. In the tabular representation of data, the assumed dependent and independent variables and their relationship—if one exists—are expressed by listing corresponding values

1

or properties of the variables in an orderly arrangement. As illustrated by newspaper radio programs, stock-market reports, railroad timetables, logarithm tables, and trigonometric tables, there are many types.

In this chapter we shall first discuss the general advantages of tables, and then give the structural forms of each of three types. Specific rules are included for the construction of the one showing $y = f(x)$, together with two simple methods of smoothing data. The important problem of interpolation is discussed, and several interpolation formulas are developed and illustrated. The chapter concludes with a discussion of extrapolation.

2. Advantages of Tables. In favor of tables generally, it may be said that (a) they are simple and inexpensive to construct, requiring no special types of paper, curve forms, etc.; (b) they permit easy reference to data; (c) they facilitate comparisons of values, and (d) they provide a compact form for filing. In certain applications they possess special advantages. Thus, a table may show variations for several dependent variables as satisfactorily as for just one. It would be difficult to present the same data on a single graph without confusion. The table is generally preferable to the graph for presenting data which may be classified and subclassified in various ways. Finally, when the table is of the type showing $y = f(x)$, the element $f(x)$ can often be differentiated or integrated directly from the table to the desired accuracy without knowledge of its mathematical form, and with less labor than is involved when a graph is used.

3. Types of Tables. Tables may be grouped into three general classes. The first and least important class—the qualitative class—contains those tables which relate quantities in a qualitative way. Table I is a typical example. Its construction and interpretation are sufficiently simple to require no explanation. The occurrence of the qualitative table is relatively infrequent despite the fact that it contains data which cannot be well presented in any other way.

The second class of tables—the statistical class—contains tables in which some of the variables are expressed quantitatively, while others, usually including the variable assumed independent, are not. (See Table II.) This class includes most statistical tables such as those in the *World Almanac* and U. S. Census reports, tables of equivalents, and the periodic table of the chemical elements.

The third class of tables—the functional class—is composed of tables which show one or more relations of the type $y = f(x)$. Table III is a typical example.

We are here principally concerned with the construction and interpretation of tables of the second and third classes.

TABLE I. An Example of the Qualitative Type of Table

Parallelism of Physical Theories [1]

THEORIES OF LIGHT	THEORIES OF MATTER
1. *Corpuscular Theory:* Corpuscles obey Newton's laws of mechanics.	1. *Corpuscular Theory:* Particles obey Newton's laws of mechanics.
2. *Modified Corpuscular Theory of Planck and Einstein:* Quantum laws govern the behavior of photons.	2. *Modified Corpuscular Theory of Heisenberg:* Quantum laws govern the behavior of particles.
3. *Wave Theory:* Theory deals with continuous waves, yielding interference and diffraction effects. Standing waves produced by interference correspond to quantization. No mention of particles.	3. *Wave Theory:* Theory deals with continuous waves, yielding interference and diffraction effects. Quantization . . . corresponds to standing waves. No mention of particles in certain extreme forms of the theory.
4. *Einstein's "Ghost Field" Interpretation:* Interpretation reconciles corpuscular and wave theories . . .	4. *Born's Probability Interpretation:* Interpretation reconciles corpuscular and wave theories . . .

[1] Physics Staff of the University of Pittsburgh, *An Outline of Atomic Physics*, p. 142, 2nd Ed., New York, John Wiley & Sons, 1937.

TABLE II. An Example of the Statistical Type of Table

Certain Elements of the Solar System [1]

Name	Mean Dist. from Sun in 10^6 Km.	Period in Years	Mass / Mass of Earth	Mean Specific Gravity	Relative Surface Gravity
Sun	. . . .	. . . .	331950	1.41	27.89
Moon	149.45	. . . .	0.012261	3.33	0.165
Mercury	57.85	0.2408	0.04	3.8	0.27
Venus	108.10	0.6152	0.81	4.86	0.85
Earth	149.45	1.0000	1.000	5.52	1.00
Mars	227.72	1.8808	0.108	3.96	0.38
Ceres	413.58	4.6035	0.00012	3.3(?)	0.037(?)
Eros	217.94	1.7610	. . . .	3.3(?)	0.001(?)
Jupiter	777.6	11.862	316.94	1.34	2.64
Saturn	1425.6	29.457	94.9	0.71	1.17
Uranus	2868.1	84.013	14.66	1.27	0.92
Neptune	4494.1	164.783	17.16	1.58	1.12
Pluto	5937.	247.7	0.8(?)	. . . .	. . . .

[1] Russell, H. N., Dugan, R. S., and Stewart, J. Q., *Astronomy*, Boston, Ginn & Co., 1926. Data relating to Pluto have been taken from other sources.

TABLE III

An Example of the Functional Type of Table

Some Properties of Compressed Hydrogen at 0° C [1]

p atm	v cm^3/mole	d gm/l	f atm	c_p	c_v
				cal/mole K°	
200	127.1	15.86	227.4	7.07	4.91
300	90.12	22.37	365.1	7.14	4.94
400	71.62	28.14	521.6	7.19	4.98
500	60.56	33.28	699.2	7.22	5.00
600	53.19	37.90	900.2	7.24	5.04

[1] Deming, W. E., and Shupe, Lola E., *Phys. Rev.*, **40**, 850 (1932).

4. The Statistical Class of Tables. The general form of the statistical table and the names of its various parts are illustrated in the following plan:

TABLE NUMBER

Title

Stub Heading	Box Heading	
	Column Heading	Column Heading
Stub item	Item	Item
Stub item	Item	Item
Stub item	Item	Item
Stub item	Item	

(*a*) *The Title.* The title of a table should describe its contents briefly. It should be clear, requiring no reference to the context. It should be complete, telling what is listed, the source of the data if not original or if not widely published already, and possibly the date and the scheme of classification. Such phrases as "A Table Showing the Relationship Between . . ." should ordinarily be omitted. If completeness must be sacrificed for brevity, the necessary descriptive material may be added as separate sentences in a headnote below the title proper or as a footnote to the table.

(*b*) *The Stub*.   The first column at the left, the stub, lists the separate categories or values of the assumed independent variable.   Like all columns, the stub should have a descriptive heading naming the quantity listed and its units if expressed numerically.   An exception is a stub that contains heterogeneous items not classifiable under a single class name.

The choice of independent variable for tabulation is often arbitrary. When the stub is not quantitative the most appropriate order of entering the discrete line headings depends on the purpose of the table.   The alphabetical order is convenient for locating a particular heading.   Some suggestions follow.

1. Geographical, chronological, and magnitude subdivisions are often listed in the stub.

2. Stub items within any subdivision of the stub or within the stub as a whole should be listed in some logical classified order based on geographical location, time, magnitude, or other qualification.

3. It is usually easier to accommodate a long phrase in a stub than in a column heading.

4. It is usually easier to accommodate a long list of values in a vertical column than in a horizontal line.

(*c*) *The Columns*.   Each column should have a heading naming the quantity listed and, if appropriate, the units used in expressing the values tabulated.   Abbreviations or symbols should be used only when their meanings are clear.

In many tables, certain of the column headings as a group represent subclassifications of a more general quantity named in a box heading. All such subclassifications should be both all-inclusive and mutually exclusive.

(*d*) *The Items*.   In filling in the body of a table, numerical items should be arranged so that the decimal points are vertically aligned in each column.   Values expressed numerically should generally show zeros in all uncertain places except that which contains the first uncertain digit. Whenever the total for a group of individual items of one of the columns is given, it should preferably appear at the top of the group.   Note that a zero (0) entry may and should have a meaning different from that of a blank space.   A blank space should mean that information about the value of the particular item is lacking; a zero should mean that the item has zero value.   Sometimes a dash (—) is used to indicate that the item, though not zero, is negligibly small compared with the other items in the column.   This is not a desirable procedure since the dash is sometimes used to indicate the lack of data.   The question of significant figures will be discussed under the functional table.

5. The Functional Class of Tables. In the functional table, corresponding values of the independent (x) and dependent (y) variables are listed side by side. The form of the table is the same as that of the statistical table with the independent variable listed in the stub. If at all different, the former is usually somewhat simpler. As in the statistical table, every functional table should have a title which is clear, complete, and yet brief, and each column in the table should have a heading giving the name and the unit of the quantity listed. In the choice of the independent variable, x, the functional table is usually less arbitrary than the statistical table. The final decision must be based on the nature of the data and the purpose of the table. However, the variable so chosen should be a simple quantity, such as time, temperature, or distance, rather than a complex one such as might be desirable in plotting the same data. If the complex quantity has some special significance its values may be listed in a separate column as one of the dependent variables.

(a) *Choice of the x-Interval.* In constructing the table, one should usually (but not always) list rounded or otherwise convenient values of x in order of increasing (or, occasionally, decreasing) size, with successive values differing by a constant amount, Δx, called the common difference or x-interval. Since x-values are rounded, Δx is usually 1, 2, or 5 multiplied by $10^{\pm n}$ where n is an integer. The particular value for Δx in a given case usually represents a compromise between too small a value, which leads to an unnecessarily long table, tedious to construct, and too large a value, which leads to too short a table and to too frequent and difficult interpolations in use. For purposes of summations and finding rates of change, the smaller the Δx, the more accurate the results. A reasonable type of exception to the above indicated equal successive difference listing is that in which the successive ratios of x-values are constant.

(b) *Smoothing the Data.* For a table to be of greatest service the y-values corresponding to the tabulated x-values should generally be smoothed or graduated; i.e., the successive variations in y with successive equal variations in x should be made to vary gradually. In a truly statistical table, this smoothing process is without significance and should not be attempted.

Given an unsmoothed table of values of $y = f(x)$, values for a smoothed table may be obtained (1) from an equation of $y = f(x)$ which fits the data available, (2) from a graph of $y = f(x)$ drawn to fit the data, (3) from an arbitrary, numerical procedure, or (4) from a graph of item differences. The two last-named methods involve tabulated values of x and y in a regularly constructed but unsmoothed table.

If either of the first two methods is employed, the details of procedure and the results will depend somewhat on the smoother's idea as to what the real $y = f(x)$ is like; and a table thus smoothed may possibly be inferior to the unsmoothed table. Wherever the smoothing operation is carried through, it should always be with the purpose in mind of maintaining unchanged the general trend of the unsmoothed data and their approximate magnitudes.

Where the relation $y = f(x)$ is known, no smoothing process is involved. One is merely concerned with listing correctly computed values. Likewise, where an empirical relation has been found which maintains the general trend of the listed items as well as their approximate magnitudes, the procedure, which now may be classed technically as smoothing, is similar and obvious. Methods for finding such empirical equations are given in Chapter III.

The second-named or graphical method of smoothing consists of plotting the available data, or perhaps only a portion at a time, fitting a smooth curve, and reading the smoothed y-values therefrom. Plotting procedure is discussed elsewhere.

Many methods characterized by arbitrary numerical procedure are possible. Perhaps the one most used is one based on a least-squares relation to be derived later. It assumes a constant value for Δx and a parabolic function for $y = f(x)$. If carried through to a logical conclusion, it will usually give satisfactory results. The method should not be used, however, unless over the range of four Δx-intervals there is a reasonably close approximation to a parabolic relationship of the assumed type. The basic equation for this method is

$$a = \tfrac{1}{35} [17y_0 + 12(y_1 + y_{-1}) - 3(y_2 + y_{-2})] \qquad [1]$$

where y_{-2}, y_{-1}, y_0, y_1, and y_2 are five successive tabulated y-values and a is the smoothed value of y_0 which should replace y_0 in the smoothed table. Actually much time and effort may be saved in applying Eq. 1 if a temporary shift of origin to $(0, y_0)$ is made. In the *new* system, y_0 becomes 0. Using a', y'_1, y'_{-1}, etc., for the new a and y items, Eq. 1 changes to

$$a' = \tfrac{1}{35} [12(y'_1 + y'_{-1}) - 3(y'_2 + y'_{-2})] \qquad [1a]$$

of which the sums $(y'_1 + y'_{-1})$ and $(y'_2 + y'_{-2})$ will normally be small in magnitude. The a' obtained on this basis represents a correction to y_0 in the original coordinate system.

Obviously the second-named method may on occasions be improved upon by smoothing also the item differences. This procedure, which is also applicable directly, is likely to be justified where the precision of

TABLE IV

ILLUSTRATING THE SMOOTHING OF TABULATED DATA BY THE SMOOTHED ITEM-DIFFERENCES METHOD

The data of the first two columns, obtained by Jaeger,[1] represent constant-volume atomic heats of platinum for various temperatures. All values for c_v and Δc_v are in cal/(gm-atom C°). Columns headed $\Delta c'_v$ and $\Delta c''_v$ represent the first and the second sets of approximations of smoothed values for Δc_v as obtained from the graph of Fig. 1. Columns headed c'_v and c''_v similarly represent approximations to smoothed values for c_v. How well c''_v is smoothed is shown by the column headed $\Delta^2 c''_v$; how well it represents the given values of c_v is shown by the column headed $c''_v - c_v$. (See Table V for a first approximation in the smoothing of the same data by another method.)

T in °C	c_v	Δc_v	$\Delta c'_v$	$\Delta^2 c'_v$	c'_v	$c'_v - c_v$	$\Delta c''_v$	$\Delta^2 c''_v$	c''_v	$c''_v - c_v$
100	6.130				6.130	0.000			6.129	−0.001
		0.120	0.120				0.120			
200	.250			−0.012	.250	.000		−0.012	.249	−.001
		.105	.108				.108			
300	.355			− .012	.358	+ .003		− .012	.357	+ .002
		.099	.096				.096			
400	.454			− .011	.454	.000		− .011	.453	− .001
		.091	.085				.085			
500	.545			− .010	.539	− .006		− .011	.538	− .007
		.065	.075				.074			
600	.610			− .009	.614	+ .004		− .009	.612	+ .002
		.068	.066				.065			
700	.678			− .008	.680	+ .002		− .007	.677	− .001
		.053	.058				.058			
800	.731			− .005	.738	+ .007		− .005	.735	+ .004
		.054	.053				.053			
900	.785			− .003	.791	+ .006		− .004	.788	+ .003
		.046	.050				.050			
1000	.831			− .003	.841	+ .010		− .003	.838	+ .007
		.053	.047				.047			
1100	.884			− .003	.888	+ .004		− .003	.885	+ .001
		.046	.044				.044			
1200	.930			− .002	.932	+ .002		− .002	.929	− .001
		.039	.042				.042			
1300	.969			− .003	.974	+ .005		− .003	.971	+ .002
		.041	.039				.039			
1400	7.010			− .003	7.013	+ .003		− .003	7.010	.000
		.036	.036				.036			
1500	.046			− .003	.049	+ .003		− .002	.046	.000
		.033	.033				.034			
1600	.079			− .002	.082	+ .003		− .003	.080	+ .001
		.029	.031				.031			
1700	.108				.113	+ .005			.111	+ .003
1755	.124									

[1] Jaeger, F. M., *Optical Activity and High Temperature Measurements*, p. 371, New York, McGraw-Hill Book Company, 1930.

determination of the listed values for the dependent variable is rather high. The procedure is best described by showing how it operates when applied to a special tabulation of unsmoothed data. For this purpose, we use Jaeger's [1] values for the constant-volume atomic heats of platinum for the temperature range 100° C to 1755° C (Table IV).

The first step in the application of the item-differences method involves the determining of the differences Δc_v. These are plotted as in Fig. 1

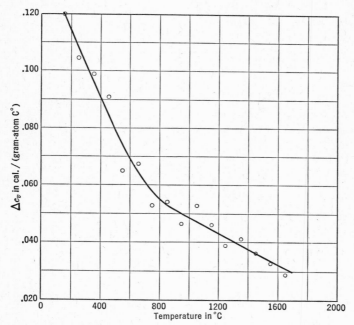

FIG. 1. Increments of constant-volume atomic heats, Δc_v, of platinum (see Table IV) for 100 C° intervals as a function of temperature, for use in smoothing tabulated data by the successive approximation, tabular method.

and a smooth curve is drawn to represent their means. Values of $\Delta c'_v$, column 4 of the table, are taken from this curve and applied to some arbitrarily chosen recorded c_v to give the first approximation c'_v to a smoothed set for c_v. As shown by the columns headed $\Delta^2 c'_v$ and $c'_v - c_v$, the first attempt at smoothing has yielded results which, though well smoothed, are generally too high in the region 600° C < T < 1700° C. Revision of the values recorded for $\Delta c'_v$, still maintaining the principle that the values for $\Delta c'_v$ need to be smoothed and

[1] Jaeger, F. M., *Optical Activity and High Temperature Measurements*, p. 371, New York, McGraw-Hill Book Company, 1930.

TABLE V

Illustrating the Smoothing of Tabulated Data by the Least-Squares Method as Expressed by Eq. 1a

The data of the first two columns obtained by Jaeger [1] represent constant-volume atomic heats for platinum. The units for c_v, Δc_v, $\Delta^2 c_v$, y', and a' are uniformly the cal/(gm-atom C°). (See Table IV where the same data have been smoothed by means of another method.)

T in °C	c_v	Δc_v	$\Delta^2 c_v$	$12(y'_1+y'_{-1})-3(y'_2-y'_{-2})$	$35a'$	c'_v-c_v	c'_v	$\Delta c'_v$	$\Delta^2 c'_v$
100	6.130						6.130		
		0.120						0.120	
200	.250		−0.015				.250		−0.014
		.105						.106	
300	.355		− .006	12(−0.006)−3(−0.035)	+0.033	+0.001	.356		− .007
		.099						.099	
400	.454		− .008	12(−0.008)−3(−0.048)	+ .048	+ .001	.455		− .013
		.091						.086	
500	.545		− .026	12(−0.026)−3(−0.057)	− .141	− .004	.541		− .013
		.065						.073	
600	.610		+ .003	12(+0.003)−3(−0.035)	+ .141	+ .004	.614		− .012
		.068						.061	
700	.678		− .015	12(−0.015)−3(−0.026)	− .102	− .003	.675		− .003
		.053						.058	
800	.731		+ .001	12(+0.001)−3(−0.023)	+ .081	+ .002	.733		− .008
		.054						.050	
900	.785		− .008	12(−0.008)−3(−0.008)	− .072	− .002	.783		.000
		.046						.050	
1000	.831		+ .007	12(+0.007)−3(−0.001)	+ .087	+ .002	.833		.000
		.053						.050	
1100	.884		− .007	12(−0.007)−3(−0.014)	− .042	− .001	.883		− .004
		.046						.046	
1200	.930		− .007	12(−0.007)−3(−0.019)	− .027	− .001	.929		− .005
		.039						.041	
1300	.969		+ .002	12(+0.002)−3(−0.008)	+ .048	+ .001	.970		− .002
		.041						.039	
1400	7.010		− .005	12(−0.005)−3(−0.011)	− .027	− .001	7.009		− .002
		.036						.037	
1500	.046		− .003	12(−0.003)−3(−0.015)	.009	.000	.046		− .004
		.033						.033	
1600	.079		− .004				.079		− .004
		.029						.029	
1700	.108						.108		
1755	.124						.124		

[1] Jaeger, F. M., *Optical Activity and High Temperature Measurements*, p. 371, New York, McGraw Hill Book Company, 1930.

keeping the differences $c'_v - c_v$ in mind, may be made to yield a second approximation which is more satisfactory than the first. Such a second approximation is shown in the column headed c''_v. How well the smoothing for the differences Δc_v and also for c_v has been done is shown in the column headed $\Delta^2 c''_v$. That the smoothed values for c_v retain closely the general trend of the original data, an important requirement for any satisfactory smoothing method, is shown by the column headed $c''_v - c_v$.

In practice, it is sometimes desirable to extend the process just described to the smoothing of second-order differences. Where the type of equation necessary to represent the data is not known and where the graph showing $y = f(x)$ is not sufficiently precise, this method would seem to be among the best if not the best.

For the sake of a comparison, the smoothing of the data on constant-volume atomic heats of platinum listed in the first two columns of Table IV is carried through in Table V according to the arbitrary-procedure method employing Eq. 1a. That the smoothed values thus obtained will maintain the general trend of the original data is evident; but, as shown by the columns headed $\Delta^2 c_v$ and $\Delta^2 c'_v$, the smoothing produced by the first application is far from being as satisfactory as that produced by the item-differences method (see columns of Table IV headed $\Delta^2 c'_v$ and $\Delta^2 c''_v$). Successive application of the method employing Eq. 1a will certainly yield successive improvements; but the rate of approach to a satisfactory limit will generally be slow. This, added to the fact that it is helpless in smoothing the two values at either end, makes the method seem rather unsatisfactory for practical purposes.

(c) *Significant Figures.* A significant figure is any digit of a number which is used to help denote the size of the number rather than to locate the decimal point. To illustrate, consider the following length measurements:

(1) 123 cm
(2) 0.00123 km
(3) 12.03 cm
(4) 12.30 cm
(5) 12,300 cm

Measurement (1) contains three significant figures. It indicates at most that the quantity is nearer 123 than 122 or 124 cm; i.e., that it lies between 122.5 cm and 123.5 cm. Measurement (2) also contains three significant figures. The two zeros to the right of the decimal point serve only to locate the decimal point. Values (1) and (2) are identical.

Measurement (3) contains four significant figures. Measurement (4) also contains four significant figures. Unfortunately, the exact significance of the final zero when written as above is somewhat uncertain. At the most, it indicates that the quantity lies between 12.295 cm and 12.305 cm. At the least, it indicates that the quantity lies between 12.275 cm and 12.325 cm. In case the latter interpretation is correct, the next lower and the next higher values that might be recorded on the same basis are 12.25 and 12.35 cm, the least count being 0.05 cm. There is no generally accepted policy which enables the reader to tell, from the expression itself, precisely what was meant by the writer. In any case, recording a measurement as 12.3 cm when it may be justly written 12.30 cm suggests a precision less than that actually attained and indicates carelessness or ignorance on the part of the recorder.

Measurement (5) as recorded is ambiguous, since it does not indicate whether the length was measured to the nearest meter, the nearest decimeter, or the nearest centimeter. For such quantities, when an indication of precision is desired, use may be made of powers of ten, or of subdigits. Thus, if measurement (5) had been written as 1.230×10^4 cm or as 123_{00} cm, the uncertainty, except as noted in connection with measurement (4), would be removed. When written in the latter form, the small zero ($_0$) farthest to the left is understood to be the first uncertain digit. Accordingly, the two expressions of length have about the same meaning.

For a table to be of greatest service, each value should contain neither more nor less than the number of significant figures it deserves. For the case of x-values, there is no point in writing 300.00, 400.00, . . . rather than 300, 400, . . . , since the independent x-values are understood to be exact. For the y-values, however, the number of significant figures in each item is an indication of the reliability of the table. If the table is based on a theoretical equation, as are mathematical function tables, the possible number of significant figures is unlimited except for convenience in construction and use. If based on an equation with experimentally determined constants, such as a table showing the radiancy, $\mathcal{R}$, of a black body as a function of temperature, T, where $\mathcal{R} = \sigma T^4$, the number of significant figures depends on the precision of the experimental constants, in this case σ. This principle also holds for an unknown law, as in a table showing the brightness of a black body as a function of temperature.

There is no generally accepted rule for deciding the exact number of digits to record when tabulating a set of values of known precision.

The American Society for Testing Materials gives rules [1] which generally result in a number containing two doubtful digits. They state, however, that for some purposes it is satisfactory to drop all digits uncertain by more than about 15 units. A value recorded as 34.7, then, may lie at best between 34.55 and 34.85, or at worst between 33.2 and 36.2. If the first set of limits is known to have too great a separation, another significant figure is permissible; or if the second set is still too small, the number should be rounded to 35. This is the practice which the authors are inclined to favor. Still another practice consists of retaining the last figure uncertain by less than 10 units. Then 34.7 would mean a value between 34.6 and 34.8 at best or between 33.7 and 35.7 at worst. Sometimes the uncertain digits are printed inferior, e.g., 34.7. A discussion of what is meant by the precision of a value may be found in Chapter VII.

(d) *Rounding Off Numbers.* If a number is to be rounded to a specific number of significant figures the following rules [2] should be observed:

1. If the first digit to be dropped is less than five, the last digit retained is left unchanged.

2. If the first digit to be dropped is greater than five, or is five followed by digits greater than zero, the last digit retained is increased by one.

3. If the digit to be dropped is five followed by zeros only, the number is rounded to its nearest even value.

Thus, rounding to one decimal place,

$$12.345 \text{ yields } 12.3$$
$$12.367 \text{ yields } 12.4$$
$$12.356 \text{ yields } 12.4$$
$$12.350 \text{ yields } 12.4$$
$$12.450 \text{ yields } 12.4$$

(e) *Abbreviated Forms of Tabulation.* Within the limits of space which may be accorded them, tables should be so constructed that a desired quantity may be obtained with the greatest ease. Doing so necessitates not only the observance of the general policies set forth above but also certain procedures for certain special cases about to be presented. For

[1] 1933 A.S.T.M. *Manual on Presentation of Data,* p. 44, Second Printing, March 1937, A.S.T.M., Philadelphia.

[2] These rules are slightly different from those recommended by the A.S.T.M. *Manual on Presentation of Data,* p. 44.

the most part, these procedures concern abbreviated forms of expression, and, in addition to making it easier for the user of a table to find desired material, save in space and in printer's ink. Five such special cases will be considered.

1. Given that all values for a variable are fractional and that, when written decimally, they have digits other than zero in the first or second place to the right of the decimal point, the customary policy is to list a zero in the units place for the first value of a column of values but not in the succeeding values of that column. See Tables I and II of Appendix 2. Often even the zero for the initial value is not listed.

2. Given, as a variation of the first case, that the first significant digit, particularly if occupying the first place to the left of the decimal point, varies only occasionally, a common practice consists in recording that significant digit for the value at the top of the column, leaving the corresponding position vacant for all following values until a change in that digit occurs, recording the new digit and proceeding as before. Table IV of this chapter contains two such illustrations.

3. For cases where the values for a variable are expressed in terms of 10^{+n} or 10^{-n} of what is considered a satisfactory unit, two procedures are rather common. (a) According to one procedure a column heading is often written in an appropriate corresponding form. See Table II of Chapter VII. (b) According to the other procedure, the first value in a column is sometimes written as, say, 0.0_5010 provided that all values for the column agree in having zero in each of the first five places to the right of the decimal point. Other values, properly aligned, then include only three digits each to correspond to the 010 of the first value.

4. Given that all values to be listed in a column are given with several significant figures of which only a few vary throughout the column, two procedures are common. (a) According to one procedure, that which is listed is the difference between actual values for the variable and some rounded convenient value. See Table III of Chapter VII, where only those portions of velocities in excess of 299,000 km/sec are recorded. (b) According to the second procedure, a complete value is recorded for the first of the column only. Succeeding values will include digits only in places where variations occur in the column. Thus, as such succeeding values for the first column of the table just referred to, we might have 299,728, 733, 738, . . . , 818, and 823. Of course, the final digits for all values must fall in the same vertical line.

5. The last-named case concerns quantities which have generally the same number of significant digits but which vary considerably in order of magnitude. A common custom here makes use of powers of ten. The details of application will naturally vary with the author. In Tables VII and VIII of Appendix 2, the power of 10 is indicated by the number enclosed in parentheses. Thus from Table VIII, we see that k_2 for $n = 6$ is $14{,}285{,}714 \times 10^{-9}$ and that k_2 for $n = 40$ is $46{,}904{,}315 \times 10^{-12}$.

(f) *Tabular Differences.* The successive tabular differences of the y-variable are of importance in certain interpolation methods and in testing the type of relationship between y and x. The first difference, denoted by the symbol Δ, is defined by the equation

$$\Delta y_n = y_{n+1} - y_n \qquad [2]$$

Higher order differences, Δ^2, Δ^3, etc., are similarly defined:

$$\Delta^2 y_n = \Delta y_{n+1} - \Delta y_n = y_{n+2} - 2y_{n+1} + y_n \qquad [3]$$

$$\Delta^3 y_n = \Delta^2 y_{n+1} - \Delta^2 y_n = y_{n+3} - 3y_{n+2} + 3y_{n+1} - y_n \qquad [4]$$

$$\cdot$$
$$\cdot$$
$$\cdot$$

Such successive differences are often arranged as in Table VI.

TABLE VI

ILLUSTRATING THE USUAL FORM OF THE DIFFERENCE TABLE

x	y	Δy	$\Delta^2 y$	$\Delta^3 y$	$\Delta^4 y$
x_0	y_0				
		Δy_0			
$x_0 + \Delta x$	y_1		$\Delta^2 y_0$		
		Δy_1		$\Delta^3 y_0$	
$x_0 + 2\Delta x$	y_2		$\Delta^2 y_1$		$\Delta^4 y_0$
		Δy_2		$\Delta^3 y_1$	
$x_0 + 3\Delta x$	y_3		$\Delta^2 y_2$		
		Δy_3			
$x_0 + 4\Delta x$	y_4				
$\cdot$					
$\cdot$					
$\cdot$					

A numerical example is given in Table VII.

TABLE VII

ILLUSTRATING THE METHOD OF CONSTRUCTING A DIFFERENCE TABLE

[Note that since x- and y-values are related by the equation $y = 1 + 3x + 3x^2$, all differences of the third and higher orders vanish.]

x	y	Δy	$\Delta^2 y$	$\Delta^3 y$	$\Delta^4 y$
−2	7				
		−6			
−1	1		6		
		0		0	
0	1		6		0
		6		0	
1	7		6		
		12			
2	19				

6. Interpolation. There are numerous interpolation procedures for finding intermediate y-values corresponding to a given x-value in the range of a particular table. The appropriate procedure depends on the accuracy of the table, the type of relationship presented, and the precision desired. One or another of the simpler methods given below will ordinarily serve for most purposes. Other methods may be found in more advanced texts.[1]

(a) *The Graph Method.* Finding by interpolation a y corresponding to a given x, x_n say, necessitates four steps: (1) selecting from the table certain convenient corresponding values of x and y in the region of x_n, (2) plotting these values on ordinary cross-section paper, (3) drawing the best curve to express $y = f(x)$, and (4) reading the desired y_n from the curve. Depending on the number of points plotted, the openness of the scales selected, and the care used in plotting and drawing the curve, this method may be used to give poor, moderate, or highly accurate interpolations. Unless the table is very detailed, a worker requiring frequent interpolations from a given table will ordinarily make such a graph and use it thereafter to the practical exclusion of the table. The principles of plotting data are treated in the following chapter.

(b) *The Proportional Part Method.* When interpolations are to be made from a given table only occasionally, or when graphing is not

[1] Whittaker, E. T., and Robinson, G., *The Calculus of Observations*, Chap. I, London, Blackie & Son, Ltd., 1924.

practicable, numerical methods can be used. Of these, the proportional part method is the simplest. It assumes that between tabulated values of x, y varies linearly with x. Using this method, the y-value corresponding to a given x lying between two successive tabulated points, (x_1, y_1) and (x_2, y_2) is obtained from

$$y = y_1 + \frac{y_2 - y_1}{x_2 - x_1} (x - x_1) \qquad [5]$$

(c) *The Gregory-Newton Method.* This method is longer but more accurate than the proportional part method. It is based on the assumed relation

$$y = A + Bx + Cx^2 + Dx^3 + \cdots \qquad [6]$$

containing unknown constants A, B, C, etc. It is derived as follows. Referring to Table VI, it is seen that

$$y_1 = y_0 + \Delta y_0$$

$$y_2 = y_1 + \Delta y_1 = y_0 + 2\Delta y_0 + \Delta^2 y_0$$

$$y_3 = y_2 + \Delta y_2 = y_0 + 3\Delta y_0 + 3\Delta^2 y_0 + \Delta^3 y_0$$

$$\vdots$$

In general, it is evident that for integral values of n,

$$y_n = y_0 + n\Delta y_0 + \frac{n(n-1)}{2!} \Delta^2 y_0 + \frac{n(n-1)(n-2)}{3!} \Delta^3 y_0 + \cdots \qquad [7]$$

where $n = (x - x_0)/\Delta x$, and in which the coefficients of the Δ's are those of the binomial theorem. Provided Eq. 6 is fulfilled, it may be shown that Eq. 7 holds for all positive values of n, fractional as well as integral. It gives directly the y corresponding to any given x in terms of a neighboring tabulated basic value, y_0 (usually the nearest smaller value), and the successive differences, Δy_0, $\Delta^2 y_0$, etc. The restriction of Eq. 7 to positive values of n does not prevent its use for values of x less than x_0. It is then necessary to consider the table in order of decreasing values of x, whereupon Δx is negative. However, n remains positive.

In general, Eq. 7 is an infinite series. Usually, however, and especially when Δx is small, the terms of the higher orders are negligible in comparison with the first few terms, so that the formula is ordinarily practicable. The exact number of terms to be used depends on the particular case at hand. Note that if the terms beyond that containing

Δy_0 are disregarded, we have the formula for the proportional part method.

Illustrating the use of Eq. 7, let us determine the value of the probability integral,

$$P_{hx} = \frac{2}{\sqrt{\pi}} \int_0^{hx} e^{-h^2 x^2} \, d(hx) \qquad [7a]$$

corresponding to $hx = 0.97$, by interpolation, using data given in the first two columns of Table VIII. Using 1.00 as the basic hx-value, the

TABLE VIII

DATA AND COMPUTATIONS FOR DETERMINING A PROBABILITY BY THE GREGORY-NEWTON INTERPOLATION METHOD

hx	P_{hx}	ΔP_{hx}	$\Delta^2 P_{hx}$	$\Delta^3 P_{hx}$
1.00	0.84270			
		−0.04579		
0.90	0.79691		−0.00902	
		−0.05481		−0.00047
0.80	0.74210		−0.00949	
		−0.06431		−0.00015
0.70	0.67780		−0.00964	
		−0.07394		
0.60	0.60386			

x_0 of the preceding discussion, and -0.10 as Δhx, n becomes 0.3 and we obtain for $P_{0.97}$ or, from the standpoint of Eq. 7, for $y_{0.3}$,

$$P_{0.97} = 0.84270 + 0.3(-0.04579) + \frac{0.3(0.3 - 1)}{2}(-0.00902) + \cdots$$

$$= 0.84270 - 0.01374 + 0.00095 - 0.00003 + \cdots \qquad [8]$$

$$= 0.82988$$

The value obtained, 0.82988, is greater by 0.00001 than that generally reported. It is much more precise than the value obtained by the proportional part method, namely, 0.82896, which is given by the first two terms of the right-hand member of Eq. 8.

(d) *The Equation Method.* This method consists in finding an empirical equation, $y = f(x)$, to fit certain selected tabulated values of x

and y, substituting therein the given value for x, and solving for the desired y. The particular type of equation to select will depend on the nature of the table. Ordinarily, the power series,

$$y = A + Bx + Cx^2 + \cdots \qquad [9]$$

suffices. For sufficiently small ranges, only three terms are necessary. Constants A, B, and C may be determined to yield an equation that will pass through any three selected points, (x_1, y_1), (x_2, y_2), and (x_3, y_3). As such points, the three nearest the given x are usually chosen. In determinant form, the desired equation is

$$\begin{vmatrix} y & 1 & x & x^2 \\ y_1 & 1 & x_1 & x_1{}^2 \\ y_2 & 1 & x_2 & x_2{}^2 \\ y_3 & 1 & x_3 & x_3{}^2 \end{vmatrix} = 0 \qquad [10]$$

Eq. 10 may be reduced to the form of Eq. 9 if values for A, B, and C are desired. If not so desired, we may substitute an appropriate value for x directly in Eq. 10 and solve the determinant for the desired y.

Where the intervals $x_2 - x_1$ and $x_3 - x_2$ have the same value Δx, much time may be saved by changing the origin of coordinates as from $(0,0)$ to (x_2, y_2). Representing the new coordinates by x' and y' where

$$x' = \frac{x - x_2}{\Delta x} \qquad [11]$$

and

$$y' = y - y_2 \qquad [12]$$

we have

$$x'_1 = \frac{x_1 - x_2}{\Delta x} = \frac{-\Delta x}{\Delta x} = -1 \qquad [13]$$

$$x'_2 = \frac{x_2 - x_2}{\Delta x} = 0 \qquad [14]$$

$$x'_3 = \frac{x_3 - x_2}{\Delta x} = 1 \qquad [15]$$

$$y'_1 = y_1 - y_2, \text{ etc.} \qquad [16]$$

In the new coordinate system Eq. 10 becomes

$$\begin{vmatrix} y' & 1 & x' & x'^2 \\ y'_1 & 1 & -1 & 1 \\ 0 & 1 & 0 & 0 \\ y'_3 & 1 & 1 & 1 \end{vmatrix} = 0 \qquad [17]$$

which reduces at once to

$$\begin{vmatrix} y' & x' & x'^2 \\ y'_1 & -1 & 1 \\ y'_3 & 1 & 1 \end{vmatrix} = 0 \qquad [18]$$

Eq. 18 may be quickly solved for y', and y may then be obtained by adding y_2.

To illustrate the use of Eq. 18, consider the problem of the previous section. Representing hx by x and P by y, the necessary tabulated data in terms of the original and the shifted coordinate systems become

x (hx)	y (P)	x'	y'
0.80	0.74210	−1	−0.05481
0.90	0.79691	0	0
1.00	0.84270	1	0.04579

For $x = 0.97$, $x' = 0.7$. Substitution in Eq. 18 yields

$$\begin{vmatrix} y' & 0.7 & 0.49 \\ -0.05481 & -1 & 1 \\ 0.04579 & 1 & 1 \end{vmatrix} = 0 \qquad [19]$$

from which $y' = 0.03300$, and $y = 0.82991$. This value is greater than that usually reported by 0.00004.

Although it has been assumed in the foregoing that there is a common x-interval, such is not necessary. The procedure for this infrequent case is left to the reader.

Eqs. 18 and 19 give the same interpolation as the Gregory-Newton formula, with the terms beyond that containing the second difference omitted.

(e) *The Lagrange Method.* This method is of particular importance because it can be used to find the y-value corresponding to a given x-value when, instead of a formal table, we have simply a group of corresponding x- and y-values not separated by the common difference, Δx.

The Lagrange interpolation formula assumes that y may be expressed as a power series in x, as in Eq. 9, namely

$$y = A + Bx + Cx^2 + \cdots \qquad [9]$$

If the determinant of Eq. 10 or a similar one, containing more terms if desired, is expanded to express y in terms of $y_1, y_2, y_3 \cdots$ and the determinant minors $Y, Y_1, Y_2, Y_3 \cdots$, one obtains directly

$$y = y_1 \frac{Y_1}{Y} - y_2 \frac{Y_2}{Y} + y_3 \frac{Y_3}{Y} - \cdots \qquad [20]$$

Expansion of the minors leads at once to the standard Lagrangian form of equation, namely

$$y = y_1 \left[\frac{(x - x_2)}{(x_1 - x_2)} \times \frac{(x - x_3)}{(x_1 - x_3)} \times \frac{(x - x_4)}{(x_1 - x_4)} \times \frac{(x - x_5)}{(x_1 - x_5)} \times \cdots \right]$$

$$\qquad [20a]$$

$$+ y_2 \left[\frac{(x - x_1)}{(x_2 - x_1)} \times \frac{(x - x_3)}{(x_2 - x_3)} \times \frac{(x - x_4)}{(x_2 - x_4)} \times \frac{(x - x_5)}{(x_2 - x_5)} \times \cdots \right] + \cdots$$

There are as many terms as there are points used in the interpolation.

To illustrate, suppose it is desired to find the current which will heat to 2500° K, in vacuo, a long tungsten filament whose radius is 0.062 mm. From a list of tabulated values, we find, for instance, that the currents for wires with radii of 0.030 mm, 0.050 mm, 0.080 mm, and 0.100 mm are 0.690 amp, 1.485 amp, 3.000 amp, and 4.200 amp, respectively. It follows, from the Lagrange formula, in case, for convenience, we use the micron values for the filament radii, that

$$I_{62} = 0.690 \text{ amp} \left[\frac{62 - 50}{30 - 50} \quad \frac{62 - 80}{30 - 80} \quad \frac{62 - 100}{30 - 100} \right]$$

$$+ 1.485 \text{ amp} \left[\frac{62 - 30}{50 - 30} \quad \frac{62 - 80}{50 - 80} \quad \frac{62 - 100}{50 - 100} \right]$$

$$+ 3.000 \text{ amp} \left[\frac{62 - 30}{80 - 30} \quad \frac{62 - 50}{80 - 50} \quad \frac{62 - 100}{80 - 100} \right]$$

$$+ 4.200 \text{ amp} \left[\frac{62 - 30}{100 - 30} \quad \frac{62 - 50}{100 - 50} \quad \frac{62 - 80}{100 - 80} \right] \qquad [21]$$

$$= (-0.0809 + 1.0835 + 1.4592 - 0.4147) \text{ amp}$$

$$= 2.047 \text{ amp}$$

This is very close to the 2.048 amp predicted by the $\frac{3}{2}$ power law for the condition of constant temperature, namely,

$$\left[\frac{I_1}{I_2} = \left(\frac{r_1}{r_2}\right)^{\frac{3}{2}}\right]_T \tag{22}$$

It is interesting to note that, with the separate omissions of terms involving the 0.030 mm and 0.100 mm wires, the values obtained for

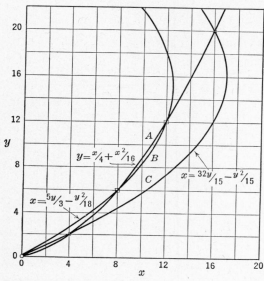

Fig. 2.   Graph showing possible dangers in assuming without testing that a simple power series expressing y in terms of x holds when the values for Δx vary considerably.   The increments of curves A and B between points of crossing are much more nearly equal than those for curves A and C.   Between the limiting points of crossing, the former pair gives more nearly the same loci of points than the latter pair.

$I_{0.062}$ are respectively 2.045 amp and 2.051 amp; and that, when the terms involving these two wires are omitted simultaneously, the proportional part value of 2.091 amp is obtained, as is to be expected. Any number of corresponding I and r values may be substituted in Eq. 20.   As might be expected, the terms involving the wires nearest the given wire in size are the most important in determining the desired current.

Although intended principally for use where the x-intervals are non-uniform, the Lagrange method applies equally well to interpolations from a formal table with a constant Δx.

In the application of methods based on the empirical power series forms of Eqs. 6 and 9, one needs to consider certain possibilities for trouble, particularly where the Δx-intervals differ considerably. To illustrate, the points $(0,0)$, $(4,2)$, and $(16,20)$ not only satisfy the equation

$$y = \frac{x}{4} + \frac{x^2}{16} \qquad [23]$$

but also the equation

$$x = \frac{32y}{15} - \frac{y^2}{15} \qquad [24]$$

How great is the danger in interpolating in these two cases is shown in Fig. 2, where both equations are graphed. If, however, the values for Δx and for Δy are separately of the same order, there is not the same great danger in the selection of the wrong power series. Thus for the points $(0,0)$, $(8,6)$, and $(12,12)$, we have the two equations

$$y = \frac{x}{4} + \frac{x^2}{16} \qquad [23]$$

and

$$x = \frac{5y}{3} - \frac{y^2}{18} \qquad [25]$$

As shown also in Fig. 2, the plot of Eq. 25 will generally yield interpolated values for y which are not so greatly different from those obtained using Eq. 23.

(f) *The Taylor's Series Method.* The usefulness of this method is limited to tables based on a known transcendental equation. For such tables the method gives good results. In accord with Taylor's series, the interpolation formula is

$$y = f(x) = f(x_0 + \delta x)$$

$$= f(x_0) + f'(x_0)\frac{\delta x}{1!} + f''(x_0)\frac{(\delta x)^2}{2!} + f'''(x_0)\frac{(\delta x)^3}{3!} + \cdots \qquad [26]$$

where $\delta x = x - x_0$ and the primes indicate differentiation with respect to x.

It suffices (1) to select from the table an x_0 as near as possible to the given x, (2) to form $f'(x_0)$, $f''(x_0)$, etc., and (3) to insert those values, together with the appropriate δx into the formula to obtain the desired y.

Suppose it is desired to find the value of $e^{-8.2}$. In a table, we find for $e^{-8.0}$ and $e^{-9.0}$ the values 335×10^{-6} and 123×10^{-6}. Applying the Taylor's series method, we have in turn

$$f(x) = e^{-x}$$

$$f'(x) = -e^{-x}$$

$$f''(x) = e^{-x}, \text{ etc.}$$

$$\delta x = 8.2 - 8.0 = 0.2$$

whence

$$y = e^{-8.2} = e^{-8.0} - e^{-8.0}\,(0.2) + e^{-8.0}\,\frac{0.04}{2} - \cdots$$

$$= e^{-8.0}\,(1 - 0.2 + 0.02 - 0.0013 + 0.00007 \cdots)$$

$$= 335 \times 10^{-6}\,(0.8188) = 274 \times 10^{-6} \qquad [27]$$

The value obtained is as precise as the value given for $e^{-8.0}$.

7. Extrapolation. When the value of y is desired for an x outside the range of values covered by the data, we must resort to extrapolation. In method, extrapolation and interpolation are alike; any of the interpolation procedures described above may be used for extrapolating. The chief differences lie in the accuracy of our results.

Where the law stating the dependency of y upon x is known, no difficulty is experienced in either interpolation or extrapolation. All methods, except the simple proportional part method, may be used with equal safety even if not with equal ease if the range of extrapolation is not too great. However, the equation and the Taylor series methods are then particularly applicable. Generally such determinations are not regarded as extrapolations. Where nothing of the law of variation is known, beyond the range for which tabular values are given, extrapolations represent little more than guesses which have a certain amount of reasonableness. Where something of the law of variation is known, extrapolations take on increased probabilities as to correctness. As a result certain extrapolations can be made with a degree of certainty which is rather high. To illustrate, the brightness of carbon at temperatures above its normal sublimation point, such as are realizable under pressure, has not been determined experimentally nor is its law of variation known. Knowing, however, that the radiations from carbon are subject to certain laws of thermodynamics permits one to set certain upper and lower limits within which extrapolated brightnesses for the carbon must fall.

8. Summary. The table, one of three forms for presenting data, lists corresponding values or properties of the dependent and independent variables in an orderly arrangement. Tables are simple and inexpensive to construct, easy to use, and compact.

There are three classes of tables: the qualitative, the statistical, and the quantitative or functional. The principal parts of the statistical table are the title, the stub, column headings, and items.

The functional table is similar to the statistical in form, but lists corresponding values of dependent, y, and independent, x, variables. Values of x differ commonly, but not always, by a constant amount. Preferably y-values should be smoothed. Depending on circumstances, this may be done (1) by taking corresponding values from an equation that represents the data, (2) by taking corresponding values from a graph in which a smooth curve has been drawn to represent the data, (3) by applying corrections obtained by an arbitrary mathematical procedure such as is connected with Eq. 1a, or (4) by smoothing the item differences, applying such differences to obtain an approximate smoothed tabulation and finally adjusting to obtain a tabulation which maintains also the general trend of the unsmoothed tabulation (Table IV and Fig. 1). Except where the law of variation in equation form is known, the last-named procedure is obviously best.

The precision of tabulated data should be indicated by the number of significant figures in the items. Generally the last digit of an item should be the first deemed uncertain digit unless the uncertainty is of the order of $1\frac{1}{2}$ or less, in which case a second uncertain digit—either a zero or five, whichever seems closer to the true value—is permissible. Some prefer not to round off these last digits.

In rounding off numbers, the last digit retained is left unchanged or increased by one as the amount dropped is less than or in excess of 0.5 of a unit in the last place retained. If the amount dropped is just 0.5 of a unit, the last digit retained is made an even digit by leaving it unchanged or by increasing it by one if necessary.

In using a table, interpolation is often resorted to for finding the y corresponding to a given x for intermediate values of x. Interpolation may be done graphically by fitting a smooth curve to the tabulated data and reading y from the curve. A second method is the proportional part method, where

$$y = y_1 + \frac{y_2 - y_1}{x_2 - x_1}(x - x_1) \qquad [5]$$

and (x_1, y_1) and (x_2, y_2) are successive tabulated points such that $x_1 < x < x_2$. The Gregory-Newton interpolation formula is

$$y = y_0 + n\Delta y_0 + \frac{n(n-1)}{2!}\Delta^2 y_0 + \cdots \qquad [7]$$

where (x_0, y_0) is the tabulated point nearest (x, y) and $n = (x - x_0)/\Delta x$.

The equation method consists in selecting three tabulated points (x_1, y_1), (x_2, y_2), and (x_3, y_3) nearest (x, y), shifting the origin and changing co-ordinates by means of the substitutions

$$x' = \frac{x - x_2}{\Delta x} \tag{11}$$

$$y' = y - y_2 \tag{12}$$

substituting values of y'_1, y'_3, and x' in the determinant equation

$$\begin{vmatrix} y' & x' & x'^2 \\ y'_1 & -1 & 1 \\ y'_3 & 1 & 1 \end{vmatrix} = 0 \tag{18}$$

and solving for y' and then y. The Lagrange formula, Eq. 20, is useful for interpolating from a list of values not arranged in a formal table. The Taylor's series method, Eq. 23, gives good results for tables based on a known transcendental equation.

Tables may be extrapolated by applying interpolation procedure to values of x outside the range of the tabulated x-values. Except where the law relating y and x is known, such extrapolations are only approximate at best. Extrapolations for values of x just beyond the limit of a table are safer than those for values considerably beyond the limit.

PROBLEMS

1. The following table is a portion of a table representing the results of an extended, important study of air by Roebuck.[1] It shows the Joule-Thompson effect μ of air expressed in C°/atm as a function of temperature T and pressure p.

P in atm \ T in °C	0	50	100	150	200	250
1	0.2746	0.1956	0.1355	0.0961	0.0645	0.0409
20	.2577	.1830	.1258	.0883	.0580	.0356
60	.2200	.1571	.1062	.0732	.0453	.0254
100	.1822	.1310	.0884	.0600	.0343	.0165
140	.1446	.1070	.0726	.0482	.0250	.0092
180	.1097	.0829	.0580	.0376	.0174	+ .0027
220	.0795	.0609	.0449	.0291	.0116	− .0025

[1] Roebuck, J. R., *Proc. Am. Acad. Arts Sci.*, **60**, 537 (1925), as corrected by the original author.

This table may be improved by smoothing both as to pressure and as to temperature. Smooth as to variations in pressure. When so smoothed, note whether there seems to be need for further smoothing as to temperature.

2. The fractional voltages and candle powers of vacuum tungsten lamps in terms of their normal voltages and candle powers at 2450° K as a function of temperature has been reported [1] as follows:

T in °K	$\dfrac{V}{V_n}$ in %	$\dfrac{I}{I_n}$ in %
2000	55.0	10.4
2100	63.6	18.6
2200	73.3	32.2
2300	83.5	52.2
2400	95.0	82.9
2450	100.0	100.0
2500	105.9	122.0
2600	118.5	179.3
2700	132.3	257.0

This table contains obvious errors due to lack of smoothing. Form a new table with smoothed values, maintaining the values as 100.0% for 2450° K. Note that end values are as likely to be in error as are other values.

3. Derive Lagrange's interpolation equation.

4. For the molal heat of air at a pressure of 20A, Roebuck [2] gives the following values as a function of temperature.

T	c_p	T	c_p
−100° C	0.2757 cal/(mole K°)	+ 75° C	0.2475 cal/(mole K°)
− 75	.2630	100	.2470
− 50	.2556	150	.2466
− 25	.2514	200	.2463
0	.2492	250	.2468
+ 25	.2487	280	.2471
+ 50	.2480		

Determine the values of c_p for air at 20A and +40° C, −20° C, and −60° C.

5. The spectral transmittances of a 6 mm thick, 28%, Corning high-transmission red glass as reported in a graph by Forsythe are:

λ	0.63 μ	0.64	0.65	0.66	0.67	0.68	0.69	0.70	0.71	0.72	0.73	0.74
t	0.00	0.02	0.25	0.60	0.735	0.770	0.770	0.765	0.760	0.750	0.745	0.735

Determine the transmittances at 0.655 μ and 0.665 μ.

[1] Forsythe, W. E., and Worthing, A. G., *Astrophys. J.*, **61**, 152 (1925).
[2] Roebuck, J. R., *Proc. Am. Acad. Arts Sci.*, **64**, 287 (1930).

6. For the variation in relative spectral brightness at 0.534μ from center to limb of the sun's disk, Abbot [1] of the Smithsonian Institution gives the following data:

$\dfrac{r}{a}$	0.00	0.40	0.55	0.65	0.75	0.825	0.875	0.92	0.95
$\dfrac{B_\lambda}{{}_0 B_\lambda}$	463	440	417	396	366	337	312	281	254

Determine, by the proportional part, the graph, and the Lagrange methods, the relative spectral brightnesses at $r/a = 0.20$ and $r/a = 0.80$. When graphing, choose the scales so that the line drawn makes an angle of roughly $45°$ with the coordinate axes.

7. Using the data of Problem 6, extrapolate to determine a relative spectral brightness for 0.534μ at $r/a = 0.98$, using a combined graph and Gregory-Newton method and the Lagrange method.

[1] Abbot, C. G., The Sun as a Source of Continuous Radiation, p. 76 of *Measurement of Radiant Energy*, Ed. by W. E. Forsythe, New York, McGraw-Hill Book Company, 1937.

CHAPTER II

REPRESENTATION OF DATA BY GRAPHS

1. Introduction. The graphical method of presenting data is an adaptation of the principles of Descartes' analytic geometry, whereby numerical values are represented in geometrical form by the length of a line, the area of a surface, the volume of a solid, or the rotation described by an angle. The fact that all measurable quantities may be given such representation does not mean that all data should be plotted. For certain data a graph means little more than wasted time and labor. For other data, failure to graph results not only in a loss of time and energy, but also in a failure to perceive significant relations. A decision as to whether or not to plot must be trusted to one's common sense.

In this chapter we set forth the general advantages and purposes of graphical representation. Examples and illustrations are given, first of the simple qualitative type, then of the more important quantitative type. Finally, specific suggestions and rules are stated for the construction of graphs of the latter type.

2. Advantages of Graphs. In favor of graphs generally, it may be said that (*a*) they facilitate comparisons of values, (*b*) they appeal to the attention of a reader, (*c*) they permit easy reference to data, and (*d*) they provide a compact form for filing. In addition, most graphs will reveal readily the presence of maxima, minima, critical inflection points, unusually high or low rates of change, and periodic or other significant features in a set of data, whereas otherwise certain of these features may be either overlooked entirely or seen only after a rather careful survey of the tabulated data. Further, with the aid of a graph, one can often determine whether or not a relationship exists between the two variables being considered, and sometimes, if a relationship exists, its mathematical form. Still further, if a satisfactory curve can be drawn, one may differentiate or integrate one variable with respect to the other directly from the graph without knowledge of the mathematical form of the relation represented. These advantages warrant a somewhat detailed study of graphs.

3. Purposes of Graphs—Qualitative and Quantitative. A graph may generally be classed as belonging to one or the other of two groups, depending on the main purpose it is to serve. Those of the first group are designed primarily to present a qualitative picture of a process (e.g., the growth of population in the United States) or of a condition (e.g., the sizes of the available armies of the European nations in 1939). Graphs of the second group are intended primarily as quantitative tools in operating and controlling mechanisms and methods or as guides in research. Commonly both purposes are served by a single graph, though usually one or the other predominates.

4. The Qualitative Graph. Of the qualitative graphs, we have those in which there is represented: (*a*) one variable, *y*, as though a function,

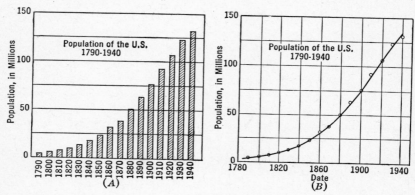

Fig. 1. Examples of two types of qualitative graphs showing their characteristic differences. (*Data from 16th Census of the U.S.*, 1940, Series P-3, No. 21, Nov. 15, 1941.)

$f(x)$, of the other variable, but actually without any suspected causal connection other than that of a simultaneity in time, coincidence in location, etc., and (*b*) $y = f(x)$ with a known or suspected causal connection between the variables. The graphs of Fig. 1 illustrate some of the differences between the two groups. Graphs (*A*) and (*B*) are both plots of the same data. In (*A*) the relative populations at the ends of succeeding decades are emphasized. In (*B*) it is assumed that population and time are somehow related and emphasis is placed on this relation. Both (*A*) and (*B*) belong to the qualitative class of graphs, for though (*B*) is of the type most commonly used as a tool, it is not intended nor is it, in many respects, able to serve any of the uses mentioned in the following section. It is seen (1) that (*A*) is a more striking presentation than (*B*), though the latter shows the rate of growth more clearly; (2) that plotted values of population can be read more quickly from (*A*); and (3) that (*B*) permits more accurate interpolations and extrapolations, uses commonly associated with the quantitative graph.

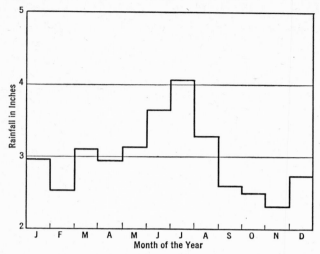

(*A*). A stepped line graph showing average rainfalls in Pittsburgh for the different months of the year for the interval 1880 to 1930. (*Report of the U. S. Weather Bureau.*)

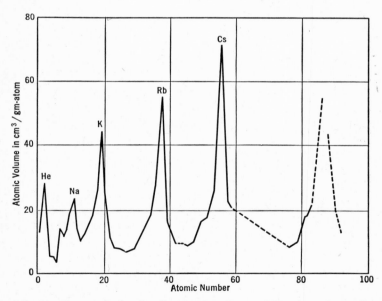

(*B*). A broken line graph showing the atomic volumes of the elements as a function of their atomic numbers. (*Univ. of Pittsburgh, Atomic Physics, 2nd Ed.*, p. 190, New York, John Wiley & Sons, 1937.)

FIG. 2.   Four types of qualitative line graphs.

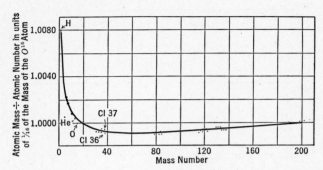

(*C*). A smooth line graph showing losses of mass sustained in the synthesizing of the different types of atoms from the simpler atoms. (*Univ. of Pittsburgh, Atomic Physics, 2nd Ed.*, p. 45, New York, John Wiley & Sons, 1937.)

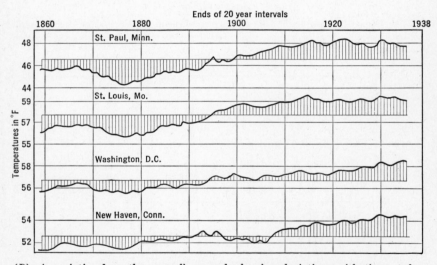

(*D*). A variation-from-the-mean line graph showing deviations with time at four American cities of the average autumn temperatures (strictly 20 year moving averages) from the mean autumn temperature for the 100 year interval 1837 to 1939. (*Kincer, J. B., Temperature Distribution, Extremes, and Trend Tendencies Over the Earth's Surface*, from the symposium entitled *Temperature, Its Measurement and Control in Science and Industry*, p. 355, New York, Reinhold Publishing Corp., 1941.)

FIG. 2.   Four types of qualitative line graphs.—*Continued.*

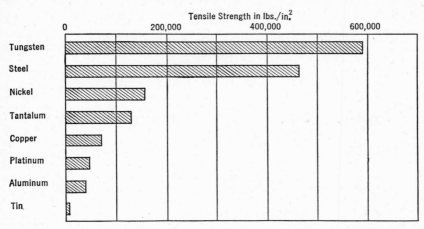

(A). The approximate maximum tensile strengths of wires of various metals. (*Handbook of Chemistry and Physics, 26th Ed.*, p. 1629, Cleveland, Chemical Rubber Publishing Co., 1942.)

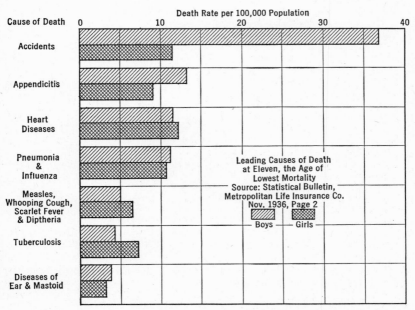

(B). The leading causes of death at the age of eleven, the age of lowest mortality. (*Metropolitan Life Insurance Co. Statistical Bulletin*, Nov. 1936.)

FIG. 3.   Four types of qualitative bar charts.

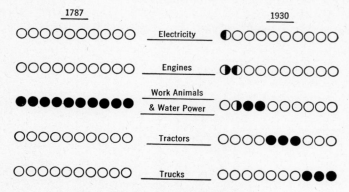

Each Disc Represents 10% of the Total Power

(*C*). Types of power other than human labor power available on U. S. farms in 1930 compared with 1787—a multiple unit bar chart. (*Cohen, P., Technology Review,* **42**, 112, 1940.)

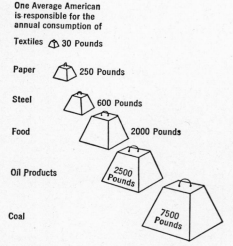

(*D*). The utilization of resources by an average individual—a pictorial bar chart. (*Cohen, P., Technology Review,* **43**, 203, 1941.)

Fig. 3.   Four types of qualitative bar charts.—*Continued.*

Since the qualitative graph is usually drawn for the layman, it should be particularly clear, simple, and attractive. There are various types which satisfy these requirements. Which to choose for a particular case

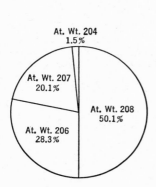

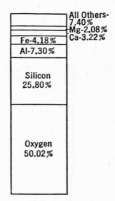

(A). The stable isotopes of lead. (*Committee on Atoms, International Union of Chemistry, Rev. Sci. Instruments,* **7**, 334–335, 1936.)

(B). The composition of the earth's crust to the depth of 10 miles, including the lithosphere, the hydrosphere, and the atmosphere. (*Clarke, F. W., Data of Geochemistry, 4th Ed.,* p. 35, *U. S. Geol. Survey Bull.* 695, Washington, D. C., 1920.)

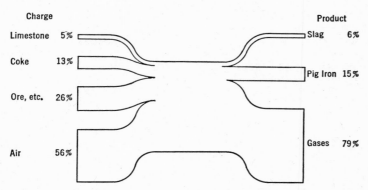

(C). Relative weights of materials charged into and produced by a typical blast furnace.

FIG. 4. Three types of qualitative graphs for expressing percentages.

depends somewhat upon the data, but often the choice is a matter of personal preference. Some common types of qualitative graphs are illustrated in Figs. 2 to 4.

5. The Quantitative Graph. A graph of the second or quantitative class ordinarily shows the relation between two related variables in the form of a regular curve, which may or may not be expressed mathematically.

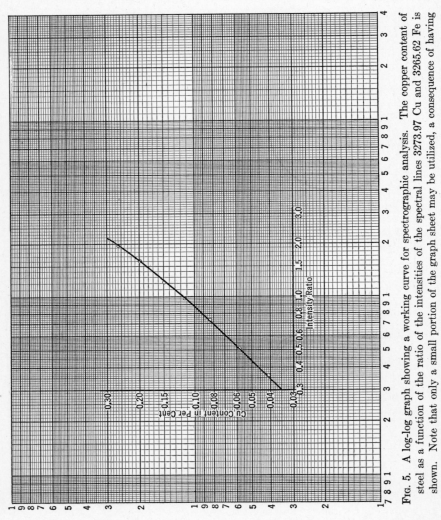

Fig. 5. A log-log graph showing a working curve for spectrographic analysis. The copper content of steel as a function of the ratio of the intensities of the spectral lines 3273.97 Cu and 3265.62 Fe is shown. Note that only a small portion of the graph sheet may be utilized, a consequence of having the scales forced upon the user.

The vast majority of graphs in this class are drawn on ordinary rectangular coordinate paper with uniform scale divisions (Fig. 1B). Other papers in rather common use are the logarithmic or log-log (Fig. 5), the semi-log (Fig. 6), the polar (Fig. 7), and the probability (Fig. 8). Their characteristics as to arrangement of axes and spacing of scales are readily seen. When the relation connects more than two variables, the nomo-gram (Fig. 9) is frequently a satisfactory form of graphical presentation.

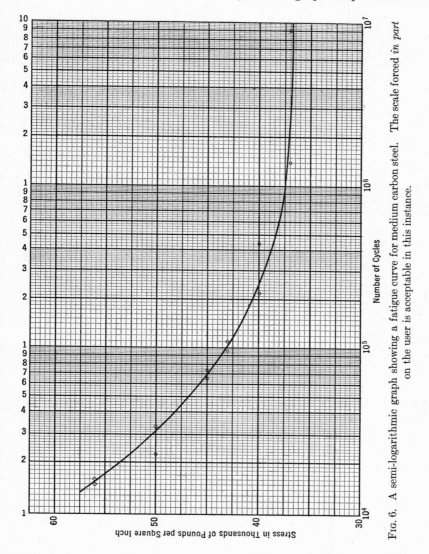

FIG. 6. A semi-logarithmic graph showing a fatigue curve for medium carbon steel. The scale forced *in part* on the user is acceptable in this instance.

In certain cases trilinear paper (Fig. 10) can be used. These latter forms will not be discussed further.

A graph, like any other tool, loses much in effectiveness when certain easily followed principles of construction are disregarded. There are

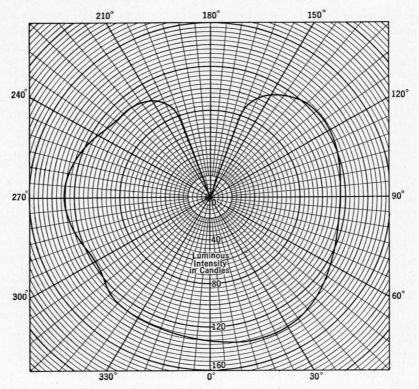

Fig. 7. A polar graph showing the luminous intensity of an incandescent lamp as a function of angle of view.

seven main steps to the preparation of a satisfactory graph. They relate to

(a) choosing the graph paper,
(b) choosing the coordinate scales,
(c) labeling the coordinate scales,
(d) plotting the data,
(e) fitting a curve to the plotted points,
(f) preparing a descriptive caption, and
(g) acknowledging the source of the data.

(a) *Choosing the Graph Paper.* Important questions to consider here are:

1. Is ordinary rectangular paper or log-log paper or something else the most satisfactory for the particular case under consideration?

2. Is there the necessary preciseness of separation of the coordinate lines?

3. Are the lines not so close to one another as to be confusing, yet sufficiently numerous as not to require excessive interpolation?

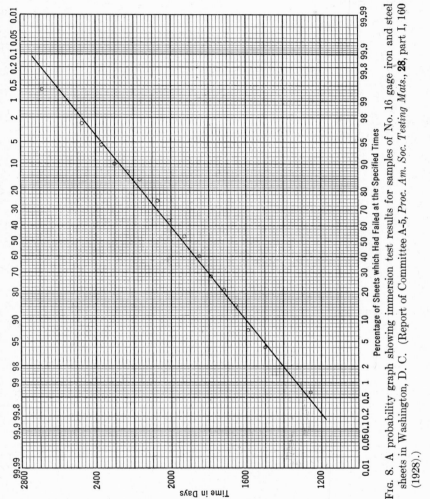

FIG. 8. A probability graph showing immersion test results for samples of No. 16 gage iron and steel sheets in Washington, D. C. (Report of Committee A-5, *Proc. Am. Soc. Testing Mats.*, **28**, part I, 160 (1928).)

4. Is the paper of such quality that it will stand erasures and possible frequent handling?

5. Is the paper of the needed transparency or opacity, on the one hand, to permit of tracing or blueprinting or, on the other hand, to prevent the print on pages below from showing through?

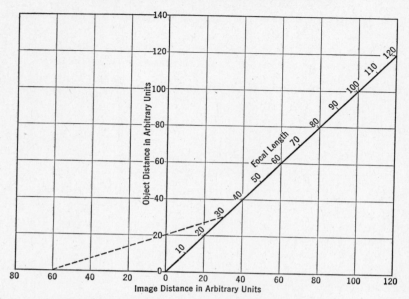

Fig. 9. A nomogram relating object distances, image distances, and focal lengths of mirrors and lenses. The dotted line shows, for example, that an object 20 cm from a 30 cm focal length convex lens is seen through the lens as a virtual image 60 cm back of the lens.

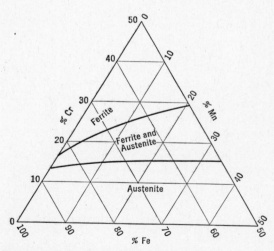

Fig. 10. A trilinear graph showing metallographic phases present in Fe—Mn—Cr alloys at 1830° F. (*Burgess, C. O., and Forgeng, W. D., Metals Technology,* **5**, 1933, *Am. Inst. Mining Met. Engrs. Tech. Pub.* 911.)

6. If the graphs are to be reproduced in print, are the coordinate lines black so that they may show up well or blue so that they may not show at all?

7. Are the sheets of such size as not, on the one hand, to lead to cramped scales, to the elimination of significant figures which the data may justify, and to errors due to the finite widths of the plotted points and the lines that may be drawn; or, on the other hand, to lead to such large scales as to indicate an accuracy greater than that which the data justify? Often the need for a large sheet may be satisfied by pasting together two or more small sheets. Sometimes the margin of a single sheet may be used to extend the scales a sufficient amount.

(b) *Choosing the Coordinate Scales.* A poor choice of scales for the coordinates, more than any other single factor, will make an otherwise acceptable graph unsatisfactory as a tool. Such being the case, the need of suitability rules is evident. Although none can be given to fit all cases, where the maximum revelation of content of data plotted or the maximum of ease and comfort in the use of the plot as a tool are concerned, certain general rules may be stated. Granted the best selection of graph paper, experience has shown it generally desirable to choose the coordinate scales in accord with the following rules.

Rule 1. The scale for the independent variable should be measured along the so-called x-axis.

This rule is a statement of an established custom. Which of two variables shall be viewed as independent is usually greatly influenced, if not actually determined, by either the experimental procedure or the nature of the resulting data. Where in a process of measurement involving two or more variables, the values for one are fixed arbitrarily and corresponding values of the others are then determined, the former is generally regarded as the independent variable. At other times, which variable shall be so regarded is a matter of opinion.

Rule 2. The scales should be so chosen that the coordinates of any point on the plot may be determined quickly and easily.

No scale is acceptable if it is difficult to read. How much scales may differ in this respect is shown by (A) and (B) of Fig. 11, where extremes of readability are presented. Compare the two curves for ease and accuracy with which refractive indexes corresponding to wavelengths of 0.47μ, 0.65μ, etc., can be located and read.

For rectangular graph paper with the space between successive main lines divided into ten equal small spaces, the most convenient scales are those in which such distances between successive main lines represent a difference in value of one, two, four, or five units, or these values multiplied by 10^n where n is an integer. Scales in which this distance represents three, six, seven, nine, or eleven units, etc., should seldom if ever be used. Other scales, corresponding to 1.25, 2.5, or eight units per main scale division may occasionally be found desirable.

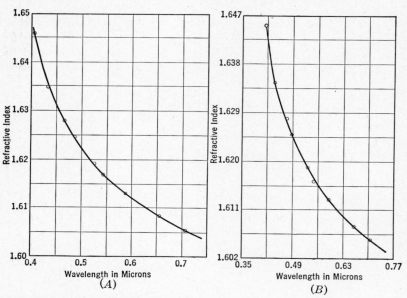

FIG. 11. Refractive index of dense flint glass as a function of wavelength, on graphs with (A) convenient scales, (B) inconvenient scales.

Rule 3. The scales should be numbered so that the resultant curve is as extensive as the sheet permits, provided the uncertainties of measurement are not made thereby to correspond to more than one or two of the smallest divisions.

Coordinate scales need not, in fact generally do not, start from zero values. The scale for each variable may well begin, in accord with this rule, at or just below the lowest rounded value in the data and end at or just above the highest. There is, however, no justification for extending a scale to such an extent that the uncertainties for the values plotted correspond to more than one or two of the finer scale divisions (Fig. 12).

Rule 4. Other things being equal, the variables should be manipulated to give a resultant curve which approaches as nearly as practicable to a straight line.

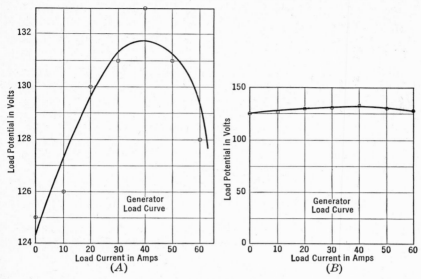

FIG. 12. Showing over extension and under extension of a graph scale. In describing the performance of a generator, graph A exaggerates and graph B minimizes the accuracy.

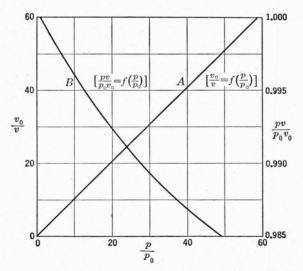

FIG. 13. Showing an advantage possessed by a differential graph. With p_0 representing 1 atmosphere and v_0 1 gmv/mole, curve A shows, for nitrogen at $0°$ C, v_0/v as a function of p/p_0, and curve B shows pv/p_0v_0 as a function of p/p_0. The deviation from the ideal gas law is evident in curve B but not in curve A. (*Michels, Wouters, and de Boer, Physica* (7), **1**, 587, 1934.)

The straight line is the simplest curve to construct and to use. Where precision is a matter of concern, it is usually advantageous to plot, when possible, variables which cause the resultant curve to approximate a straight line. This is especially true when the graph is to be used for finding slopes or the constants of a rational equation by the methods to be described later. For example, if we wish to find the constants of an equation of state of the type

$$pv = RT(1 + ap + bp^2 + cp^4) \qquad [1]$$

a graph of p as a function of v (Fig. 13A) is of little value. If, however, the product pv is plotted as a function of p (Fig. 13B), the resultant curve will approximate a line whose deviation from the horizontal will show the first order deviation of the gas from an ideal gas, and whose deviation from straightness will show the second order variation from an ideal gas.

Many other types of equation can be rectified. Thus, the equation

$$B_\lambda = {}_0B_\lambda \, e^{-c_2/\lambda[(1/T)-(1/T_0)]} \qquad [2]$$

gives the Wien approximation for the spectral brightness, B_λ, of a black body at temperature T in terms of the value ${}_0B_\lambda$ for a black body at a standard temperature, T_0. If experimental values of ln (B_λ) are plotted against $1/T$, the curve will approximate a straight line, since by taking natural logarithms of the original equation one obtains

$$\ln (B_\lambda) - \ln ({}_0B_\lambda) = \frac{c_2}{\lambda}\left(\frac{1}{T_0} - \frac{1}{T}\right) \qquad [3]$$

an equation linear in ln (B_λ) and $1/T$. The departure of such an experimental curve from a straight line (for any one of many non-black sources) is a measure of the deviation of the spectral emissivity of the source from constancy. Similarly, data thought to satisfy the Steinmetz law for work done in a magnetization cycle

$$W = aB^k \qquad [4]$$

should give a straight line if log W is plotted as a function of log B. Many other equations may be handled similarly. (See Fig. 8.)

Sometimes when the data fit a certain type of equation, a straight line graph can be obtained by plotting the measured variables on other than regular rectangular graph paper more simply than by manipulating the variables in some such manner as above. Thus, where the difference in temperature, θ, between a body and its surroundings at any time, t, is given by Newton's law of cooling

$$\theta = \theta_0 e^{\alpha t} \qquad [5]$$

a cooling curve approximating a straight line may be obtained by plotting $\log \theta$ as a function of t. When semi-log paper is used, plotting θ as a function of t suffices. This eliminates looking up and tabulating logarithms. This latter method, however, in view of suitability rules 3 above and 5 below, is often unsatisfactory, and especially so if the constants θ_0 and α are to be evaluated.

Rule 5. Scales should be chosen such that the curve shall, to the extent possible, have a geometrical slope approximating unity.

The geometrical slope of a curve at a point is the tangent of the angle between the x-axis and the tangent to the curve at that point, and is different from the physical slope of the curve dy/dx at the point in question, whose value contains the units of the quantities plotted. The latter quantity does not depend on the scales chosen for plotting, while the former depends completely on the scales chosen.

Though rather generally ignored, the rule is of great value where precision is concerned. This is especially true when a graph consisting of a straight line, obtained in accord with rule 4, is to be used as a tool.

With scales chosen as suggested above, it is often found that a curve results whose geometrical slope does not vary much from unity at any point. This is quite desirable, for then deviations of the plotted points from the line will show up most markedly. Conversely, the line to be drawn may be drawn most precisely. An illustration is furnished in Fig. 14 by the work of Hecht [1] and others in their important study of "Energy at the Threshold of Vision." Using Fig. 14B leads to greater certainty of correct assignments of quantum numbers than does using Fig. 14A. Doubters may well trace the base lines and the computed curves for $n = 6$ quanta on translucent paper and attempt to fit the curves to the other sets of data. On the other hand, if one wishes to cover up departures of observed plotted points from a line to be drawn, he should choose the coordinate scales so that the geometrical slope of the line to be drawn shall be far from unity. The main objection to the use of log-log and semi-log papers, noted under rule 4, depends on these considerations. Usually the scales which they force lead to geometrical slopes differing widely from unity, and automatically many variations are covered up.

There are many cases, it is true, where the precision of one coordinate is so low with regard to the other that nothing is gained by following the unity slope rule and where in the interest of economy of space one should deviate from the rule (see Fig. 12).

[1] Hecht, S., Shaler, S., Pirenne, M. H., *Science*, **93**, 585 (1941).

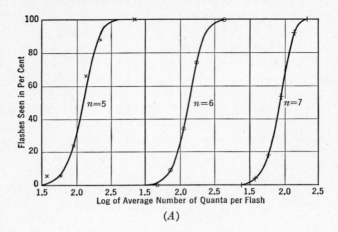

(A)

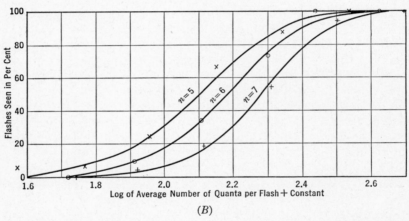

(B)

FIG. 14. Showing an advantage due to having an approximate geometrical slope of unity for the important portion of a line graph. The points graphed represent results obtained by three observers at the threshold of vision, using light whose wavelength coincides with the maximum of the luminosity curve of the eye, and show the fractional part of the time that flashes were perceived as a function of the average number of quanta of light received per flash at the cornea. The lines represent the expected responses of the three observers in case just 5 ($n = 5$), just 6, and just 7 quanta of the light used are required to produce just perceptible flashes. For the sake of separating the curves in graph B, 0.050 has been added to the observed log abscissa values for $n = 6$ and 0.350 for $n = 7$. That the expectation curves are properly associated with the observed data is more evident when one makes use of graph B than when using graph A. (*Hecht, S., Shaler, S., and Pirenne, M. H., Science,* **93**, 585, 1941, and personal correspondence.)

(c) *Labeling the Coordinate Scales.* Scales are marked on graphs by labeling certain main coordinate lines with the values they represent. Not all main lines need be so marked. Often labeling every second main line results in the shortest time of location of a desired coordinate. Whatever the plan, it should be uniform. One need not begin with the first line at the left or at the bottom of the graph unless the scale begins at zero, in which case the 0 should be recorded. It is suggested that the numbers used in marking the scale contain as many significant figures as the data justify, or as are readable from the curve if, as is usually the case, the data are roughly equally accurate throughout. That is, 3.50 may well be written instead of 3.5 when it is possible to distinguish 3.51 from 3.50 in the data and on the plot. An essential part of a satisfactory scale designation is the inclusion along each axis of the name of the quantity represented and the units in which it is measured, e.g., Temperature in °K, Pressure in atmospheres, etc. When the logarithm of a quantity is being plotted, the units in which the quantity itself is measured should be stated, e.g., log of Radiancy in watts/cm^2, although strictly speaking it is impossible to take the logarithm of anything but a pure number.

(d) *Plotting the Data.* Plotting the points to represent the data at hand is a simple process, but it should be done carefully if an accurate tool is desired. If the data to be plotted are experimental or computed and subject to computational errors, each point should be indicated by a suitable symbol, such as a cross (x) or a circle (O). Different sets of data on the same graph should be denoted by different symbols if there is a possibility of confusion otherwise. When computed data which are subject to negligible computational errors are plotted, the curve necessarily passes through all points plotted and nothing is gained by indicating plotted points. The point symbols should be omitted in such cases.

(e) *Fitting a Curve to the Plotted Points.* Two types of cases are to be considered. In one, owing to the fewness of the observed points, the uncertainty as to the law of dependency of the assumed dependent variable on the assumed independent variable, or the possibility of unknown variables entering, the plotted points are connected by straight lines. (Fig. 15.) [1] In the other type, sufficient points are assumed present to justify drawing a smooth continuous curve to represent the actual variation of the related variables under consideration in the regions between the plotted points. For these cases the curves are generally so drawn. What is said here applies almost wholly to this type.

[1] Hardy, J. D., and DuBois, E. F., "The Significance of the Average Temperature of the Skin," p. 537 of report of symposium on *Temperature—Its Measurement and Control in Science and Industry*, New York, Reinhold Publishing Corporation, 1941.

Proficiency in judging the most likely course of a smooth curve through a set of plotted points requires practice. In the case of a single-valued function one may always include all plotted points on a

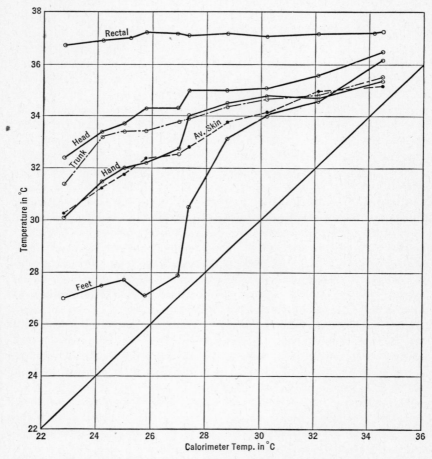

FIG. 15. Illustrating the irregular broken line graph. Data, obtained with subjects in a calorimeter, show variations in the temperatures of various portions of the human body with different environmental temperatures. (*Du Bois, E. F., Report on the Temperature of the Human Body in Health and Disease,* in the symposium on *Temperature, Its Measurement and Control in Science and Industry,* p. 24, New York, Reinhold Publishing Corp., 1941.)

single smooth curve of many inflections. It is absurd, however, to think that such a curve will represent the true relation between y and x, for many curves can be drawn which will pass through the plotted points.

Usually a much better curve for representing the relation sought is obtained by following the principles listed below.

1. The curve should be smooth, with few inflections.

2. The curve should pass as close as reasonably possible to all of the plotted points.

3. The curve need not pass through a single point, much less through either of the end points. Very often they are end points because of limits in the accuracy of the instrument or of the method used. In such cases less weight should be given to them than to the other points of the plot.

4. The curve should usually, but not always, contain no inexplicable discontinuities, cusps, or other peculiarities.

5. When taken in moderate-sized groups, about one-half of the plotted points of each group should fall on one side of the curve and the other half on the other side.

In addition to the pencil or the pen, transparent frames such as the ordinary so-called celluloid triangles, irregular curves, and ships curves are desirable for curve-drawing. In place of the last-named instrument, certain adjustable curves may often be conveniently employed. The transparency feature is of decided importance in connection with the application of the principles stated above.

Granted the desired instruments, the procedure to follow in locating and drawing the best curve consists of (a) locating with the unaided eye, or, perhaps with the aid of fixed transparent frames, certain points through which or close to which it seems that the curve should be drawn; (b) drawing lightly through the selected points, in pencil and in a preliminary way, one section of the curve and then successive adjacent sections; and (c) drawing the desired curve in its final form, changing where necessary the lightly drawn preliminary curve in accord with the principles stated above.

In the drawing of both the preliminary and final curves, when a shift or a change of a frame is made, one should see that the frame in the adjacent shifted position permits of the smooth joining on of the new section without a sharp change of slope at the junction. The satisfactory carrying out of this procedure may be readily judged by the *squint test*. In making this test, the eye is held close to the plane of the graph sheet in such a manner that one can sight along the curve. If the adjoining sections have not been correctly matched, a sudden change in direction of the curve will be quite noticeable. Figs. 16A and 16B represent the same data. As regarded ordinarily, both curves seem smooth and satisfactory. The squint test, however, reveals that one

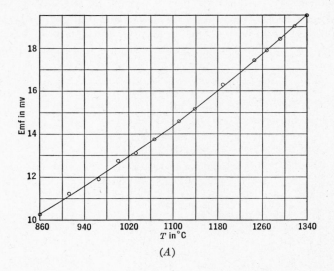

(A)

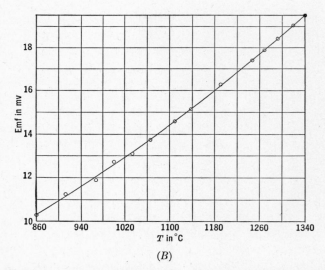

(B)

FIG. 16.   Showing two graphs which differ in that, as revealed by the squint test, the curve of A shows a kink while the curve of B does not.   When slopes of curves are determined graphically such kinks are dangerous and may lead to erroneous conclusions.   See discussion relating to Fig. 2 of Chapter XI.   The data plotted show the emf of Rh vs. Pt as a function of the temperature of the hot junction.

of the curves fails to pass the test. Where the curve is to be differentiated graphically, the need for its application is great. As will appear in Chapter XI, a suspected kink in a graph of the data of Fig. 16 was the source of a difference of opinion that was later settled by least-squares treatment.

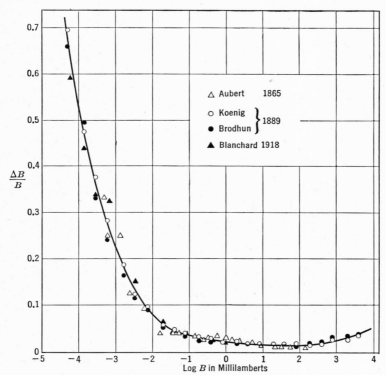

FIG. 17. A combined graph, as presented by Hecht, showing for various individuals the brightness discrimination factor $\Delta B/B$ as a function of the logarithm of the brightness B.

Kinks in curves are not always to be avoided. Their presence may reveal important processes or changes of process. An interesting case is furnished by the work of Hecht.[1] It concerns the explanation of the observed variations in brightness discrimination, $\Delta B/B$, where ΔB represents the least perceptible change in the brightness B, as a function of that brightness. Results of previous reliable work relating to what is commonly referred to as the Weber-Fechner law was combined in a single

[1] Hecht, Selig, *Proc. Natl. Acad. Sci. U. S.*, **20**, 644 (1934); *J. Psychol.* (6) **33**, 161 (1936).

graph (Fig. 17). Except perhaps for the results of Aubert, there seems no indication of a kink or break in the curve. By the proper choice of scales and with the aid of an assumed explanatory law, Hecht, however, found significant breaks in the data for each observer and made them obvious. We here consider the observations reported by Blanchard.[1] His data, disregarding for lack of space the value for the lowest brightness, are replotted in Fig. 18 on the same basis as for Fig. 17, but with scales so chosen that the presence of a kink or break might well show up. Except for the single value of $\Delta B/B$ corresponding to -3.17 for log B, there seems to be no indication of a break. Most workers in this field passed over it as just another rather unsatisfactorily determined point. Hecht, however, believing that the two types of visual processes corresponding respectively to the cone and the rod receptors of the retina might well follow different laws, sought for indications in such brightness-discrimination curves. With log $\Delta B/B$ rather than $\Delta B/B$ graphed as a function of log B (Fig. 19), the evidence became unmistakable. Not only that, but there were verified the two theoretical equations,

$$\frac{\Delta B}{B} = c\left(1 + \frac{1}{K_B}\right) \tag{6}$$

which with properly chosen values for c and K holds for the rod or low-brightness region, and

$$\frac{\Delta B}{B} = c\left(1 + \frac{1}{\sqrt{KB}}\right)^2 \tag{7}$$

which similarly holds for the cone or high-brightness region. The kink, which with the proper function graphed became a break, is highly important here. Without doubt other similar breaks are waiting for discoverers.

When the curve to be drawn is known or judged to be a straight line, its course may be located by moving about among the points a stretched black thread, the straight edge of a transparent frame or, best of all, a straight line scratch on the under surface of a transparent frame. In any case the final line should be drawn with the aid of a straight edge.

If a curve is to be used for the exact determination of corresponding values of y and x, or if it is to be used for obtaining highly precise derivatives, it is necessary to make the curve as fine a line as is practicable.

Some authors, in drawing curves among plotted points, draw them in segments, with a break occurring wherever the curve if continued would cut through a point symbol. The questionable argument in its favor seems

[1] Blanchard, Julian, *Phys. Rev.*, **11**, 81 (1918).

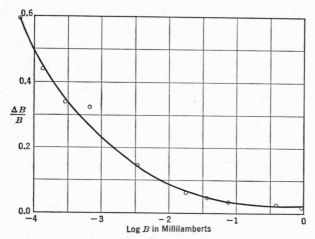

FIG. 18. A graph similar to Fig. 17, but with much more favorable scales for showing kinks or breaks, in which only data by Blanchard are regraphed. (*Blanchard, Julian, The Brightness Sensibility of the Retina, Phys. Rev.,* **11**, 81, 1918.)

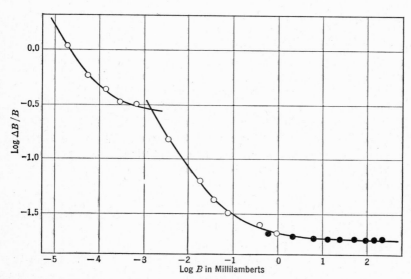

FIG. 19. Showing, as presented by Hecht, the data of Fig. 18 replotted with log ($\Delta B/B$) rather than $\Delta B/B$ as a function of log B. The open circles represent data obtained by Blanchard in 1918, the full circles added data obtained by Lowry in the same laboratory in 1931. The full line curves represent the predictions of Eqs. 6 and 7.

to be one of artistic appearance. For the qualitative graph, that suffices. For the quantitative graph, however, it seems wise to continue the curve as a line regardless of the point symbols intersected. Where the squint test is of value, the curve must continue thus uninterrupted.

(*f*) *Preparing a Descriptive Caption.* The caption accompanying a graph when completed should include an accurate description of what the graph is intended to show. How complete this should be is somewhat a matter of opinion. If the graph is to be a part of a publishable report, it should be remembered (1) that graphs and tables are often the portions of an article which excite the interest of a possible reader; (2) that time is saved in the reading of an article if suitable descriptive captions are found adjacent to the figures; (3) that certain material incorporated in a caption may appropriately be left out of the body of the text; and (4) that in referring to a paper some time after a reading, a reader hopes to find certain quantitative data that it contains in its figures and tables, and that a search in the body of the paper for that which may appropriately be placed in a caption is likely to be a source of irritation. On the other hand, one can hardly include the whole of the text in figure and table captions.

(*g*) *Acknowledging the Source of the Data.* Wherever the data for a graph are taken from a published report or the work of another, the source should be plainly stated in the caption. An exception occurs where the data have been widely published, e.g., the Maxwellian distribution of molecular speeds for a gas. Wherever a graph by itself is presented as a report, it should carry the name of the author and an appropriate date.

6. Summary. As devices for presenting data, graphs have many advantages over other forms of presentation. Two classes of graphs are considered: the qualitative, including those intended for a convenient and picturesque way of presenting data, and the quantitative, including those intended for use as tools, either in research or in operating or controlling mechanisms or processes.

There are many types of qualitative graphs which possess the attributes of clarity, simplicity, and attractiveness desirable in graphs of this class. Regardless of type, each such graph should contain an appropriate and complete descriptive caption.

Though the quantitative graph usually takes the form of a regular curve, there are many different types in this class since the curve may often be plotted on any one of about six different general types of papers. The quantitative graph should be carefully drawn and certain general principles of good construction should be followed. These principles are listed and discussed in detail for each of seven main steps in the preparation of a satisfactory graph: (1) choosing the graph paper, (2) choosing the coordinate scales, (3) labeling coordinate scales, (4) plotting the data, (5) fitting a curve to the plotted points, (6) preparing a descriptive caption, and (7) acknowledging the source of the data.

PROBLEMS

1. Following the instructions given in the text, and using the data given below showing the radiancy of tungsten [1] as a function of temperature, plot curves showing $\mathcal{R} = f(T)$ on ordinary rectangular graph paper, $\mathcal{R} = f(T)$ on log-log paper, and $\log \mathcal{R} = f(\log T)$ on ordinary rectangular paper.

T	$\mathcal{R}$	T	$\mathcal{R}$
1600° K	7.74 watts/cm^2	2400° K	55.70 watts/cm^2
1800	14.15	2600	80.6
2000	23.65	2800	112.5
2200	37.20	3000	154.5

2. Using the following data [2] showing the brightness of incandescent tungsten as a function of temperature, plot with care four curves on one or more two-page sized or larger sheets of rectangular graph paper. Use ships or other equivalent curves and apply the squint test. For the first graph plot $B = f(T)$; for the others plot $\log B = f(\log T)$, but choose the coordinate scales to yield approximate geometrical slopes of 1.0, 0.5, and 0.25. Keep this plot for use in a graphical differentiation problem in Chapter IV.

T	B	T	B
2000° K	20.0 c/cm^2	2600° K	345 c/cm^2
2100	35.9	2700	495
2200	61.0	2800	690
2300	100.1	2900	950
2400	156.0	3000	1270
2500	234.0		

[1] Forsythe, W. E., and Watson, E. M., *J. Optical Soc. Am.* **24**, 114 (1934).
[2] Idem.

CHAPTER III

REPRESENTATION OF DATA BY EQUATIONS

1. Introduction. It is often desirable to express in equation form the relationships between variables which may be suggested by graphs or tables. On the one hand such a derived equation or one or more of its coefficients may represent the objective of a research. On the other hand, it may be desired as an aid to differentiation, integration, or interpolation. Moreover, an equation is a compact, easily remembered, and convenient form for the presentation of data. Methods for obtaining such equations will be discussed here. However, only forms involving one dependent variable will be treated. Periodic curves will be taken up in Chapter V; distribution functions for statistical data in Chapter VII.

2. Rational and Empirical Equations. An equation for representing experimental data is said to be rational if it is derivable theoretically. For example, the equation

$$q = a \sin \frac{d}{2} \qquad [1]$$

relating the throw, d, of a ballistic galvanometer to the electric charge, q, causing the throw, is rational, since it is based on established physical laws. In this case the finding of an equation reduces to the finding of a value for the constant, a.

An equation for representing experimental data is said to be empirical if its form has not been derived theoretically. In the process of obtaining such an equation, one must first find a suitable form. Given that form, the further procedure becomes the same as that for the rational equation.

3. Choosing a Suitable Form for an Empirical Equation. The ideal empirical equation is one that represents the experimental data closely, yet has only a few arbitrary constants—two generally opposing characteristics. As a consequence a choice must sometimes be made involving a sacrifice either of simplicity or of precision of fit. On the other hand, a choice must sometimes be made from two or more functions which, in a given case, approach the ideal form about equally. There is no straightforward method of obtaining a most suitable function for a given

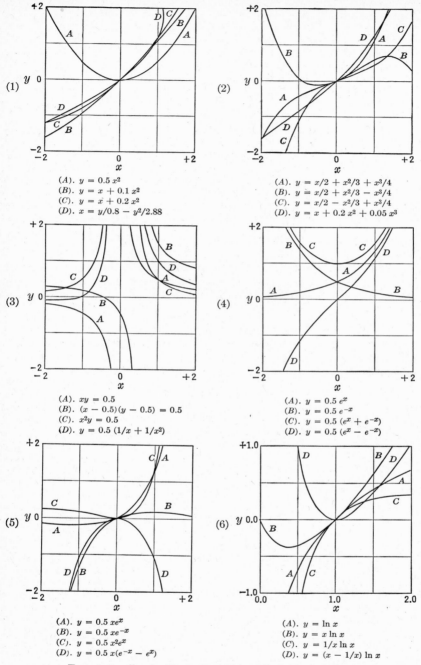

(1)
(A). $y = 0.5\,x^2$
(B). $y = x + 0.1\,x^2$
(C). $y = x + 0.2\,x^2$
(D). $x = y/0.8 - y^2/2.88$

(2)
(A). $y = x/2 + x^2/3 + x^3/4$
(B). $y = x/2 + x^2/3 - x^3/4$
(C). $y = x/2 - x^2/3 + x^3/4$
(D). $y = x + 0.2\,x^2 + 0.05\,x^3$

(3)
(A). $xy = 0.5$
(B). $(x - 0.5)(y - 0.5) = 0.5$
(C). $x^2y = 0.5$
(D). $y = 0.5\,(1/x + 1/x^2)$

(4)
(A). $y = 0.5\,e^x$
(B). $y = 0.5\,e^{-x}$
(C). $y = 0.5\,(e^x + e^{-x})$
(D). $y = 0.5\,(e^x - e^{-x})$

(5)
(A). $y = 0.5\,xe^x$
(B). $y = 0.5\,xe^{-x}$
(C). $y = 0.5\,x^2e^x$
(D). $y = 0.5\,x(e^{-x} - e^x)$

(6)
(A). $y = \ln x$
(B). $y = x \ln x$
(C). $y = 1/x \ln x$
(D). $y = (x - 1/x) \ln x$

FIGS. 1–6. Graphs illustrating frequently used equations.

57

set of data. Usually one simply plots the data, represents them approximately by means of a curve, and, guided by experience and a knowledge of analytic geometry, makes a guess as to the form of the equation. If, on being tested, this form is found unsatisfactory, a new guess is made and tested. This process is repeated until one is satisfied. With the ease and precision of such testing in mind, it is usually advisable, where possible, to select coordinates which yield as nearly a straight line as possible.

The selection of such coordinates and the drawing of a best curve whose equation is sought brings up the question of the changed reliabilities (more precisely weights) assigned, in effect, to the various plotted points, which accompany changes of coordinates. The significance of weights, how coordinate changes affect them, and the account that should be taken of changed weights will be discussed in Chapters IX to XI.

To assist the less experienced, the curves of Figs. 1 to 6 are presented as examples of the shapes of curves which may be obtained from several of the more common types of equations by varying the arbitrary constants.

4. Testing the Suitability of an Empirical Function to Represent a Set of Data. Fortunately, one need not evaluate the constants for a particular form of equation to see whether or not that form fits the data satisfactorily. Certain preliminary tests often not only give the information desired, but help later on when the constants are to be calculated. For simple types of equations with only one or two arbitrary constants, the following graphical test is convenient. For more complex forms, a tabular test may be used.

(a) *The Graphical Suitability Test.* The procedure here consists of three steps.

1. Write the assumed relation, $f(x, y, a, b) = 0$, in a form that is linear with respect to two selected functions, F_1 and F_2, which do not include the arbitrary constants, a or b, thus

$$F_1 = A + BF_2 \qquad [2]$$

Of these two functions, often one may involve x only while the other involves y only, and the new constants A and B will be functions of a and b only.

2. Calculate F_1 and F_2 for a few, four say, widely separated pairs of values for x and y.

3. Plot F_1 as a function of F_2. Insofar as a straight line is obtained, the assumed equation would seem to be satisfactory. Greater certainty is obtained by taking into account the remaining pairs of F_1 and F_2.

To illustrate, we shall use the method to determine whether or not the data of Table I may be represented by an equation of the form

$$y = ae^{bx} \qquad\qquad [3]$$

TABLE I

DATA FOR ILLUSTRATING A GRAPHICAL TEST FOR THE SUITABILITY OF AN EMPIRICAL
FUNCTION

x	1	2	3	4	5	6	7	8	9
y	1.78	2.24	2.74	3.74	4.45	5.31	6.92	8.85	10.97
$\log y$	0.250	0.350	0.438	0.540	0.648	0.725	0.840	0.947	1.040
y_c	1.76	2.21	2.78	3.51	4.39	5.52	6.93	8.71	10.94

Eq. 3 written in a form similar to Eq. 2 becomes

$$\log y = \log a + (b \log e)x \qquad\qquad [3a]$$

in which $\log y$ corresponds to F_1, x to F_2, $\log a$ to A, and $(b \log e)$ to B. Plotting $\log y$ for four selected points, marked by $\odot$ in Fig. 7, as a function of x, a straight line results. The choice of Eq. 3 seems satisfactory

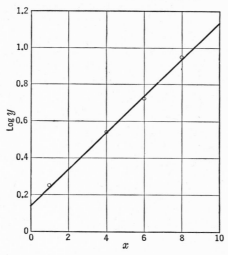

FIG. 7. A plot for testing whether Eq. 3 fits the data of Table I.

for representing the given data. This conclusion is verified by the further plotting of points and finally by comparing the observed y-values with the computed values (shown as y_c in Table I) eventually obtained.

Methods for determining the constants of the equation $y_c = f(x)$ are given below.

Certain two-constant equations, such as $y = a(1 - e^{bx})$, $y = x^a + bx$, etc., which cannot be written in the form of Eq. 2 cannot be tested by this method. Among those which can, however, be so tested are

$$y = ax \tag{4}$$

$$y = a + bx \tag{5}$$

$$y = ab^x \tag{6}$$

$$y = ae^{bx} \tag{7}$$

$$y = ax^b \tag{8}$$

$$y = \frac{x}{a + bx} \tag{9}$$

$$y = e^{(a+bx)}, \text{ etc.} \tag{10}$$

(b) *The Tabular Suitability Test.* When more than two arbitrary constants are involved, a tabular method is convenient for testing an assumed equation form. The procedure depends on the equation assumed, but in general it consists of (a) making a plot of the experimental data, (b) constructing a table from the graph, (c) forming certain successive differences, and (d) examining the final set of differences for approximate constancy, the criterion of suitability for the assumed equation.

For data already in a suitable tabular form, steps a and b are unnecessary. Procedures and criteria for testing several of the more common types of equations are given in Table II.

Just what successive differences are to be obtained is not difficult to determine. Consider case 1 of the table. If

$$y = a + bx + cx^2 + dx^3 \tag{11}$$

then also

$$y + \Delta y = a + b(x + \Delta x) + c(x + \Delta x)^2 + d(x + \Delta x)^3 \tag{12}$$

and

$$\Delta y = (b\Delta x + c\Delta x^2 + d\Delta x^3 + \cdots) + (2c\Delta x + 3d\Delta x^2 + \cdots)x$$
$$+ (3d\Delta x + \cdots)x^2 \tag{13}$$

Since Δx is to be kept constant during the test, Eq. 13 takes the form

$$\Delta y = a' + b'x + c'x^2 \tag{14}$$

of which a', b', and c' are constant.

TABLE II

Procedures and Criteria for Testing the Suitability of Various Assumed Forms of Equations to Represent Given Data

Case	Assumed Form of Equation	Procedures Based on a Constant Value for Δx		Criterion of Suitability
		Plot, Then Make Table of	Obtain These Successive Differences	
1	$y = a + bx + cx^2 + \cdots + qx^n$	$y = f(x)$	$\Delta y; \Delta^2 y; \Delta^3 y; \cdots; \Delta^n y$	$\Delta^n y$ is constant
2	$y = a + \dfrac{b}{x} + \dfrac{c}{x^2} + \cdots + \dfrac{q}{x^n}$	$y = f\left(\dfrac{1}{x}\right)$	$\Delta y; \Delta^2 y; \Delta^3 y; \cdots; \Delta^n y$	$\Delta^n y$ is constant
3	$y^2 = a + bx + cx^2 + \cdots + qx^n$	$y^2 = f(x)$	$\Delta y^2; \Delta^2 y^2; \Delta^3 y^2; \cdots; \Delta^n y^2$	$\Delta^n y^2$ is constant
4	$\log y = a + bx + cx^2 + \cdots + qx^n$	$\log y = f(x)$	$\Delta(\log y); \Delta^2(\log y); \cdots; \Delta^n(\log y)$	$\Delta^n(\log y)$ is constant
5	$y = a + b(\log x) + c(\log x)^2$	$y = f(\log x)$	$\Delta y; \Delta^2 y$	$\Delta^2 y$ is constant
6	$y = ab^x = ae^{b'x}$	$\log y = f(x)$	$\Delta(\log y)$	$\Delta(\log y)$ is constant
7	$y = a + bc^x = a + be^{c'x}$	$y = f(x)$	$\Delta y; \log \Delta y; \Delta(\log \Delta y)$	$\Delta(\log \Delta y)$ is constant
8	$y = a + bx + cd^x = a + bx + ce^{d'x}$	$y = f(x)$	$\Delta y; \Delta^2 y; \log \Delta^2 y; \Delta(\log \Delta^2 y)$	$\Delta(\log \Delta^2 y)$ is constant
9	$y = ax^b$	$\log y = f(\log x)$	$\Delta(\log y)$	$\Delta(\log y)$ is constant
10	$y = a + bx^c$	$y = f(\log x)$	$\Delta y; \log \Delta y; \Delta(\log \Delta y)$	$\Delta(\log \Delta y)$ is constant
11	$y = axe^{bx}$	$\ln y = f(x)$	$\Delta \ln y; \Delta \ln x$	$(\Delta \ln y - \Delta \ln x)$ is constant

Repetition of the above procedure leads similarly to

$$\Delta^2 y = a'' + b'' x \qquad [15]$$

and finally to

$$\Delta^3 y = a''' \qquad [16]$$

This last equation shows that, if Eq. 11 holds and Δx is maintained constant throughout, the third-order tabular differences will be constant. Conversely, if such third-order tabular differences are found constant except for uncertainties of measurement, etc., the data may be represented by Eq. 11.

TABLE III

TABULAR TEST FOR THE SUITABILITY OF AN EQUATION OF THE FORM $y = a + bc^x$ TO REPRESENT CERTAIN OBSERVED DATA

Observed Values		Taken from Graph		Computations of Successive Differences		
x	y	x	y	Δy	$\log (\Delta y)$	$\Delta \log (\Delta y)$
0.50	17.3	0	16.6			
				1.3	0.114	
1.75	19.0	1	17.9			0.090
				1.6	.204	
2.75	21.0	2	19.5			.097
				2.0	.301	
3.50	22.5	3	21.5			.079
				2.4	.380	
4.50	25.1	4	23.9			.097
				3.0	.477	
5.25	28.0	5	26.9			.091
				3.7	.568	
6.00	30.5	6	30.6			.085
				4.5	.653	
6.50	33.0	7	35.1			.103
				5.7	.756	
7.50	38.0	8	40.8			

As inspection will show, the underlying theory for the other cases of the table is much the same. Consider case 7. The equations corresponding to Eqs. 11 to 16 are

$$y = a + be^{c'x} \qquad [17]$$

$$y + \Delta y = a + be^{c'(x+\Delta x)} = a + be^{c'\Delta x}e^{c'x} \qquad [18]$$

$$\Delta y = be^{c'x}(e^{c'\Delta x}-1) \tag{19}$$

$$\ln \Delta y = \ln[b(e^{c'\Delta x}-1)] + c'x = b' + c'x \tag{20}$$

$$\Delta(\ln \Delta y) = c'\Delta x = b'' \tag{21}$$

Many other functions may be handled similarly.   In the case of still other functions, there seems no possibility of such treatment as a criterion of suitability of equation form, e.g.,

$$y = ae^{-bx} + ce^{+dx} \tag{22}$$

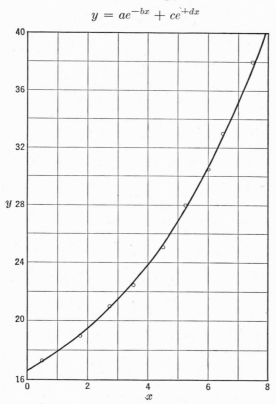

FIG. 8. A plot constructed to test the suitability of Eq. 23 to represent the data in the first two columns of Table III.

To illustrate the use of Table II, we shall test whether or not an equation of the form

$$y = a + bc^x \tag{23}$$

can suitably represent the data in the first two columns of Table III. We first plot y as a function of x (Fig. 8).   Then, using the curve, we list values of y corresponding to equally spaced values of x (Table III).

Next we obtain, in turn, the successive differences, Δy, log (Δy), and Δ log (Δy). The values of Δ log (Δy) are essentially constant, indicating for Eq. 11 a certain suitability of choice.

5. Evaluating the Arbitrary Constants. Once a satisfactory form of equation has been chosen, or, in the rational case, derived, the problem has been reduced to finding suitable values for the constants. Numerous procedures, varying in ease and in accuracy, are available. The most accurate is the method of least squares, discussed in detail in Chapter XI. Since it ordinarily involves much computation, other methods, less accurate but also less cumbersome, are very much used. Frequently one of these methods is used to give an approximate result which may be later improved by the successive approximation method or, in cases where the labor is justified, by the method of least squares. If it is known in advance in any case that either the successive approximation or the least-squares method is to be used finally, considerable time may often be saved by definitely dealing at first with only rounded convenient values for the desired constants.

(a) *Straight-Line Graph Method—Equations with Two Arbitrary Constants.* For the simple equation with one or two arbitrary constants, the constants can be evaluated by a continuation of the graphical test for suitability outlined above. The method is best explained by an illustration. If was shown that the data of Table I may be represented by $y = ae^{bx}$ because log y plotted against x gave a straight line. The slope of this line is $(b \log e)$. The intercept on the (log y)-axis is log a. From Fig. 7, the slope is found to be 0.0991, and the intercept, 0.147, whence

$$b = \frac{0.0991}{\log e} = \frac{0.0991}{0.4343} = 0.228 \qquad [24]$$

and

$$a = 10^{0.147} = 1.403 \qquad [25]$$

The final form of Eq. 3 is, then,

$$y = 1.403e^{0.228x} \qquad [26]$$

Values of y calculated with the aid of this empirical equation (listed in Table I as y_c) agree well with the listed values for y.

In obtaining the slope of the line, the familiar two-point formula

$$b = \frac{y_2 - y_1}{x_2 - x_1} \qquad [27]$$

may be used. Here (x_1,y_1) and (x_2,y_2) may be any two points on the line, but for greatest accuracy they should be as far apart as practicable.

For convenience they may be taken as the intersections of the curve with two main x-coordinate lines, so that $(x_2 - x_1)$ shall be a convenient divisor. Similarly, the intercept, a, when it cannot be read directly from the plot, can be calculated by the two-point formula

$$a = \frac{y_1 x_2 - y_2 x_1}{x_2 - x_1} \qquad [28]$$

The advantages of using the same two points in evaluating a and b are obvious. Those familiar with the general determinant method of finding equations will conveniently substitute the given values for x and y in the determinant equation

$$\begin{vmatrix} y & x & 1 \\ y_1 & x_1 & 1 \\ y_2 & x_2 & 1 \end{vmatrix} = 0 \qquad [29]$$

and simplify.

The extension of the above method to Eqs. 4 to 10 listed above should be evident.

(b) *The Straight-Line Graph Method—Equations with Three Arbitrary Constants.* To evaluate the constants of a three-constant equation by the straight-line graph method, one must first eliminate one of the constants and then treat the resultant two-constant equation as described above. The scheme to be used in eliminating a constant depends on the type of equation being fitted. Methods follow for three of the most common types of equations

$$y = a + bx + cx^2 \qquad [30]$$

$$y = a + bx^c \qquad [31]$$

and

$$y = a + bc^x \qquad [32]$$

For straight-line methods of treating other three-constant and many four-constant equations, the reader is referred to more complete sources.[1]

$$(1) \quad y = a + bx + cx^2$$

The equation is that of a parabola, of which a is the y-intercept. If data are given close to $x = 0$, or if the $y = f(x)$ curve may be safely extrapolated to the y-axis, a may be determined directly. It is then a

[1] Running, T. R., *Empirical Formulas*, New York, John Wiley & Sons, 1917. Lipka, J., *Graphical and Mechanical Computation*, New York, John Wiley & Sons, 1918.

simple matter to treat $(y - a)$ as a new variable, y' say, and to evaluate b and c, as shown above, using the form

$$\frac{y'}{x} = b + cx \tag{33}$$

When a cannot be thus evaluated, we may possibly shift the origin of the coordinate system to some convenient point (x_0, y_0) in the neighborhood of the actual plotted points, through which it has been decided that the curve shall pass. The coordinates (x', y') of the observed points in the new system are given in magnitude by $(x - x_0, y - y_0)$. Since the curve now passes through the origin it takes the form

$$y' = b'x' + c'x'^2 \tag{34}$$

which may be rewritten as

$$\frac{y'}{x'} = b' + c'x' \tag{35}$$

Values for b' and c' are found from a plot of $y'/x' = f(x')$. Then c, b, and a are given by

$$c = c' \tag{36}$$

$$b = b' - 2c'x_0 \tag{37}$$

and

$$a = y_0 - b'x_0 + c'x_0^2 \tag{38}$$

The method will not be illustrated, since it is generally less acceptable for parabolic equations than the selected-points method, combined, if necessary, with the successive-approximation method.

$$(2) \quad y = a + bx^c$$

Here the constant a represents the y-intercept of the curve if c is positive, or of an asymptote parallel to the x-axis if c is negative. It may sometimes be obtained directly from the $y = f(x)$ curve. Usually a satisfactory value cannot be so obtained, and we must evaluate or eliminate it by some alternate method. Probably the simplest suitable method of evaluation proceeds as follows.

Select from the experimental curve, three widely separated points, (x_1, y_1), (x_2, y_2), and (x_3, y_3) such that

$$x_3 = (x_1 \cdot x_2)^{\frac{1}{2}} \tag{39}$$

Then

$$bx_3^c = (bx_1^c \cdot bx_2^c)^{\frac{1}{2}}$$

or, since for every point on the curve, $bx^c = y - a$

$$y_3 - a = \sqrt{(y_1 - a)(y_2 - a)}$$

whence

$$a = \frac{y_1 y_2 - y_3{}^2}{y_1 + y_2 - 2y_3} \qquad [40]$$

We may then treat $(y - a)$ as a new variable, y', and write Eq. 31 as

$$y' = bx^c \qquad [41]$$

for which b and c can be evaluated by the straight-line graph method for two constants. If the plot $\log y' = f(\log x)$ is concave downward, the computed a is too small, and vice versa. Corrections for such errors may be obtained by the method of repeated trials.

$$(3) \quad y = a + bc^x$$

When this type of equation fits the data, the value of a cannot be read directly from the curve of $y = f(x)$. It can, however, be calculated as follows.

Choose three widely separated points on the curve such that

$$x_3 = \tfrac{1}{2}(x_1 + x_2) \qquad [42]$$

Then

$$(\log c)x_3 = \tfrac{1}{2}[(\log c)x_1 + (\log c)x_2] \qquad [43]$$

or, since for any point on the curve,

$$(\log c)x = \log \frac{(y - a)}{b} \qquad [44]$$

$$\log \frac{(y_3 - a)}{b} = \tfrac{1}{2}\left[\log \frac{(y_1 - a)}{b} + \log \frac{(y_2 - a)}{b}\right]$$

$$= \log \sqrt{\frac{y_1 - a}{b} \frac{y_2 - a}{b}} \qquad [45]$$

Hence

$$y_3 - a = \sqrt{(y_1 - a)(y_2 - a)} \qquad [46]$$

and

$$a = \frac{y_1 y_2 - y_3{}^2}{y_1 + y_2 - 2y_3} \qquad [47]$$

As before, we may then set $(y - a) = y'$, whereupon

$$y' = bc^x \qquad [48]$$

for which b and c may be evaluated by the straight-line graph method for two constants given above. If in the plot of $\log y' = f(x)$, the line is slightly concave downward, the computed a is too large, and vice versa. As before, corrections for such errors may be obtained by the method of repeated trials.

(c) *Method of Selected Points.* The procedure of this method consists of four steps.

1. Plot y as a function of x and fit a smooth curve as carefully as is needed.

2. From the curve choose a number of points equal to n, the number of arbitrary constants in the equation selected to represent the data. For convenience these points should lie on main x-coordinate lines; for accuracy they should be widely separated without lying at the relatively uncertain extremes of the curve.

3. Substitute in turn each of these n pairs of x- and y-values into the chosen equation, thus obtaining a set of n equations with n unknowns.

4. Solve these n equations simultaneously for the unknowns, i.e., for the desired arbitrary constants.

When the chosen equation is transcendental with three or more arbitrary constants, step 4 may prove to be very difficult. When, however, the equation is, or can be made, linear with respect to its arbitrary constants, the procedure may be simplified by the use of determinants. Steps 3 and 4 then combine to a single step.

Illustrating the simplified procedure, consider the curve of Fig. 9, for which an equation linear with respect to its arbitrary constants, of the type

$$y = a + bx + cx^2 \tag{49}$$

is desired. The first step of plotting has been carried through. As the second step, we select the points where the curve crosses convenient x-coordinate lines at 4, 8, and 12. The corresponding y-coordinates are 8.1, 12.8, and 16.0. As the third and fourth steps combined, we write the determinant equation

$$\begin{vmatrix} y & 1 & x & x^2 \\ 8.1 & 1 & 4 & 16 \\ 12.8 & 1 & 8 & 64 \\ 16.0 & 1 & 12 & 144 \end{vmatrix} = 0 \tag{50}$$

Simplified, this determinant yields

$$y = 1.90 + 1.738x - 0.0469x^2 \tag{51}$$

as the equation sought. Equations thus derived should always be tested for errors and for goodness of fit. Substitutions, accordingly, of 4, 8, and 12 for x show that no computational error has been made in obtaining Eq. 51. However, tests for $x = 2$ and $x = 16$ yield values for y that do not check with the curve as drawn. Two possible conclusions may be drawn. (1) It is dangerous to extrapolate beyond observed regions. (2) Perhaps the desired form of equation is not capable of

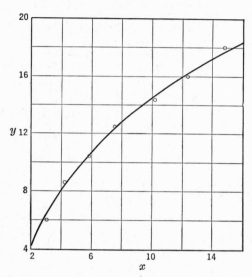

FIG. 9. A parabolic curve whose constants may be evaluated by the selected points method.

satisfactorily representing the data, and one should try another form. Reference to Figs. 1 to 6 reveals a similar curve in curve A of Fig. 6 and suggests that an equation of the form

$$y = a \ln x \qquad [51a]$$

might satisfy. Actually, however, additional terms, similar to those of Eq. 51, are needed for a satisfactory representation.

Essentially the same procedure may often be used for less obvious cases where linearity with respect to the arbitrary constants themselves does not exist, but where linearity with respect to certain functions of those constants does exist. Where the desired equation is of the form

$$y = a \sin (\omega t + \phi) \qquad [52]$$

with y and ωt as variables and a and ϕ as the unknown constants, a change of form yields

$$y = a \cos \phi \sin \omega t + a \sin \phi \cos \omega t \qquad [53]$$

of which $a \cos \phi$ and $a \sin \phi$ are now the unknown constants in linear form. As such they may be obtained easily by using the above method. To obtain separate values for a and ϕ thereafter, we make use of the two obvious relations

$$a = (a^2 \cos^2 \phi + a^2 \sin^2 \phi)^{\frac{1}{2}} \qquad [54]$$

and

$$\phi = \tan^{-1} \frac{a \sin \phi}{a \cos \phi} \qquad [55]$$

Where the desired equation is, for example, of the type

$$y = ae^{(bx + cx^2)} \qquad [56]$$

linearity with respect to arbitrary constants may be obtained by changing the form of the equation to

$$\ln y = \ln a + bx + cx^2 \qquad [57]$$

Obviously, determining $\ln a$ is equivalent to determining a. For equations like Eq. 56 which are made linear by writing them in linear form, it will usually prove advantageous in step 1, to plot $\ln y$ as a function of x rather than to plot one variable as a function of the other.

As a second example illustrating this very important method, let us fit Eq. 56 to the data of Table IV by the method of selected points. An examination of the range of y-values in Table IV shows the impracticability of trying to draw a curve of $y = f(x)$ from which to choose the points with sufficient accuracy. Hence, we follow the suggestion of the previous paragraph and write the equation in the linear form of Eq. 57, or, even better for computational purposes, in the form

$$\log y = \log a + (0.4343b)x + (0.4343c)x^2$$
$$= a' + b'x + c'x^2 \qquad [58]$$

We then tabulate values of $\log y$ and plot them as a function of x, Fig. 10. Remembering the convenience and accuracy suggestions of step 2 above, we select the three points $(0.250, 0.356)$, $(0.550, 1.031)$, and $(0.850, 2.158)$. If, further, we make the simplifying substitutions

$$x' = \frac{x - 0.550}{0.300} \qquad [59]$$

and

$$z = \log y - 1.031 \qquad [60]$$

we obtain a simple expression capable of easy evaluation, namely

$$
\begin{vmatrix}
z & 1 & x' & x'^2 \\
-0.675 & 1 & -1 & 1 \\
0 & 1 & 0 & 0 \\
+1.127 & 1 & 1 & 1
\end{vmatrix} = 0 \qquad [61]
$$

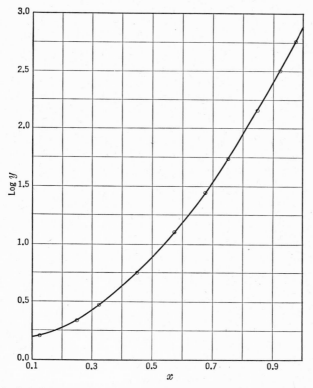

FIG. 10. A plot showing log $y = f(x)$, Table IV, for obtaining an equation by the selected points method.

To one familiar with determinants, inspection yields the solution

$$
z = \left(\frac{1.127 + 0.675}{2}\right)x' + \left(\frac{1.127 - 0.675}{2}\right)x'^2
$$

$$
= 0.901x' + 0.226x'^2 \qquad [62]
$$

Substituting for z and x' in accord with Eqs. 59 and 60, we obtain

$$\log y = 0.1388 + 0.2411x + 2.5111x^2 \qquad [63]$$

and

$$y = 1.377e^{(0.5552x + 5.782x^2)} \qquad [64]$$

TABLE IV

DATA FOR ILLUSTRATING THE SELECTED POINTS METHOD OF FINDING AN EMPIRICAL EQUATION

[The prime of y'_c is intended to indicate that these computed values are first approximations only]

x	y	$\log y$	y'_c	$\log y'_c$	$\log y - \log y'_c$
0.125	1.595	0.2028	1.615	0.2082	−0.0054
.250	2.239	0.3500	2.269	0.3559	− .0059
.325	2.995	0.4764	3.037	0.4824	− .0060
.450	5.626	0.7502	5.698	0.7557	− .0055
.575	12.97	1.1069	12.81	1.1076	− .0007
.675	27.92	1.4459	27.90	1.4455	+ .0004
.750	53.88	1.7314	53.95	1.7320	− .0006
.850	141.7	2.1514	143.8	2.1579	− .0065
.925	320.8	2.5062	323.8	2.5103	− .0041
.975	571.3	2.7569	576.7	2.7610	− .0041

Values of y and $\log y$ calculated by Eq. 64 are given in Table IV in the columns headed y'_c and $\log y'_c$. Inspection shows that the computed $\log y'_c$ values are uniformly too great. A value of $\log a$ less by 0.0038, yielding 1.365 for a itself gives a much better check between y and y'_c. However, even with the suggested change, it is evident that the fit is not as satisfactory as it might be. With the −0.0038 change assumed made, values of $\log y - \log y'_c$ are uniformly too great for low and for high values of x and too small for intermediate values. The further application of the successive approximation method, as shown later, yields corrections which eliminate this tendency.

For equations with more than two arbitrary constants, the method of selected points is recommended whenever applicable, for it is generally simpler to carry through than the straight-line graph method, and more accurate than the method of averages to be described.

(d) *Method of Averages.* This method is a *selected-points* method based on a particular method of selecting points, which can be used only when the type of equation dealt with is linear with respect to its arbitrary constants; i.e., when the equation may be written in the form of Eq. 49. It is also known as Norman Campbell's *zero-sum* method,[1] so called because, for the straight line, it yields zero as the sum of all the deviations. For this case with points randomly and similarly distributed with respect to the straight line to be drawn, this method yields results comparable with those obtained by the least-squares method (Chapter XI).

The procedure for the equation, $y = f(x)$, containing n arbitrary constants consists in (1) dividing the N observed pairs of x, y values into n approximately equal groups, choosing for each group only pairs that correspond to adjacent points when graphed; (2) averaging the x- and the y-values for each group separately to obtain n pairs of x, y values; (3) with these average x, y values to describe selected points, using the selected-point method as described above.

The results depend somewhat on the way the original N pairs of values are grouped and accordingly cannot be expected to yield the most precise results in the general case. This method does not require a graph and generally speaking is much shorter than most other methods. However, when one departs from the straight-line equation, for which it is particularly acceptable, it still serves well in giving a first approximation which may be improved by further approximations.

Let us apply the method to data (Table V), given by Osborne and Meyers [2] of the Bureau of Standards in an attempt to obtain an equation for use in determining the boiling point of water as a function of barometric pressure. For this purpose only data in the neighborhood of the normal boiling point is needed. The successive-difference test shows that a three term equation of the type

$$T = T_0 + a(p_0 - p) + b(p_0 - p)^2 \qquad [65]$$

in which the subscript (0) refers to standard conditions, namely, 100° C and 760 mm–Hg, should suffice. Certain data as selected are shown grouped in columns two and three. The averages are shown in the next two columns. For carrying the work further, it is desirable to introduce new variables

$$x = \frac{p - 720 \text{ mm–Hg}}{60 \text{ mm–Hg}} \qquad [66]$$

$$y = \frac{T - 98.486°\text{C}}{1.000 \text{ C}°} \qquad [67]$$

[1] *Phil. Mag.*, VI, **39**, 177 (1920).

[2] Osborne, N. S., and Meyers, C. H., *J. Research Nat. Bur. Standards*, **13**, 1 (1934).

TABLE V

DATA SHOWING THE BOILING POINTS OF PURE WATER FOR VARIOUS PRESSURES IN
THE NEIGHBORHOOD OF NORMAL ATMOSPHERIC PRESSURE GIVEN BY OSBORNE AND
MEYER,[1] FOR USE IN ILLUSTRATING THE METHOD OF AVERAGES FOR DETERMINING
EQUATIONS

Group No.	p in mm–Hg	T in °C	Group p in mm–Hg	Average T in °C
1	800 780 760	101.443 100.729 100.000	780	100.724
2	740 720 700	99.255 98.492 97.712	720	98.486
3	680 660 640	96.914 96.095 95.256	660	96.088

In determinant form, the equation using x and y becomes

$$\begin{vmatrix} y & x & x^2 \\ 2.238 & 1 & 1 \\ -2.398 & -1 & 1 \end{vmatrix} = 0 \qquad [68]$$

which simplifies to

$$y = 2.318x - 0.080x^2 \qquad [69]$$

and to

$$T = 98.486° \text{ C} - 0.03863 \frac{\text{C}°}{\text{mm–Hg}} (p - 720 \text{ mm–Hg})$$

$$- 0.0000222 \frac{\text{C}°}{\text{mm–Hg}^2} (p - 720 \text{ mm–Hg})^2 \quad [70]$$

On transferring to standard conditions this becomes

$$T = 99.995° \text{ C} - 0.03686 \frac{\text{C}°}{\text{mm–Hg}} (760 \text{ mm–Hg} - p)$$

$$- 0.0000222 \frac{\text{C}°}{\text{mm–Hg}^2} (760 \text{ mm–Hg} - p)^2 \quad [71]$$

[1] Idem.

Though the fit of this equation is not bad, it is quite inferior to that of the equation which follows.

$$T = 100.000° \text{ C} - 0.03682 \frac{\text{C}°}{\text{mm–Hg}} (760 \text{ mm–Hg} - p)$$

$$- 0.0000219 \frac{\text{C}°}{(\text{mm–Hg})^2} (760 \text{ mm–Hg} - p)^2 \quad [72]$$

(e) *Method of Moments.* This method is sometimes used when the equation sought is of the form

$$y = f(x) = a + bx + cx^2 + \cdots + px^q \quad [73]$$

The procedure requires that the x-coordinates of the points to which the equation is to be fitted differ by a constant, Δx. If the original data do not satisfy this condition, it is necessary to plot the original data, fit a smooth curve, and choose from the curve a series of points with equidistant abscissas. For such a set of points we define, in succession, the zero moment, μ, the first moment, μ', the second moment, μ'', etc., of y with respect to x as

$$\mu = \Sigma y \Delta x = \Delta x \Sigma y$$
$$\mu' = \Sigma x y \Delta x = \Delta x \Sigma x y \quad [74]$$
$$\mu'' = \Sigma x^2 y \Delta x = \Delta x \Sigma x^2 y, \text{ etc.}$$

It is then assumed that these moments are related to the desired curve as follows:

$$\mu = \int_\alpha^\beta f(x) dx = \Delta x \Sigma y$$

$$\mu' = \int_\alpha^\beta x f(x) dx = \Delta x \Sigma x y \quad [75]$$

$$\mu'' = \int_\alpha^\beta x^2 f(x) dx = \Delta x \Sigma x^2 y, \text{ etc.,}$$

where α represents the lowest x-value less $\frac{1}{2}\Delta x$, and β the highest x-value plus $\frac{1}{2}\Delta x$. If the desired equation is linear in x, only the first two equations of Eqs. 75 are used; if of the second degree, the first three are used; etc. Substituting for $f(x)$ its equal, Eq. 73, and integrating, we obtain for the linear case

$$a(\beta - \alpha) + \frac{b(\beta^2 - \alpha^2)}{2} = \Delta x \Sigma y$$

$$\frac{\alpha(\beta^2 - \alpha^2)}{2} + \frac{b(\beta^3 - \alpha^3)}{3} = \Delta x \Sigma x y \quad [76]$$

The values of a and b may then be obtained by solving Eqs. 76 simultaneously.

Equations obtained by this method deviate from those obtained by more reliable methods, the more so the fewer the number of points. Its use is not recommended, since it is faulty in theory and usually entails more computational labor than far more reliable methods.

6. Successive Approximations. For cases where the desired equation is, or can be made, linear with respect to its arbitrary constants, the results obtained using one of the methods above may generally be improved by taking successive approximations. Let the equation, transformed if necessary to a form linear with respect to the arbitrary constants or functions of them, be written

$$y = a + bx + cx^2 + \cdots \qquad [77]$$

and let the values for the arbitrary constants and the computed y-values calculated as first approximations, using one of the above described methods, be represented by primes, a', b', y'_c, etc.

Ordinarily, in accord with a suggestion made above, it will be advantageous to use rounded values for a', b', etc., but not for the y'_c's computed with their aid. So doing greatly reduces computational labor.

The procedure for obtaining a second approximation follows: (1) Compute for the various given x-values the corresponding values of $y - y'_c$. (2) Plot $(y - y'_c)$ as a function of x and fit, if possible, a smooth curve to the plotted points. Note that in this plot the distances of the points from the x-axis represent deviations of the first approximation equation from the observed data, and that the distances from the plotted points to the curve represent deviations of the observed data from the second approximation equation which is to be derived. (3) If a curve can be fitted, obtain its equation, either by the method used to obtain $y' = f(x)$, or by any other suitable method. (4) Add this correction equation to the first approximation equation to obtain the second approximation equation.

If a third approximation is needed, steps 1 to 4 may be repeated. If necessary, still further approximations may be made until the best possible fit is obtained. This condition is attained when the curve obtained by step 2 coincides with the x-axis.

On the other hand, the least-squares method may be used to obtain the second approximation equation. So obtained, it is identical with that obtained by least-squares treatment of the original data and cannot be further improved. This procedure, involving the obtaining of a first approximation by some simpler method as outlined above, which generally lightens the computational labor connected with the method of least squares, and increases greatly the ease of detection of computational errors, is further explained in Chapter XI.

At the close of the discussion of the selected-points method, it was indicated that the equation there derived to represent the data of Table IV, namely

$$y = 1.377e^{(0.5552x + 5.782x^2)} \qquad [64]$$

or in linear form for the undetermined constants,

$$\log y = 0.1388 + 0.2411x + 2.5111x^2 \qquad [63]$$

could be bettered to overcome certain deficiencies in fit. With this purpose in mind, let us attempt improvement by successive approximations, using the selected-points method.

That Eqs. 64 and 63 fail to a certain extent is indicated in the last column of Table IV. To correct for the deviations shown, we seek an equation of the same form as Eq. 63 to represent ($\log y - \log y'_c$) as a function of x. One first plots, as in Fig. 11A, ($\log y - \log y'_c$) = $f(x)$. Then, selecting $(0.3, -0.0052)$, $(0.6, -0.0004)$, and $(0.9, -0.0040)$ as probable points for the first approximation correction, one obtains for that correction

$$\Delta'(\log y'_c) = -0.0184 + 0.0580x - 0.0467x^2 \qquad [78]$$

Plotting next, as taken from the graph, the differences ($\log y - \log y'_c$) $- \Delta'(\log y'_c) = f(x)$ gives the distribution shown in Fig. 11B. A second approximation correction seems desirable. Selecting the points $(0.3, 0.0006)$, $(0.6, -0.0010)$, and $(0.9, 0.0006)$, the following second correction equation is obtained:

$$\Delta''(\log y'_c) = 0.0054 - 0.0213x + 0.0178x^2 \qquad [79]$$

Plotting the new differences in Fig. 11C, one sees the possibility for a third approximation correction. For such correction, there is shown

$$\Delta'''(\log y'_c) = 0.0015 - 0.0025x \qquad [80]$$

Whether or not this correction should be represented by a straight line, and if so, by the one indicated, is a matter of opinion. At any rate, that given can hardly be bettered with certainty without recourse to the least-squares method.

Adding the three correction equations to Eq. 63 one obtains the fourth approximation

$$\log y''''_c = 0.1273 + 0.2747x + 2.4828x^2 \qquad [81]$$

and finally, writing y in place of y''''_c

$$y = 1.3406e^{(0.6325x + 5.7170x^2)} \qquad [82]$$

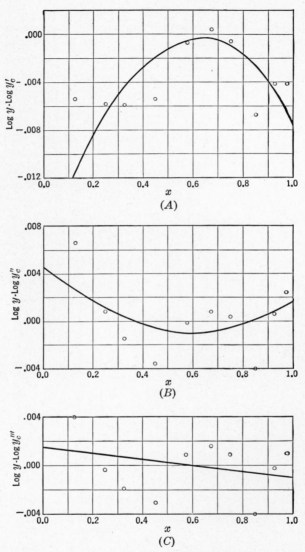

FIG. 11. Graphs used to improve, by successive approximations, the fit of Eqs. 60 and 64 in representing the data of Table IV. *A*, *B*, and *C* are graphs leading to first, second, and third correction equations respectively.

The next question concerns the extent to which the computed constants are significant. Their probable errors (see Chapter VIII) cannot be determined, though, as will be shown in Chapter XI, probable errors can be determined for constants obtained by the least-squares method. Here we must be content with estimates. Inspection of Fig. 11C indicates that, at the most, reliance on computed values for log y to represent the measurements given in Table IV cannot exceed 0.0005. With log y varying from 0.12 for $x = 0$ to 2.7 for $x = 1.0$, this means for dy/y, the differential of log y, a variation from about 1/240 to about 1/5000. It is therefore desirable to include in the way of significant digits in the computed constants of Eq. 81 only as many as will contribute 1/5000th of the whole or more. For $x = 1$, where the value of log y is roughly 2.9, this means a $\Delta(\log y)$ of 0.0006. To the extent of six in the ten thousandth place, it is to be seen that contributions are made by the last digits given in each of the computed constants, and that none could be made by additional digits had they been included. It follows that the computed constants for Eq. 81 are significant only to the extent shown. As to whether or not the coefficients of x and x^2 in Eq. 82 should be rounded off to 0.632 and 5.717, the answer is difficult, since these are borderline cases.

The rather irregular nature of the distribution of plotted points as shown in Fig. 11 was largely responsible for the need of the unusually large number of approximations made before the final equation was obtained in the case illustrated above. Often, particularly if the data are highly consistent, only one approximation correction is needed. Consider in this connection data by Regnault as reported by Fowle.[1] (Table VI.) The equation to be fitted is based on the extremely important thermodynamic relation known as the Clapeyron equation

$$L = T \frac{dp}{dT} (v_2 - v_1) \qquad [83]$$

of which L is a heat of transformation, e.g., vaporization, from phase 1 to phase 2, and T, p, and v are, in order, temperature, pressure, and specific volume. The data selected concern the saturated vapor pressure of CCl_4. (See Table VI and Fig. 12.) From the plot of log $p = f(1/T)$, the first approximation equation, that of a straight line in accord with thermodynamic reasoning, is readily obtained. With rounded values

---

[1] Fowle, F. E., *Smithsonian Physical Tables*, 7th Revised Edition, p. 176, The Smithsonian Institution, Washington, D. C., 1920.

TABLE VI

THE SATURATED VAPOR PRESSURE OF CARBON TETRACHLORIDE CCl₄ FOR VARIOUS
TEMPERATURES AS DETERMINED BY REGNAULT AND REPORTED BY FOWLE,[1] AND
CERTAIN COMPUTATIONS TO ILLUSTRATE THE SUCCESSIVE APPROXIMATION METHOD
OF FINDING AN EQUATION TO REPRESENT GIVEN DATA

T in °C	p in mm–Hg	$\log \dfrac{p}{1\text{ mm–Hg}}$	T in °K	$\dfrac{1}{T}$ in $\dfrac{1}{\text{K}°}$	$\dfrac{1600\,°\text{K}}{T}$	$\log \dfrac{p'}{1\text{ mm–Hg}}$	$10^5 \log \dfrac{p}{p'}$
55.0	376.3	2.57553	328.16	0.0030473	4.87568	2.57432	121
60.0	447.4	2.65070	333.16	.0030016	4.80256	2.64744	326
65.0	528.7	2.72321	338.16	.0029572	4.73152	2.71848	473
70.0	621.1	2.79316	343.16	.0029141	4.66256	2.78744	572
75.0	725.7	2.86076	348.16	.0028722	4.59552	2.85448	628
80.0	843.3	2.92598	353.16	.0028316	4.53056	2.91944	654
85.0	975.1	2.98905	358.16	.0027920	4.46720	2.98280	625
90.0	1122.3	3.05010	363.16	.0027536	4.40576	3.04424	586
95.0	1286.9	3.10955	368.16	.0027162	4.34592	3.10408	547

for the constants, and hence no expectation of a close fit, we use as such
the straight line

$$\log \frac{p'}{1\text{ mm–Hg}} = 2.97 - 1600\,°\text{K}\left(\frac{1}{T} - 0.00280\,\frac{1}{\text{K}°}\right) \qquad [84]$$

Values for this function are given in the next to the last column of the
table. In the last column, headed $10^5 \log (p/p')$, is shown the extent
to which Eq. 84 fails to represent the data. These values are plotted
in Fig. 12. The points shown as ○ are seen on the magnified scale,
which may now be used, to lie on a smooth curve which seems slightly
off that for a second-degree parabola. Selection of a power series of the
third degree in $\left(\dfrac{1}{T} - 0.0028\,\dfrac{1}{\text{K}°}\right)$ and using positions where the curve,
if drawn, would intersect the ordinates at 0.0027, 0.0028, 0.0029, and
0.0030 lead to the correction equation

$$\log \frac{p''}{p'} = 635 \times 10^{-5} + 4.75\,\text{K}°\left(\frac{1}{T} - 0.0028\,\frac{1}{\text{K}°}\right) - 7.5 \times 10^4\,\text{K}°^2$$

$$\left(\frac{1}{T} - 0.0028\,\frac{1}{\text{K}°}\right)^2 - 125 \times 10^6\,\text{K}°^3\left(\frac{1}{T} - 0.0028\,\frac{1}{\text{K}°}\right)^3 \qquad [85]$$

[1] Idem.

That this correction equation has succeeded well is shown by the curve that has been drawn according to the equation.

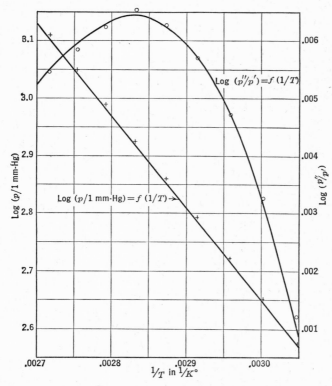

Fig. 12. A graph showing the saturated vapor pressure of CCl₄ as a function of temperature. The straight line represents a rounded first approximation. The points plotted as small circles represent the failure of that approximation. How well the second approximation accounts for the failure of the first is shown by the fit of the third-degree curve of Eq. 85 which has been drawn.

Equation 85 added to Eq. 84 yields the relation desired, namely

$$\log \frac{p''}{1 \text{ mm–Hg}} = 2.97635 - 1595.25 \text{ K}° \left(\frac{1}{T} - 0.0028 \frac{1}{\text{K}°}\right)$$

$$- 7.5 \times 10^4 \text{ K}°^2 \left(\frac{1}{T} - 0.0028 \frac{1}{\text{K}°}\right)^2$$

$$- 125 \times 10^6 \text{ K}°^3 \left(\frac{1}{T} - 0.0028 \frac{1}{\text{K}°}\right)^3 \qquad [86]$$

Differentiation of Eq. 86 and substitution in Eq. 83, once $(v_2 - v_1)$ is known, leads to a desired heat of vaporization.

7. Summary. Data which yield a smooth curve on plotting may often be profitably represented by an equation. For the empirical case, the problem of fitting an equation to a set of data involves two steps: (1) finding a suitable form of equation to represent the data, and (2) obtaining suitable values for the arbitrary constants. For the rational case, the form of the equation is known from theoretical considerations, so that only step (2) is involved.

For the empirical equation, there is no straightforward way of performing step (1); one can only guess at a suitable form from the shape of the curve representing the data. There are, though, methods of testing whether a particular guess is a good one. For most equations with only one or two arbitrary constants, a graphical test may be used; for equations with three or more arbitrary constants, a tabular method (Table II) is often applicable.

There are several methods for finding values for the arbitrary constants. The method of least squares (Chapter XI) is the most reliable, but generally the most laborious. Of the substitute methods, (1) the straight-line graph method may be used for most two-constant forms of equations as well as several three- and four-constant forms. It will generally give more accurate results with less labor than any other substitute method for the two-constant forms for which it is applicable. (2) The method of selected points may be used for almost all forms of equations but is most suitable for linear forms or forms which can be made linear with respect to their arbitrary constants. This method is generally the most accurate for equations with three or more arbitrary constants, and is especially recommended when successive approximations are to be made. (3) The method of averages, a special selected-points method, may be used only for equations which can be written in a form linear with respect to the arbitrary constants. For the straight line case it is highly precise. It does not require the construction of a graph. (4) The method of moments is applicable only to equations expressing y as a polynomial in x, and is considerably less reliable than any of the other methods discussed in this chapter.

When fitting equations which are linear with respect to their arbitrary constants, the results obtained by applying one of the above methods may generally be improved by employing successive approximations. Generally also, the time involved may be shortened by following from the beginning the procedure of using for the first approximation only rounded values for the arbitrary constants. This method also provides a convenient way of simplifying the least-squares procedure.

PROBLEMS

1. The α-ray activity of a sample of radon, expressed in terms of its initial activity at the beginning of a test to determine its decay constant and half life, is found to have the following fractional values at the ends of succeeding 24-hour intervals: 0.835, 0.695, 0.580, 0.485, 0.405, 0.335, 0.280, and 0.235. On the assumption that the activity obeys an exponential decay law, find the equation that represents the activity, and determine the decay constant and half life.

2. Find a tabular suitability test for the equation

$$y = \frac{ae^{-bx}}{x}$$

3. Using the following data for the resistivity of tungsten as a function of temperature,[1] find the equation for $\rho = f(T)$.

T °K	ρ μ ohm cm	T °K	ρ μ ohm cm
1000	25.70	2500	77.25
1500	41.85	3000	96.2
2000	59.10	3500	115.7

4. The emf of a standard Pt to (90% Pt—10% Rh) thermocouple [2] as a function of temperature when the cold junction is at 0.0° C is given as

T 0° C	E	T	E
0° C	0.000 mv	1000° C	9.569 mv
200	1.436	1200	11.924
400	3.250	1400	14.312
600	5.222	1600	16.674
800	7.330		

Apply the successive-differences test and determine how many terms in a power series in $(T - 0°\,C)$ are needed to give a rather precise description of $E = f(T - 0°\,C)$. Derive an equation of the form

$$E = a(T - 0°\,C) + b(T - 0°\,C)^2 + c(T - 0°\,C)^3$$

to represent the data given. Form a table showing, for the temperatures given, the differences between the given emf's and your computed emf's.

5. Using the data of Problem 2, Chapter I, in which unsmoothed data were given for incandescent tungsten vacuum lamps relating percentage of normal voltage of operation to the temperature of the filament, compute a best curve of the type

$$\frac{V}{V_n} = \left(\frac{T}{T_n}\right)^{a(1 + b \log T/T_n)}$$

Use the method of successive approximations. Compare the results with those obtained by tabular smoothing.

---

[1] Forsythe, W. E., and Worthing, A. G., *Astrophys. J.*, **61**, 153 (1925).

[2] Roeser, W. F., "Thermoelectric Thermometry," p. 194 of report of symposium on *Temperature— Its Measurement and Control in Science and Industry*, New York, Reinhold Publishing Corporation, 1941.

6. As the result of a porous-plug test for air, Roebuck reports that air, started with the first pressure-temperature condition shown, will assume the succeeding conditions shown on passage through a succession of porous plugs properly controlled.

p	T	p	T
215.8 A	0.00° C	128.1 A	−10.80° C
180.9	−3.35	109.7	−14.02
168.4	−4.63	91.2	−17.69
154.4	−6.51	73.5	−21.56
140.7	−8.67		

Find the best power series, using successive approximations, for representing these data.

CHAPTER IV

TABULAR AND GRAPHICAL DIFFERENTIATION AND INTEGRATION

1. Introduction. The solutions of many problems include finding the slope of a curve or the area of a closed figure. Of such great importance have these processes been historically that their solutions lead directly to the invention of the calculus. Mathematically the derivative, dy/dx, of a function, $y = f(x)$, and the definite integral, $\int_{x_1}^{x_2} y\,dx$, are involved. The function $f(x)$ is often known explicitly. Here, however, we are concerned principally with those that are not known.

The derivative problem has already been encountered in Chapter III, where the slope of a straight line was required for the evaluation of one of the constants of an empirical equation. More often the slope itself is desired because of what it itself represents.

Often, slopes that are desired are those of nonlinear curves as (1) in the field of chemical thermodynamics, where values of dE/dT are sought in order that we may obtain heats of reactions which proceed in voltaic cells, in accord with the Gibbs-Helmholtz equation,

$$\Delta U = -Q\left(E - T\frac{dE}{dT}\right) \qquad [1]$$

of which ΔU is the change of internal energy, Q the quantity of electricity transferred, E the emf of the cell, and T the absolute temperature; (2) in the field of electrical engineering, when the power loss, P, of a motor or generator is obtained by the retardation method, and values of $d\omega/dt$ are needed for use with the equation

$$P = I\omega\frac{d\omega}{dt} \qquad [2]$$

of which I is the moment of inertia of the rotor, ω its angular velocity, and $d\omega/dt$ its angular acceleration; and (3) in the field of heat measurements, when the conductivity, k, of a metal in rod form is measured by the Biot, Wiedemann, and Franz method. Here the equation used is

$$k = \frac{\dfrac{dQ}{dt}}{A\left[\left(\dfrac{dT}{dl}\right)_1 - \left(\dfrac{dT}{dl}\right)_2\right]} \qquad [3]$$

of which dQ/dt is the rate of transfer of heat, dT/dl temperature gradient, and A cross-sectional area.

Problems involving integrations are equally important and numerous. Typical examples occur (1) in the field of mechanical engineering, when the mean effective pressure in the cylinder of a steam engine is obtained from the area of an "indicator diagram" showing the pressure as a function of the position of the piston; (2) in the field of chemical thermodynamics, when the absolute entropy, S, of a pure substance at the absolute temperature, T, is calculated, using the defining equation

$$S = \int_0^T \frac{c_p}{T}\, dT + \sum \frac{L}{T} \qquad [4]$$

of which c_p represents a specific heat and L a heat of transformation; and (3) in the field of electrical measurements, when the hysteresis energy loss per unit volume, W, for a magnetic material is obtained from the area of its "hysteresis loop," using

$$W = \frac{1}{4\pi} \oint H\, dB \qquad [5]$$

of which H represents magnetic field strength and B magnetic induction.

There are numerous methods of solving both the slope and the area problem. Which method is best depends on the nature of the problem and the form in which the data are presented. If the data are available in equation form as $y = f(x)$, the derived equation, $(dy/dx) = f'(x)$, or the integrated equation, $\int y\, dx = F(x)$, can generally be obtained by mathematical differentiation or integration. Particular values of dy/dx for any value of x, or of $\int y\, dx$ for any set of limits, can then usually be obtained with ease and with precision. When the data are presented in tabular or graphical form there are two possibilities. It may be best, and particularly is this so when a general expression for dy/dx or $\int y\, dx$ is desired, to find $y = f(x)$ empirically by the methods covered in Chapter III, and then to differentiate or to integrate mathematically.

However, if only a few particular values of dy/dx or of $\int y\,dx$ are wanted, or if the equation $y = f(x)$ is too complicated, one of the graphical or tabular methods to be described may be preferable.

2. Graphical Methods of Finding dy/dx. (a) *Tangent and Normal Methods.* The procedure for the graphical determination of the slope of a curve at a particular point, that corresponding to x say, consists of three steps: (1) plotting with considerable care the curve $y = f(x)$, (2) locating the line tangent (or normal) to the curve at x, and (3) calculating the slope of the curve. For the tangent

$$\frac{dy}{dx} = \frac{y_2 - y_1}{x_2 - x_1} \qquad [6]$$

where (x_1, y_1) and (x_2, y_2) are two conveniently chosen points on the tangent (or normal) line.

Seemingly slight variations in the curve representing $y = f(x)$ may result in large variations in dy/dx. For this reason it is important that, in step 1, one should follow with care the rules of good practice stated in Chapter II. It is especially desirable to have the tangent line at x inclined at about 45° to the x-axis. Also for greatest accuracy and convenience, the points chosen for step 3 should be as far apart as is practicable and should be intersections of the tangent (or normal) with main coordinate lines.

There are several methods of performing step 2. The simplest method of locating the tangent line at x is that of slowly rotating a straight edge on the convex side of the curve about the point until it seems to be tangent to the curve. Much depends on good illumination. With practice, rather accurate results may be obtained by this method. Performance is improved by the use of a transparent rule with a long narrow scratch or cut on its under side.

Some workers prefer to determine the dy/dx of a given curve by the indirect method, which involves first determining the normal. This method requires distinguishing between the geometric slope of a curve at a particular point and its physical slope. The former for the common plot of $y = f(x)$ at a particular point is the tangent of the angle which the tangent to the curve at that point makes with the x-axis. For a given function and a particular x, the value of the geometric slope varies with the scale choice. Its unit is the numeric one. The physical slope for a particular x, however, does not change with the scale choice. Its value is dy/dx. Its unit is that of y divided by that of x as, for example, cm/sec, K°/cm, etc.

With subscripts gc and gn referring to the geometric slopes of a curve and its normal, we may write

$$\left(\frac{dy}{dx}\right)_{gc} = -\frac{1}{\left(\dfrac{dy}{dx}\right)_{gn}} \qquad [7]$$

correspondingly with subscripts pc and pn referring to the physical slopes of the curve and its normal, we may write

$$\left(\frac{dy}{dx}\right)_{pc} = -\frac{\left(\dfrac{\delta y}{\delta x}\right)^2}{\left(\dfrac{dy}{dx}\right)_{pn}} \qquad [7a]$$

Here $(\delta y/\delta x)$, a scale factor for the graph, is the ratio of a physical δy corresponding to a length measured along the y-axis to the physical δx corresponding to the same length measured along the x-axis. As is apparent,

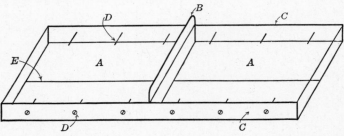

FIG. 1. The Simons tangentmeter. Parts A, A are lucite blocks. B is a first surface metal mirror. C, C are brass binding strips. D, D are machine screws. E is an index line perpendicular to mirror B scribed on the bottom of the lucite blocks.

the introduction of the scale factor makes it possible for the equation to check dimensionally. Proof of Eq. 7a is left for a problem at the end of the chapter.

Given Eq. 7a, the procedure for determining a physical slope follows. One first finds the position of the normal. A satisfactory method for doing this consists of placing a long narrow piece of plane, first-surface mirror across the curve, rotating it until the curve and its reflection in the mirror form a smooth curve as shown by the "squint test" (Chapter II). The plane of the mirror is then normal to the curve. Though a short mirror may be used, a long one is preferred in order that the calculation of its slope may be as accurate as possible. Next, one determines the scale factor in accord with the definition given above and then finally the physical slope, using Eq. 7a.

A convenient apparatus, which employs the normal principle yet permits of the direct determination of the physical tangent from the graph, is the tangentmeter (Fig. 1) described by Simons.[1] The polished, plane, first-surface, metal mirror mounted between the lucite blocks is first set normal to the curve. The scratch perpendicular to the mirror is then parallel to the desired tangent and permits determining dy/dx at once.

In Chapter III it was noted that, if a graph of $y = f(x)$ is to be used for determining the derivative dy/dx, one should select scales for plotting which give an approximate geometric slope of unity. We can now

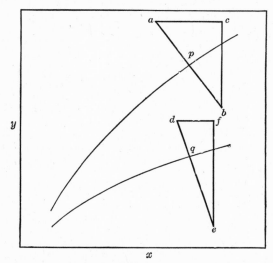

FIG. 2. A graph showing that greater precision for determining a dy/dx is possible when the geometric slope is approximately unity than when it deviates considerably from this value.

show why this is the case. Consider the determination of the dy/dx's at p and q, corresponding points on the two curves of Fig. 2 with geometric slopes of approximately 1 and $\frac{1}{2}$, using the normal method. Obviously their relative accuracies will depend on the accuracies with which the geometric slopes of the normals may be obtained, and these in turn on the accuracies with which the lengths ac, bc, df, and ef may be determined. Given that ab and de are of equal lengths and that the uncertainty in the other linear measurements is a certain small amount, say 0.2 mm, it is obvious that the relative accuracies of the two dy/dx's will depend most of all on the relative accuracies of the measurements

[1] Simons, H. P., *Ind. Eng. Chem.* (Anal. Ed.), **13**, 563 (1941). See also Latishaw, J. J., *Am. Chem. Soc.*, **47**, 793 (1925). Richards and Raspe, *Science*, **71**, 290 (1930).

of ac and df and that the accuracy for the determination of dy/dx at p is greater than at q. Just how much greater will depend on principles to be discussed later in Chapter IX.

(b) *Secant Method.* For a possibly greater accuracy than that yielded by the tangent or the normal methods, the secant method may be used. In this instance the slope of the tangent line is obtained as the limiting position of the secant line drawn through (x,y) and nearby points P_1, P_2, etc., as P approaches x. For this purpose, four or five or more positions of P are chosen. It is convenient to let the values $\Delta_1 x$, $\Delta_2 x$, $\Delta_3 x$, etc., representing changes in x in passing from (x,y) to points P_1, P_2, etc., be multiples of a chosen Δx. Let the corresponding changes in y be $\Delta_1 y$, $\Delta_2 y$, etc. The quotients $\Delta_1 y/\Delta_1 x$, $\Delta_2 y/\Delta_2 x$, etc., representing slopes of secants passing through the point (x,y), are then plotted as a function of Δx, and a curve giving $\Delta y/\Delta x = f(\Delta x)$ is drawn. The value of $\Delta y/\Delta x$ for $\Delta x = 0$ is, of course, the dy/dx desired. With values for x and y taken from a suitable table, the only graphing that may need to be performed is that showing $\Delta y/\Delta x = f(x)$. The points P_1, P_2, etc., need not all be on the same side of the point (x,y).

Illustrating the secant method, consider the data of Table I showing the pyrometer current, I_p, of a certain disappearing filament optical

TABLE I

THE PYROMETER CURRENT, I_p, OF A CERTAIN DISAPPEARING FILAMENT PYROMETER FOR DISAPPEARANCE AGAINST A BACKGROUND AT VARIOUS SPECTRAL BRIGHTNESSES, B_λ ($\lambda = 0.665\mu$), EXPRESSED IN TERMS OF $_0B_\lambda$ FOR A BLACK BODY AT THE GOLD POINT, $1336°$ K

$\dfrac{B_\lambda}{_0B_\lambda}$	I_p in ma	$\log \dfrac{B_\lambda}{_0B_\lambda}$	$\log I_p$	$\log I_p - \log I_{p0}$	$\dfrac{\Delta \log I_p}{\Delta \log \dfrac{B_\lambda}{_0B_\lambda}}$
0.125	193.8	−0.9031	2.2873	−0.1141	0.1263
0.250	210.8	−0.6021	2.3238	− .0776	.1288
0.500	230.1	−0.3010	2.3619	− .0395	.1312
1.000	252.0	0.0000	2.4014	.0000	. . . .
2.000	277.1	0.3010	2.4426	.0412	.1369
4.000	305.8	0.6021	2.4854	.0840	.1395
8.000	338.5	0.9031	2.5296	.1282	.1420
16.000	376.0	1.2041	2.5752	.1738	.1444
32.000	419.5	1.5052	2.6227	.2213	.1470
64.000	470.2	1.8062	2.6723	.2709	.1500

pyrometer as a function of the spectral brightness, B_λ, of a source of light. Let us find (B_λ/I_p) (dI_p/dB_λ) for the pyrometer lamp when matching a black body background at the gold point. The quantity sought is the slope of the curve $\log I_p = f[\log (B_\lambda/_0B_\lambda)]$ at $\log (B_\lambda/_0B_\lambda)$ $= 0$.

Computed values for $\Delta \log I_p/\Delta \log (B_\lambda/_0B_\lambda)$ are included in Table I. These values are graphed in Fig. 3. For $\log (B_\lambda/_0B_\lambda) = 0.000$ the slope

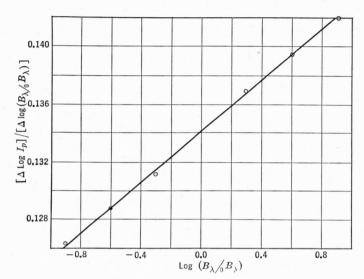

FIG. 3. Illustrating, with the aid of the data of Table I, the secant method for the precise determination of a slope. The slope sought is that of $(B_\lambda/I_p)(dI_p/dB_\lambda)$ for $\log (B_\lambda/_0B_\lambda) = 0.000$.

is seen to be 0.1341. Generally the inverse of $(B_\lambda/I_p)(dI_p/dB_\lambda)$ is desired. This inverse value is 7.45, and states that for a black body at the gold point the spectral brightness at $\lambda = 0.665\mu$ varies 7.45% for a 1.00% variation in the matching pyrometer current. The work required is considerable in comparison with that required by the tangent or the normal method.

There are mechanical devices for evaluating dy/dx from a plot of $y = f(x)$ [1] and other devices which automatically draw out the curve of $dy/dx = f'(x)$ when their tracer arms are made to follow the $y = f(x)$ curve in a particular manner.[2] Such instruments are rather compli-

[1] Evans, D. L. C., *Engineering*, **144**, Sept. 3, 1937.

[2] Lipka, J., *Graphical and Mechanical Computation*, p. 255, New York, John Wiley & Sons, 1918.

cated to use, however. They yield no increase in accuracy, but are very valuable as time savers in certain specialized routine problems.

3. Tabular Methods of Finding dy/dx. When the tabulations are precise, these methods equal, or are superior to, graphical methods in accuracy, and permit the calculation of derivatives of the second and higher orders directly from the original data. The necessary equations are obtained by differentiating the interpolation formulas of Chapter I. Thus, the Gregory-Newton formula (Eq. 7 of Chapter I) expresses $y = f(x)$ in terms of the successive differences of y obtained from a table of $y = f(x)$ as

$$y = y_0 + n\Delta y_0 + \frac{n(n-1)}{2!} \Delta^2 y_0 + \cdots \qquad [8]$$

Here (x_0, y_0) is a tabulated point near (x, y), Δx is the constant tabular x-interval, and n is defined by

$$n = \frac{x - x_0}{\Delta x} \qquad [9]$$

The terms Δy_0, $\Delta^2 y_0$, etc., are the first, second, etc., order of differences of the tabulated y's (see Chapter I). There follows

$$\frac{dy}{dx} = \left(\frac{dy}{dn}\right)\left(\frac{dn}{dx}\right) = \left(\frac{dy}{dn}\right)\left(\frac{1}{\Delta x}\right) \qquad [10]$$

Hence,

$$\frac{dy}{dx} = \frac{1}{\Delta x}\left[\Delta y_0 + (2n - 1)\left(\frac{\Delta^2 y_0}{2!}\right) \right.$$

$$+ (3n^2 - 6n + 2)\left(\frac{\Delta^3 y_0}{3!}\right)$$

$$+ (4n^3 - 18n^2 + 22n - 6)\left(\frac{\Delta^4 y_0}{4!}\right)$$

$$\left. + \cdots \right] \qquad [11]$$

An example illustrating the method follows.

Example. From the values for $y = f(x) = \log x$, given in Table II, find dy/dx for $x = 1.726$.

TABLE II

Showing Several Values for $y = f(x) = $ Log x for a Limited Range of x and Their Successive Differences Δy, $\Delta^2 y$, Etc.

x	y	Δy	$\Delta^2 y$	$\Delta^3 y$	$\Delta^4 y$	$\Delta^5 y$
1.0	0.00000					
		0.17609				
1.5	.17609		−0.05115			
		.12494		0.02312		
2.0	.30103		− .02803		−0.01282	
		.09691		.01030		0.00802
2.5	.39794		− .01773		− .00480	
		.07918		.00550		.00257
3.0	.47712		− .01223		− .00223	
		.06695		.00327		.00108
3.5	.54407		− .00896		− .00115	
		.05799		.00212		
4.0	.60206		− .00684			
		.05115				
4.5	.65321					
5.0	.69897					

As x_0 we select 1.500 and as Δx, 0.500. There follows from Eq. 9

$$n = \frac{x - x_0}{\Delta x} = \frac{1.726 - 1.500}{0.500} = 0.452 \qquad [12]$$

Substituting into Eq. 11, yields

$$\left(\frac{dy}{dx}\right)_{1.726} = \frac{1}{0.500}\left[0.12494 + (2 \times 0.452 - 1)\frac{-0.02803}{2} \right.$$

$$\left. + (3 \times 0.452^2 - 6 \times 0.452 + 2)\frac{0.01030}{6} + \cdots \right]$$

$$= 2.000(0.12494 + 0.00135 - 0.00017 - 0.00014 \cdots) \qquad [13]$$

The final result depends on the number of terms included:

Number of Terms	$\dfrac{dy}{dx}$	Correction
1	0.24988	+0.00174
2	.25258	− .00096
3	.25224	− .00062
4	.25196	− .00034

4. Tabular Methods of Finding $\int y\,dx$. There is a wide choice of tabular methods for finding areas and the final equations—the so-called quadrature formulas. To data in graph form, they may be applied with the same ease that attends their application to tabulated data. In fact, their significance and use are best shown graphically.

(a) *Trapezoidal Rule.* The value of the integral $\int_{x_1}^{x_p} y\,dx$ which we seek is represented in Fig. 4 by the area $x_1 A P x_p x_1$. Except for a remainder $x_p - x_n$ in width, let this area be subdivided, as shown, into

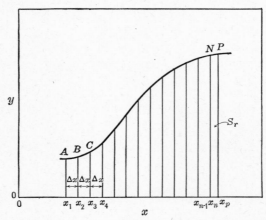

FIG. 4. Illustrating the derivation of the trapezoidal rule and of Simpson's ⅓ rule.

$(n–1)$ strips of equal and convenient width, Δx, by ordinates at x_1, $x_2, \cdots x_n$. The approximation is made such that between two successive intersections of the curve with the ordinates, such as the points A and B, the curve may be replaced by a straight line without appreciably changing the area of the strip. Hence, by the trapezoidal rule, the area of the strip $x_1 A B x_2 x_1$ is taken as $\Delta x (y_1 + y_2)/2$, and the area under the curve as the sum of the areas of $(n - 1)$ such strips, plus the remainder of width $x_n x_p$, or

$$\int_{x_1}^{x_p} y\,dx = \Delta x \left(\frac{y_1}{2} + y_2 + y_3 + \cdots + y_{n-1} + \frac{y_n}{2} \right)$$
$$+ (x_p - x_n) \left(\frac{y_n + y_p}{2} \right) \quad [14]$$

It is apparent that the smaller the value of the interval Δx, the closer the value given by the rule approaches the true value of the integral.

As Δx decreases, however, the number of ordinates to be added together increases, so that unless an adding machine is available, the work becomes more tedious and chances for error increase. When the data are given in tabular form, Δx cannot be taken smaller than the x-interval of the table, so that one of the other formulas must be used if an approximation better than that given by the trapezoidal rule is desired.

(b) *Simpson's* ⅓ *Rule.* Let the area desired be subdivided, except possibly for a remainder at one end whose area, s_r, may be found otherwise, into an even number of strips of equal width, Δx, by ordinates at $x_1, x_2 \cdots x_n$, as in Fig. 4. The assumption is then made that between points A and C the curve may be replaced by a parabola of the second degree passing through points A, B, and C without changing appreciably the area of the two strips underneath. On the basis of this assumption, it can be shown that the area of these two strips is $\Delta x(y_1 + 4y_2 + y_3)/3$. Hence, by Simpson's ⅓ rule the desired area is the sum of $(n-1)/2$ such double-strip areas, or

$$\int_{x_1}^{x_p} y \, dx = \frac{\Delta x}{3} \, (y_1 + 4y_2 + 2y_3 + 4y_4 + \cdots + 4y_{n-1} + y_n) + s_r$$

$$= \frac{\Delta x}{3} \, [(y_1 + y_n) + 2(y_3 + y_5 + \cdots) + 4(y_2 + y_4 + \cdots)]$$

$$+ \tfrac{1}{2} \, (x_p - x_n)(y_n + y_p) \quad [15]$$

Simpson's ⅓ rule will usually, but not always, yield a closer approximation to the actual area sought than will the trapezoidal rule using the same Δx. When the data for the interval over which the integral is to be taken are given an odd number of strips, Simpson's rule may be used for all but the last strip, whose area may then be combined with that represented by s_r and calculated by the trapezoidal rule.

(c) *Simpson's* ⅜ *Rule.* By reasoning similar to that for the ⅓ rule, it can be shown, if the area under the curve $y = f(x)$ is assumed subdivided into $(n-1)$ strips of equal width, Δx, where $(n-1)$ is now divisible by three, and it is further assumed that the curve above any three adjacent strips approximates a third degree parabola, that the formula known as Simpson's ⅜ rule becomes applicable. In algebraic form it states

$$\int_{x_1}^{x_n} y \, dx = \frac{3\Delta x}{8} \, [(y_1 + y_n) + 2(y_4 + y_7 + y_{10} + \cdots)$$

$$+ 3(y_2 + y_3 + y_5 + y_6 + \cdots)] \quad [16]$$

For a given value of Δx, Simpson's ⅜ rule will usually, but not always, give a closer approximation than Simpson's ⅓ rule.

(d) *Weddle's Rule.* By subdividing the desired area into a number of strips divisible by some integer m, and approximating the curve above m such adjacent strips by an mth degree parabola, it is possible to approximate curve boundaries more closely than is possible with the simpler trapezoidal and Simpson's rules. One such procedure known as Weddle's rule is obtained by simplifying somewhat the general formula for $m = 6$. It states that

$$\int_{x_1}^{x_n} y \, dx = \frac{3\Delta x}{10} \left[(y_1 + y_n) + 5(y_2 + y_6 + y_8 + y_{12} + y_{14} + \cdots) \right.$$

$$+ (y_3 + y_5 + y_9 + y_{11} + y_{15} + \cdots)$$

$$+ 6(y_4 + y_{10} + y_{16} + \cdots)$$

$$\left. + 2(y_7 + y_{13} + y_{19} + \cdots) \right]   [17]$$

The increased chances for error in using this equation are evident. Few cases justify the use of this rule rather than one of the simpler rules.

(e) *Illustrative Example.* Let us consider the results which these various quadrature formulas yield when applied to a particular case. For this we choose theoretically computed values for spectral black body radiancy, $\mathcal{R}_\lambda$, at any given temperature, expressed in terms of the maximum, $\mathcal{R}_{\lambda \max}$, as a function of the product of wave length and temperature λT. The values of $\mathcal{R}_\lambda / \mathcal{R}_{\lambda \max}$ for various λT values as given by Lowan and Blanch [1] are given in Table III.

TABLE III

SHOWING $\mathcal{R}_\lambda / \mathcal{R}_{\lambda \max}$ FOR BLACK BODY RADIATION AS A FUNCTION OF λT

λT in cm K°	$\dfrac{\mathcal{R}_\lambda}{\mathcal{R}_{\lambda \max}}$	λT in cm K°	$\dfrac{\mathcal{R}_\lambda}{\mathcal{R}_{\lambda \max}}$
0.08	0.0014	0.22	0.8188
.10	.0167	.24	.9139
.12	.0735	.26	.9719
.14	.1880	.28	.9974
.16	.3476	.30	.9968
.18	.5230	.32	.9765
.20	.6860		

[1] Lowan, A. N., and Blanch, G., *J. Optical Soc. Am.*, **30**, 70 (1940).

For the average $\mathcal{R}_\lambda/\mathcal{R}_{\lambda\max}$ for the range 0.08 cm K° $< \lambda T <$ 0.32 cm K° as expressed by

$$\text{Average } \frac{\mathcal{R}_\lambda}{\mathcal{R}_{\lambda\max}} = \frac{1}{0.24 \text{ cm K°}} \int_{0.08 \text{ cm K°}}^{0.32 \text{ cm K°}} \frac{\mathcal{R}_\lambda}{\mathcal{R}_{\lambda\max}}\, d(\lambda T) \qquad [18]$$

the trapezoidal rule, the Simpson ⅓ rule, the Simpson ⅜ rule, and the Weddle rule in order yield 0.5852, 0.5854, 0.5853, and 0.5855, all of which are close to the value 0.5854 which is yielded by more precise calculations using smaller intervals. That the trapezoidal rule should have deviated most from the true average is to be expected, but that the Simpson

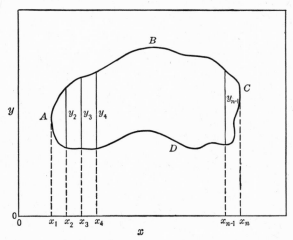

Fig. 5. To find the area of $ABCD$, the lengths y_2, y_3 $\cdots$ may be substituted into any quadrature formula.

⅓ rule should have come closest is hardly to be expected. The comparison supports the fact that often, and especially where Δx is small, the simple trapezoidal rule will frequently yield results as accurate as the data justify. Only rarely is it necessary—and hence desirable—to use any formula beyond the easily remembered Simpson's ⅓ rule. This conclusion is commensurate with that reached in Chapter III, where it was found that short portions of most curves can be represented empirically by second-degree parabolas.

When the area of an irregular closed figure such as that of Fig. 5 is to be measured by one of the quadrature formulas, we may divide the figure into the proper number of strips by the parallel equidistant lines at x_1, x_2, $\cdots$ x_n, and then substitute the lengths of these lines into the formula used. This procedure is equivalent to subtracting the area $x_1ADCx_nx_1$ from the area $x_1ABCx_nx_1$.

5. Graphical Methods of Finding $\int y\,dx$. (a) *Polar Planimeter*

Method. There are many mechanical devices for measuring areas. Most of them, provided the data are once satisfactorily graphed, are more rapid than using quadrature rules. Further, they are sometimes more accurate, especially so when the desired area has very irregular boundaries. The instruments range from the extremely simple hatchet planimeter [1] to such complex mechanisms as that which automatically integrates the product of two empirical functions in a few seconds.[2] Between these extremes, the polar planimeter is probably the most suitable

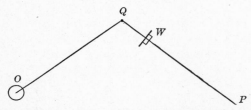

Fig. 6. A diagram showing the main characteristics of the polar planimeter. *OQ* represents the pivot arm pivoted at *O*, *QP* the tracer arm with tracer point at *P*, and *W* the recording wheel.

compromise with regard to simplicity, applicability, cost, availability, and accuracy. There are several forms of polar planimeters, differing in minor details of construction and refinement, but the essential parts of the instrument (Fig. 6) are (1) the polar arm, *OQ*, with a point *O* which is maintained fixed during an operation; (2) the tracer arm, *QP*, adjustable usually as to length, which is hinged to the polar arm at *Q* and terminates at one end in a tracer point *P*; and (3) the recording wheel, *W*.

To measure an area with the polar planimeter, the following steps are performed:

1. Locate the fixed point, *O*, so that in tracing the figure, the wheel, *W*, does not go off the edge of the paper, or over any folds or other irregularities; the more uniform the surface on which the wheel rolls, the greater the possible accuracy of the measurement.

2. Place the tracer point, *P*, on the perimeter of the area, noting the reading of the recording mechanism attached to the integrating wheel.

[1] Haynes, F. B., and Haynes, I. C., *Rev. Sci. Instruments*, **2**, 396 (1931).
[2] Sears, F. W., *J. Optical Soc. Am.*, **29**, 77 (1939).

3. Trace the boundary of the figure carefully until the starting point is reached once more (this is important), and note the new reading of the recording mechanism.

4. Subtract the two readings to obtain the number of rotations of the wheel.

5. Multiply the number of rotations so obtained by the calibration constant to obtain the area measured. This constant may be calculated from the dimensions of the instrument by Eq. 19 below, or it may be found by noting the number of rotations produced in tracing a figure of known area, such as a triangle or a rectangle.

More reliable values for areas using a polar planimeter are obtained if the figure is traced a number of times—five say. It may also help to trace the figure five more times in a direction opposite to the first, and to average the results thus obtained. If proper precautions as to their locations are taken, a straight edge or a transparent drawing curve that coincides with the boundary of the figure measured for a reasonable distance may be used as a guide for the tracer arm point. Other suggestions concerning the use and care of the polar planimeter may be found elsewhere.

That the number of rotations of the integrating wheel is directly proportional to the area traced is easily shown. Consider the three movements for the tracer arm shown at *A*, *B*, and *C*, Fig. 7. In *A*, the arm

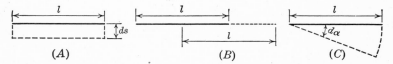

Fig. 7. Diagrams showing areas swept out by the tracer arm of a polar planimeter during each of the three possible elementary motions.

moves a distance ds at right angles to its length, l. The area swept out is $l\,ds$; and, if r represents the radius of the integrating wheel, the angle through which the wheel rotates is $d\theta\ (= ds/r)$. In *B*, the arm moves parallel to itself. The area swept out is zero; so also is the angle through which the wheel rotates. In *C*, the arm rotates about a fixed end. The area swept out is $\frac{1}{2}l^2 d\alpha$; the angle $d\phi$ through which the integrating wheel rotates depends on its position with respect to the fixed end. In any case it is proportional to $d\alpha$ and may be written as $c\,d\alpha$.

All motions, no matter how complicated, that are possible for the tracer arm of a polar planimeter as used (Fig. 8), may be viewed as a combination of infinitesimal motions similar to those of *A*, *B*, and *C* of Fig. 7. If, for such a motion, we add the condition that at the end of the movement the tracer arm shall occupy its intitial position, we have the result, taking account of the vector nature of ϕ, that the sum of the $d\phi$'s, all of which have taken place about the Q end of the arm, is zero. In actual instruments this condition is assured by having end O (Fig. 6) of the polar arm fixed so that the Q end of the tracer arm is limited to the arc of a circle. It follows, when an area is traced, that the integrating

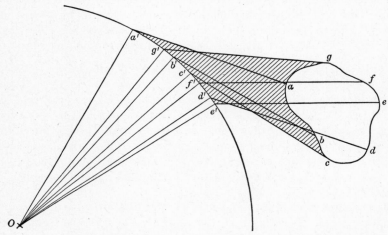

Fig. 8. A diagram showing several successive positions of the tracer arm of a polar planimeter when, with the fixed point of the polar arm at O, the tracer point is moved around the area *abcdefga*. During this movement, the whole of the enclosed area is swept out by the tracer arm in the same direction, namely, counterclockwise, and only once. The cross-hatched area, however, is swept out twice, once clockwise and once counterclockwise.

wheel will show only the vector sum of a number of $d\theta$'s. We see at once that the area A is given by

$$A = \Sigma dA = lr\Sigma d\theta = lr\theta \qquad [19]$$

In actual use, it is customary, though not necessary, to move the tracer point counterclockwise about the area to be measured, and to reckon as positive an area that is swept out by counterclockwise rotation of the tracer arm about the end which is limited in motion to the arc of a circle.

It is interesting to follow through the motions of the tracer arm in Fig. 8, and to see what area has been measured. Let *abcdefga* be the area traced out by tracer point P. As the tracer arm takes the successive positions aa', bb', cc', etc., back to aa', the area that is cross-hatched is swept over first clockwise and then counterclockwise. In the summation of dA's this area yields zero. Only the area *abcdefga* is swept once, and all in the same direction. Hence the A of Eq. 19 refers to this area only. In certain irregular areas, portions of the enclosed area to be measured may be swept out three times, or five times, or some odd number of times, but never an even number of times. Moreover, the net effect of the sweepings in excess of one for these portions are always in directions such as to annul one another in pairs. In effect, even in these very irregular areas, the tracer arm sweeps the enclosed area only once, and all in the same direction.

A slight difficulty arises in the use of a polar planimeter when, in sweeping out the area with the tracer point P, the point Q at the junction of the two arms describes a complete circle about the fixed point O. When QP is less than OP and for most other cases, area A is then given by

$$A = lr\theta + \pi(R^2 + l^2) \qquad [20]$$

of which R is the length of polar arm OQ, and θ the angle through which the recording wheel turns in consequence of motions described in Fig. 7A only. It is not the total angle through which the wheel has turned. It is that angle less the angle ϕ which corresponds to $\alpha = 2\pi$ radians.

(b) *Average Ordinate Method.* This method, like the polar planimeter method, requires that the data be graphed. It is not suitable for the determination of all areas. Practically it is limited to cases where the whole area can be broken up into several parallel-sided approximations to trapezoids such as were assumed for the various above-listed tabular methods for finding $\int y\,dx$. For such cases, it combines with high accuracy the simplicity of the inaccurate counting squares procedure.

The method can best be described in connection with an application. Fig. 9 shows a temperature-time curve for a standard compensated-loss calorimeter such as might be obtained when, with its aid, one seeks to determine the amount of heat lost by a heated specimen of material on cooling from some high temperature to that of the calorimeter. The fore interval is the period previous to the receipt of the heated specimen and during which stirring of the calorimetric fluid is principally responsible for the change of temperature. The test interval is the period during which heat is transferred to the fluid by the heated specimen and a near equilibrium of temperature is being established. The after interval is the final period during which temperature variations are a combined result of stirring and of Newtonian leakage. One seeks the temperature interval $T_c - T_b$. This involves finding the area $b'bdd'b'$.

The approximations to trapezoids which we will use here are those determined by the $0C°$ line, the temperature-time curve, and the ordinates at 4, 6, 8, 10, 12, and 14 min. We first locate a straight edge so that it passes through the intersections of the 4-min and the 6-min ordinates with the temperature-time curve. Then on the 5-min line we locate the point m which is two-thirds of the way from the straight edge to the curve. Insofar as Simpson's $\frac{1}{3}$ rule is applicable, $m'm$ is the average ordinate for the area between the 4-min and the 6-min ordinates. Next in order points n, o, p, and q are located similarly, and similarly they represent the upper limits of other average ordinates.

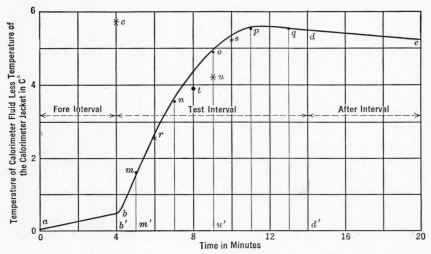

Fig. 9. The temperature-time curve for a standard, compensated loss calorimeter to which a heated specimen of material has been transferred.

The upper limit of the average ordinate for the area between the 4-min and the 8-min ordinates is now determined. It is the point r on the middle or 6-min line where that ordinate is cut by a straight line between m and n. Similarly s is the upper limit of the average ordinate for the area between the 8-min and the 12-min lines. On the same basis, position t on the 8-min ordinate is the upper limit for the average ordinate for the area between the 4-min and the 12-min lines. The area between the 12-min and the 14-min lines may be similarly combined with the area associated with point t. Since, however, the time width of this area is only one-fifth that of the combined areas, one must select, on the straight line passing through t and q, a point u which is but one-fifth of the way from t to q. Accordingly the ordinate $u'u$ is the average ordinate for the area between the 4-min and the 14-min ordinates and the area sought is 422 min C°. How this may be used in determining $T_c - T_b$ will be found elsewhere.

Depending on the scale and the care used, this method is susceptible of high precision. If the data are available in the form of an acceptable curve rather than in a tabulation of y-values for equal x-intervals, this method might well be superior to all other methods, particularly if time is a factor.

(c) *Cut-and-Weigh Method.* If the figure whose area is desired is cut out and weighed, its area can be found by dividing its weight by the weight per unit area of the paper on which it is drawn. Obviously this procedure would make the figure unfit for any further use, so that in practice the outline of the figure is traced onto a second sheet, preferably of heavy paper or metal foil, which is then cut and weighed. Errors may arise in faulty tracing, cutting, and weighing, and through nonuniformity of surface density of the heavy paper or foil. This method is relatively inaccurate. For rough work, it may prove convenient if a polar planimeter is not available.

(d) *Photoelectric Method.* A photoelectric device for measuring areas developed in part by the Botany Department of the University of Chicago is now offered commercially by the American Instrument

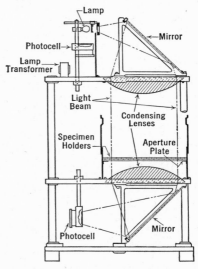

FIG. 10. A photoelectric device for measuring areas. (*Courtesy of the American Instrument Co.*)

Company. Light from a low-voltage lamp (Fig. 10) is made parallel by a condensing lens, and then focused by a second lens onto a barrier layer photocell. The output of this cell is balanced in a suitable bridge arrangement by the output of a second cell, illuminated by the same lamp. The object whose area is desired must be opaque or translucent and must fit into a 10-inch circle. It is placed into the parallel light beam, thus reducing the output of the first photocell. The bridge circuit is then rebalanced by adjusting a slide-wire resistance which is calibrated directly in units of area. Advantages claimed by the manufacturer are high accuracy, high speed, and no required operator experience.

6. Summary. Methods other than those of differential and integral calculus are often desirable for obtaining values of dy/dx and $\int y\, dx$.

To find dy/dx at the point (x,y) when the data are presented graphically, we may determine the slope of the tangent (or sometimes of the normal) line, or obtain it by the more laborious and more exact secant method. The slope of the tangent line, and hence of the curve, is given by

$$\left(\frac{dy}{dx}\right)_x = \frac{y_2 - y_1}{x_2 - x_1} \qquad [6]$$

where (x_1,y_1) and (x_2,y_2) are two points on the tangent line.

If the slope of the curve at a specified point is to be obtained from the slope of the normal to the curve at that point, the equation to be used is

$$\left(\frac{dy}{dx}\right)_{\text{curve}} = -\frac{\left(\dfrac{dy'}{dx'}\right)^2}{\left(\dfrac{dy}{dx}\right)_{\text{normal}}} \qquad [7a]$$

of which (dy'/dx'), a scale factor for the graph, represents the ratio of the change in y corresponding to a length measured along the y-axis to the change in x corresponding to the same length measured along the x-axis.

When the secant method is used to determine the slope of a curve at a specified point, the slopes of various secants, all of which cut the curve at that point, are graphed as a function of Δx, the change in x in going from one point of crossing to the next. The secant slope for $\Delta x = 0$ is the slope desired. It is convenient for data in tabular form.

When the data are tabulated, we may use the equation

$$\frac{dy}{dx} = \frac{1}{\Delta x}\Bigg[\Delta y_0 + (2n - 1)\left(\frac{\Delta^2 y_0}{2!}\right)$$

$$+ (3n^2 - 6n + 2)\left(\frac{\Delta^3 y_0}{3!}\right)$$

$$+ (4n^3 - 18n^2 + 22n - 6)\left(\frac{\Delta^4 y_0}{4!}\right)$$

$$+ \cdots \Bigg] \qquad [11]$$

where (x_0,y_0) is a tabulated point, Δy_0, $\Delta^2 y_0$, etc., are successive tabular differences, Δx is the common tabular x-interval, and $n = (x - x_0)/\Delta x$.

To find $\displaystyle\int y\,dx$, we may use one of the quadrature formulas for either tabular or graphical data. Important rules and formulas are

(1) the trapezoidal rule:

$$A = \int_{x_1}^{x_n} y\, dx = \Delta x \left(\frac{y_1}{2} + y_2 + y_3 + \cdots + y_{n-1} + \frac{y_n}{2} \right) \quad [14]$$

(2) Simpson's ⅓ rule:

$$A = \frac{\Delta x}{3} \left[(y_1 + y_n) + 2(y_3 + y_5 + \cdots) + 4(y_2 + y_4 + \cdots) \right] \quad [15]$$

(3) Simpson's ⅜ rule:

$$A = \frac{3\Delta x}{8} \left[(y_1 + y_n) + 2(y_4 + y_7 + y_{10} + \cdots) \right.$$
$$\left. + 3(y_2 + y_3 + y_5 + y_6 + \cdots) \right] \quad [16]$$

(4) Weddle's rule:

$$A = \frac{3\Delta x}{10} \left[(y_1 + y_n) + 5(y_2 + y_6 + y_8 + \cdots) \right.$$
$$+ (y_3 + y_5 + y_9 + y_{11} + \cdots)$$
$$+ 6(y_4 + y_{10} + y_{16} + \cdots)$$
$$\left. + 2(y_7 + y_{13} + y_{19} + \cdots) \right] \quad [17]$$

Measurement with a polar planimeter is a second method of finding $\int y\, dx$. Although especially well suited for measuring irregular areas, the planimeter may be used for all graphical data as well as for tabular data if these are first plotted. In "emergencies," or for rough work, the cut-and-weigh method may be used for finding $\int y\, dx$.

PROBLEMS

1. Using the plot containing three curves drawn in connection with Problem 2 of Chapter II, construct with care a graph showing $TdB/BdT = f(T)$ for tungsten for the range $2000°\,\text{K} < T < 3000°\,\text{K}$. Use the straight edge tangent or normal methods. Use different symbols for values obtained from the three different curves. What is your conclusion as to probable accuracies for the three sets of values?

2. Using the data reported in Problem 2 of Chapter II, determine with the aid of a tabular method the value of TdB/BdT for tungsten at $2000°\,\text{K}$, $2500°\,\text{K}$, and $3000°\,\text{K}$. Compare these values with those obtained in connection with Problem 1 above.

3. Repeat Problem 2, making use of the graphical secant method.

4. Using the data given below for the spectral brightness of a black body at $2400°\,\text{K}$ as a function of wavelength, determine its brightness at that temperature using (1) the tabular trapezoid method using a $0.01\ \mu$ interval, (2) the tabular trapezoid method using a 0.02 μ interval, (3) the tabular Simpson's $\frac{1}{3}$ method, and (4) the graphical polar planimeter method.   For (1), (2), and (3) use an adding machine if available.   How do the four determinations check?

λ in μ	B_λ in $\dfrac{candles}{cm^2\,\mu}$	λ in μ	B_λ in $\dfrac{candles}{cm^2\,\mu}$
0.41	0.09	0.61	619
.42	0.38	.62	506
.43	1.36	.63	379
.44	3.30	.64	268
.45	6.59	.65	175.5
.46	12.45	.66	106.0
.47	22.4	.67	59.2
.48	40.0	.68	33.3
.49	69.6	.69	16.95
.50	124.0	.70	8.95
.51	221	.71	4.80
.52	358	.72	2.50
.53	487	.73	1.30
.54	606	.74	0.65
.55	706	.75	0.32
.56	786	.76	0.17
.57	828	.77	0.08
.58	830		
.59	791		
.60	716		

5. Prove the relation expressed by Eq. 7a.

CHAPTER V

FOURIER SERIES

1. Introduction. A Fourier series is a convergent infinite series composed of sine and cosine terms whose successive angular values are proportional to the cardinal numbers, thus:

$$y = f(\theta) = a_1 \sin \theta + a_2 \sin 2\theta + a_3 \sin 3\theta + \cdots + \frac{b_0}{2}$$
$$+ b_1 \cos \theta + b_2 \cos 2\theta + b_3 \cos 3\theta + \cdots$$
$$= \frac{b_0}{2} + \sum_{m=1}^{\infty} (a_m \sin m\theta + b_m \cos m\theta) \tag{1}$$

Some authors use b_0 not $b_0/2$ for the constant term. The reason for the present use will appear later. That certain series of this type could be developed was known long before Fourier's time, but certain of their properties as well as their possibilities in the solution of problems in the field of heat were not then appreciated. Fourier's views, first presented to the French Academy in 1811, were published in 1822 in his *Theorie analytique de la chaleur*.

Fourier series represent means whereby a very large number of problems of certain types may be solved. In such instances, their value lies in the fact that with their aid boundary conditions, even when highly complicated, may usually be expressed in forms which are compatible with the underlying differential equations of Laplace and of Poisson. Given the boundary conditions as to temperature for a sheet, a rod, or a block of material, certain of its physical characteristics, such as density, specific heat, and thermal conductivity, and the distribution of temperature throughout at some one instant, it is generally possible to specify with the aid of these series the distribution of temperature throughout thereafter. In case, however, the distribution of temperature at some instant cannot be ascertained, it is still possible to specify the steady state distribution. Analogous problems in acoustics, radiation, and electricity may be handled similarly.

Industrial applications occur wherever vibrations are a matter of concern, as in the fields of electrical engineering, aerodynamics, telephony, music, radio, and sound projection. The designer for electrical generators and transformers must meet a requirement of noninjurious harmonics (vibrations, multiples of the fundamental, which correspond mathematically to succeeding terms of a Fourier series), and the tester must know how to determine their presence and their intensities. The airplane designer must similarly guard against possible harmonics of frequencies that are unavoidably present in engine operation. The tester again must know how to detect their presence and to measure their intensities. In telephony, radio, and sound projection, distortions due to emphasizing or minimizing harmonics need to be reduced. In musical instruments, the harmonics introduced and properly controlled determine the quality of the instrument. In all the cases named, experimentally observed or recorded effects for a definite angle swept out, for a definite distance traversed, or for a definite period of time, are the bases for design, correction, or control.

2. Functions Expressible by Fourier Series. Most of the functions which the experimental worker desires to expand into Fourier series involve angular displacement, time, or distance as the independent variable. Other physical quantities, of course, may be and are similarly involved. The dependent variables concerned are much more numerous. Of the many combinations, we may mention three of importance to industry: those concerned with (1) the graph of the electrical engineer showing instantaneous emf's or other electrical quantities for an AC generator, transformer, or circuit as a function of the phase angle, (2) the graphs of the builder of musical instruments showing the displacements of some portion of a string from its normal position as a function of time, and (3) the graphs of the vibration specialist showing displacements of the various parts of a structure in vibration as a function of position.

Corresponding to these three groups of particular interest with independent variables represented in order by θ, t, and x, we shall develop Fourier series of the types,

$$y = f(\theta), \text{ for } 0 < \theta < 2\pi \tag{2}$$

$$y = f\left(\frac{2\pi}{T} t\right) = F_1(t), \text{ for } 0 < t < T \tag{3}$$

$$y = f\left(\frac{2\pi}{\lambda} x\right) = F_2(x), \text{ for } 0 < x < \lambda \tag{4}$$

in which T represents the period of a simple harmonic motion and λ a wavelength. In all three equations, the quantities in parentheses represent angles, a necessary condition, since the series are trigonometric.

Often, as suggested by Eqs. 2 to 4, the functions to be developed into Fourier series are cyclical. When graphed, inspection shows that a certain portion by successive repetition forms the whole. The minimum such portion forms a cycle.

Illustrating such cyclical variations, Fig. 1 shows the supplied potential difference, the current, and the instantaneous power for a particular capacitative circuit as a function of time. Harmonic frequencies which are multiples of the fundamental AC frequency are quite evident.

Frequently in theoretical physics we are concerned with a distribution of some quantity with distance in which there is no cyclical repetition for the function $f = \left(\dfrac{2\pi}{\lambda} x \right)$, although the function itself extends to infinity. In this case, a Fourier

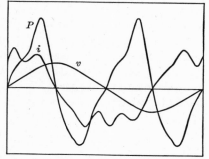

FIG. 1. Oscillograms showing supplied potential difference, current, and instantaneous power for a particular capacitative circuit. (*Kerchner, R. H., and Corcoran, G. F., Alternating Circuits*, p. 129, John Wiley & Sons, Inc., New York, 1938.)

series may be used, in which in effect λ becomes infinite. The form of the series is modified, however, to become a double integral known as Fourier's integral. This will be discussed later.

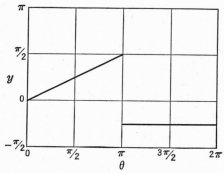

FIG. 2. Graph of a function given by $y = 0.5\theta$ for the range $0 < \theta < \pi$ and by $y = -\pi/4$ for the range $\pi < \theta < 2\pi$.

The limitations as to form for a function of a single independent variable which may be expressed as a Fourier series, are surprisingly few. In fact, so long as a function is real, finite, single valued for the independent variable and possesses only a finite number of finite discontinuities, a series may be found to represent it. One part of a cycle, if cycles are present, may have no apparent relation to another part. Illustrating this feature, Fig. 2 shows a graph for which we shall develop a series later.

3. Types of Fourier Series. The most common type of Fourier series is that represented by Eq. 1. It is known as a whole range sine-cosine series. However, for many purposes, it is desirable to have a different form of series in which the series of cosine and sine terms of Eq. 1 in pairs are combined to yield a series containing sine or cosine terms only. Doing so involves introducing phase angles in accord with the following equation.

$$a_m \sin m\theta + b_m \cos m\theta = \sqrt{a_m{}^2 + b_m{}^2} \sin\left(m\theta + \tan^{-1}\frac{b_m}{a_m}\right)$$

$$= \sqrt{a_m{}^2 + b_m{}^2} \cos\left(m\theta - \tan^{-1}\frac{a_m}{b_m}\right) \qquad [5]$$

Verification of Eq. 5 follows at once when its right-hand members are expanded in terms of sines and cosines of $m\theta$ and $\tan^{-1}(b_m/a_m)$. Eq. 1 may be rewritten as

$$y = f(\theta) = \frac{b_0}{2} + \sum_{m=1}^{\infty} A_m \sin(m\theta + \epsilon_m)$$

$$= \frac{b_0}{2} + \sum_{m=1}^{\infty} A_m \cos\left(m\theta + \epsilon_m - \frac{\pi}{2}\right) \qquad [6]$$

of which

$$A_m = \sqrt{a_m{}^2 + b_m{}^2} \qquad [7]$$

and

$$\epsilon_m = \tan^{-1}\frac{b_m}{a_m} \qquad [8]$$

Eq. 6, in all respects the equivalent of Eq. 1, has an advantage over Eq. 1 in that it shows directly the phase relations for the various frequencies, which, though present in the form of Eq. 1, are not so evident. In the form of Eq. 6, each term separately, rather than by pairs as in Eq. 1, represents the whole contribution of a given frequency or harmonic. To distinguish harmonics from one another, each is given a number corresponding to its m. Thus for $m = 1$ we have the first harmonic or fundamental. Corresponding to $m = 2, 3, 4$, etc., we likewise have the second, the third, the fourth harmonics, etc.

Making use of the well-known relations

$$\cos m\theta = \frac{e^{im\theta} + e^{-im\theta}}{2} \qquad [9]$$

and

$$\sin m\theta = \frac{e^{im\theta} - e^{-im\theta}}{2i} \qquad [10]$$

Eq. 1 may also be expressed as

$$y = f(\theta) = \frac{b_0}{2} + \frac{1}{2} \sum_{m=1}^{\infty} [(b_m - ia_m)e^{im\theta} + (b_m + ia_m)e^{-im\theta}] \qquad [11]$$

The coefficients of $e^{im\theta}$ and $e^{-im\theta}$ are conjugate, a characteristic often permitting considerable simplification of computations. It is much used.

In addition to the whole range sine-cosine series, there is a half-range sine series

$$y = f_1(\theta) = \sum_{m=1}^{\infty} \alpha_m \sin m\theta \qquad [12]$$

and a half-range cosine series

$$y = f_2(\theta) = \frac{\beta_0}{2} + \sum_{m=1}^{\infty} \beta_m \cos m\theta \qquad [13]$$

A sine series, as is more or less evident, yields a graph (Fig. 3A) which is symmetrical with respect to the origin or to points on the θ-axis where

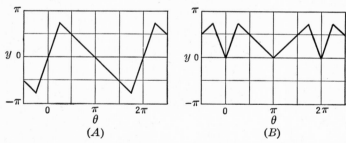

Fig. 3. (A). Graph of a sine series. (B). Graph of a cosine series. For the range $0 < \theta < \pi$, the graphs are alike.

$\theta = \pm n\pi$. Similarly the half-range cosine series yields a graph (Fig. 3B) which is symmetrical with respect to lines perpendicular to the θ-axis at these same points. These series will be discussed more fully later.

Lastly we refer again to Fourier's integral, a limiting form for a Fourier whole range sine-cosine series when the range of the cycle is infinite in extent. We shall discuss it later.

In what precedes, it has been tacitly assumed that the origin of co-ordinates for a problem has been somehow fixed and that the series has been developed accordingly. It is always possible, however, for the operator to select what shall be the beginning and the ending of a range. When the function is cyclical, certain points will appear more natural than others for such choices. If, for instance, there are two loops to the graph of a cycle, one positive and the other negative, and both are of equal length, a point of intersection of two succeeding loops with the θ-axis may be chosen as the origin. Instead, however, a point midway between two such successive intersections will sometimes be chosen. Which choice is to be made will depend to some extent on the type of series desired and that will usually depend upon other considerations.

4. Some General Considerations. That Fourier series will converge has been shown. The proof, which is said by Byerly [1] to be "elaborate," is assumed and accepted here.

Connected with this feature of convergence are the questions of inte-grability and differentiability. Granting convergence, it is easily seen that a Fourier series may always be integrated though not always differ-entiated. To illustrate, the integral of $f(\theta)$, as expressed in Eq. 1, when integrated term by term, yields

$$\int_0^\theta f(\theta)\, d\theta = a_1\,(1 - \cos\theta) + \frac{a_2}{2}\,(1 - \cos 2\theta) + \frac{a_3}{3}\,(1 - \cos 3\theta) + \cdots$$

$$+ b_0\theta + b_1 \sin\theta + \frac{b_2}{2}\sin 2\theta + \frac{b_3}{3}\sin 3\theta + \cdots \quad [14]$$

while the derivative is given by

$$\frac{d}{d\theta} f(\theta) = a_1 \cos\theta + 2a_2 \cos 2\theta + 3a_3 \cos 3\theta + \cdots$$

$$- [b_1 \sin\theta + 2b_2 \sin 2\theta + 3b_3 \sin 3\theta + \cdots] \quad [15]$$

Granted that the coefficients of Eq. 1 form a converging series, it is evident that those of Eq. 14 will also converge, since term by term, in comparison with those of Eq. 1, the coefficients of Eq. 14 are progres-sively smaller. At the same time the coefficients of Eq. 15 term by term are progressively greater. While convergence is always assured for the integral, it is not so assured for the differential.

[1] Byerly, W. E., *Fourier's Series and Spherical Harmonics*, Ginn & Company, 1893, p. 38.

Two questions may be properly asked at this point. (1) Is it probable that a smooth curve, for example one of those shown in Fig. 1, can be represented faithfully by a sine-cosine series, or is it just an approximation? (2) For a graph of the type shown in Fig. 2, what value or values does $f(x)$ possess at $\theta = \pi$ (strictly π radians)? Replying to the first question, the answer is that an equation with an infinite number of arbitrary constants can be made to yield a locus which passes through an infinite number of chosen points. Viewing a series as such an equation and the line of a graph as the aggregate of such a selection of points, the probability seems reasonable. Further, tests with actual series seem to indicate no exception to the possibility. As to question (2), the answer is that the computed value of $f(\theta)$ for $\theta = \pi$ for the function graphed in Fig. 2 is represented by a point midway between the line $y = 0.5\theta$ at $\theta = \pi$ and the line $y = -\pi/4$. The exact value is $+\pi/8$.

5. The Coefficients of the Whole Range Sine-Cosine Series for $f(\theta)$. The well-recognized procedure for determining the coefficients of Eq. 1 follows. (1) Multiply both sides of Eq. 1 by the sine or cosine factor of a selected term on the right. (2) Integrate both sides of the equation obtained with respect to θ between the limits 0 and 2π (strictly 2π radians). (3) Evaluate the coefficient of the term whose sine or cosine factor was chosen for the first step. To illustrate, we shall evaluate a_m, b_0, and b_m, of which m represents any other subscript than zero. Steps one and two yield

$$\int_0^{2\pi} f(\theta) \sin m\theta \, d\theta = \int_0^{2\pi} a_1 \sin \theta \sin m\theta \, d\theta + \int_0^{2\pi} a_2 \sin 2\theta \sin m\theta \, d\theta + \cdots$$

$$+ \int_0^{2\pi} a_m \sin^2 m\theta \, d\theta \cdots + \int_0^{2\pi} \frac{b_0}{2} \sin m\theta \, d\theta$$

$$+ \int_0^{2\pi} b_1 \cos \theta \sin m\theta \, d\theta + \cdots \qquad [16]$$

$$= \pi \, a_m$$

Step three leads at once to

$$a_m = \frac{1}{\pi} \int_0^{2\pi} f(\theta) \sin m\theta \, d\theta \qquad [17]$$

Except for the term $\int_0^{2\pi} a_m \sin^2 m\theta \, d\theta$, all terms on the right of Eq. 16 separately equate to zero. That this is true can be shown rather simply either mathematically or physically.

Similar procedure for b_0, understanding that the trigonometric factor multiplying it in the series is 1, leads to

$$\int_0^{2\pi} f(\theta)\, d\theta = \int_0^{2\pi} a_1 \sin\theta\, d\theta + \int_0^{2\pi} a_2 \sin 2\theta\, d\theta + \cdots + \int_0^{2\pi} \frac{b_0}{2}\, d\theta$$

$$+ \int_0^{2\pi} b_1 \cos\theta\, d\theta + \cdots \qquad\qquad [18]$$

$$= \pi b_0$$

$$b_0 = \frac{1}{\pi} \int_0^{2\pi} f(\theta)\, d\theta \qquad\qquad [19]\,[1]$$

In like manner b_m may be evaluated, and we obtain

$$b_m = \frac{1}{\pi} \int_0^{2\pi} f(\theta) \cos m\theta\, d\theta \qquad\qquad [20]$$

Eq. 20 evidently includes Eq. 19 as a special case. With m equal to zero $\cos m\theta$ becomes 1.

With recourse to tabular or graphical integration if necessary, it now becomes possible to determine the coefficients of the series of Eq. 1 when $f(\theta)$ is expressed either in equation form or graphically as in Fig. 1. The process may or may not be tedious, depending largely on the number of terms that must be used to obtain the desired accuracy. Fortunately, a series often converges so rapidly that only a few terms need be evaluated.

6. Evaluation of the Coefficients for a Particular Whole Range Sine-Cosine Series. To illustrate the procedure, we shall make use of the function graphed in Fig. 2. Its value is given by $f(\theta) = \theta/2$ for the range $0 < \theta < \pi$ and $f(\theta) = -\pi/4$ for $\pi < \theta < 2\pi$. There is a discontinuity at $\theta = \pi$. Eqs. 17, 19, and 20, applied directly, yield

$$a_m = \frac{1}{\pi}\left[\int_0^{\pi} \frac{\theta}{2} \sin m\theta\, d\theta + \int_{\pi}^{2\pi} \frac{-\pi}{4} \sin m\theta\, d\theta \right] \qquad [21]$$

$$\left[a_m = \frac{1}{m} \right]_{m \text{ odd}} \qquad\qquad [22]$$

$$\left[a_m = -\frac{1}{2m} \right]_{m \text{ even}} \qquad\qquad [23]$$

---

[1] As stated above, some authors use b_0 not $b_0/2$ as the constant term of Eq. 1. For them the value of b_0 is just $\tfrac{1}{2}$ that given by Eq. 19. Using $b_0/2$ for the first term has the advantage that, when so used, the general equation for the various b_m's applies to b_0 also.

$$b_0 = \frac{1}{\pi}\left[\int_0^\pi \frac{\theta}{2}\, d\theta + \int_\pi^{2\pi} \frac{-\pi}{4}\, d\theta \right] = 0 \qquad [24]$$

$$b_m = \frac{1}{\pi}\left[\int_0^\pi \frac{\theta}{2}\cos m\theta\, d\theta + \int_\pi^{2\pi} \frac{-\pi}{4}\cos m\theta\, d\theta \right] \qquad [25]$$

$$\left[b_m = -\frac{1}{m^2\pi} \right]_{m\,\text{odd}} \qquad [26]$$

$$\left[b_m = 0 \right]_{m\,\text{even}} \qquad [27]$$

$$y = f(\theta) = \sin\theta - \frac{1}{2\times 2}\sin 2\theta + \frac{1}{3}\sin 3\theta - \frac{1}{2\times 4}\sin 4\theta + \cdots$$

$$-\frac{1}{\pi}\left[\cos\theta + \frac{1}{3^2}\cos 3\theta + \frac{1}{5^2}\cos 5\theta + \cdots \right] \qquad [28]$$

Checking shows the following relation between θ and the computed $f(\theta)$

θ	0	$\dfrac{\pi}{4}$	$\dfrac{\pi}{2}$	$\dfrac{3\pi}{4}$	π	$\dfrac{5\pi}{4}$	$\dfrac{3\pi}{2}$	$\dfrac{7\pi}{4}$	2π
$f(\theta)$	$\dfrac{-\pi}{8}$	$\dfrac{\pi}{8}$	$\dfrac{\pi}{4}$	$\dfrac{3\pi}{8}$	$\dfrac{\pi}{8}$	$\dfrac{-\pi}{4}$	$\dfrac{-\pi}{4}$	$\dfrac{-\pi}{4}$	$\dfrac{-\pi}{8}$

As expected, $f(\theta)$ for θ equal to 0, π, and 2π is the mean of the values predicted separately by the two lines of the graph.

7. The Half-Range Series for $f(\theta)$. If one is interested in the values for $f(\theta)$ only for the range $0 < \theta < \pi$ or if the portion for the range $\pi < \theta < 2\pi$ is symmetrical in either of two ways with the portion for the range $0 < \theta < \pi$, one has the possibility of developing the function for one or the other of two half-range series, a sine series corresponding to the a terms of Eq. 1 and a cosine series corresponding to the b terms. Generally such half-range sine or cosine series are preferred to whole-range series since they involve less labor. Moreover, through containing terms of one type only, they make it possible in certain computations to comply with certain boundary conditions when otherwise it would be impossible.

If the graph of the whole range is symmetrical with respect to a point on the θ-axis at $\theta = 0$, π, 2π, etc., that is, if the function is odd, as in Fig. 3A, the series can evidently contain only sine terms. The term $a_m \sin m\theta$, whatever the value of m, will have values of opposite signs though of the same magnitude when successively $\pi - \delta$ and $\pi + \delta$ are substituted for θ, while, for the term $b_m \cos m\theta$, the corresponding values will be both of the same sign and the same magnitude. Obviously, on the other hand, if the graph of the whole range is symmetrical with respect to the perpendicular to the θ-axis at $\theta = 0$, π, 2π, etc., that is, if the function is even, as in Fig. 3B, the series can contain cosine terms only.

Comparing A and B of Fig. 3, we see that they are identical in the portions in the ranges $0 < \theta < \pi$, though not generally elsewhere. It appears, and is the case, that a given line in the range $0 < \theta < \pi$ may therefore be represented by either a sine or a cosine series and also any number of combinations of part sine and part cosine series. Outside the stated range, however, all will differ.

In developing a half-range series, the procedure for determining the coefficients is the same as that for the whole-range series. Assuming thus

$$y = f_1(\theta) = \alpha_1 \sin \theta + \alpha_2 \sin 2\theta + \alpha_3 \sin 3\theta + \cdots \qquad [29]$$

multiplying through by $\sin m\theta$, integrating with respect to θ between the limits 0 and π (not 2π as for the whole range), and evaluating, one obtains

$$\alpha_m = \frac{2}{\pi} \int_0^\pi f_1(\theta) \sin m\theta \, d\theta \qquad [30]$$

Similarly for the half-range cosine series, assuming

$$y = f_2(\theta) = \frac{\beta_0}{2} + \beta_1 \cos \theta + \beta_2 \cos 2\theta + \beta_3 \cos 3\theta + \cdots \qquad [31]$$

we obtain

$$\beta_0 = \frac{2}{\pi} \int_0^\pi f_2(\theta) \, d\theta \qquad [32]$$

and

$$\beta_m = \frac{2}{\pi} \int_0^\pi f_2(\theta) \cos m\theta \, d\theta \qquad [33]$$

Eqs. 30, 32, and 33 differ from Eqs. 17, 19, and 20 in that the constants preceding the integrals are twice as great and in that the upper limits of the integrals are one-half as great. It is of interest to note that, by change of the independent variable from θ to ϕ where $\phi = \theta/2$, it is possible to obtain a normal half-range series for the new variable ϕ which is equivalent to the whole-range for θ. Referring to Fig. 2, for instance, the range $0 < \theta < \pi$ would cover the whole range in θ, namely $0 < \theta < 2\pi$. Further, the appropriate half-range series in ϕ in terms of cosines, say, once developed, can be converted by substitution into a cosine series in θ with the β_1 term containing the angle $\theta/2$. The function for the whole range, as initially described, is now described by a cosine series.

8. Evaluation of the Coefficients for Particular Half-Range Sine and Cosine Series. Consider a sine series to represent, between the limits 0 and π, the straight line whose equation is

$$y = f_1(\theta) = \frac{\theta}{2} \qquad [34]$$

Substitution in Eq. 30 yields

$$\alpha_m = \frac{2}{\pi} \int_0^\pi \frac{\theta}{2} \sin m\theta \, d\theta = \pm \frac{1}{m} \qquad [35]$$

with the sign positive when m is odd and negative when even. We have therefore

$$y = f_1(\theta) = \sin \theta - \tfrac{1}{2} \sin 2\theta + \tfrac{1}{3} \sin 3\theta - \tfrac{1}{4} \sin 4\theta + \cdots \qquad [36]$$

For the cosine series representing the same straight line in the range $0 < \theta < \pi$, we obtain

$$\beta_0 = \frac{2}{\pi} \int_0^\pi \frac{\theta}{2} \, d\theta = \frac{\pi}{2} \qquad [37]$$

$$\beta_m = \frac{2}{\pi} \int_0^\pi \frac{\theta}{2} \cos m\theta \, d\theta \qquad [38]$$

When m is odd, β_m has the value $-(2/m^2\pi)$; when m is even, its value is zero. There follows

$$y = f_2(\theta) = \frac{\pi}{4} - \frac{2}{\pi}\left(\cos \theta + \frac{1}{3^2}\cos 3\theta + \frac{1}{5^2}\cos 5\theta + \cdots\right) \qquad [39]$$

By trial both Eq. 36 and Eq. 39 are found to check. The process is simple for the latter at points where θ takes the values 0, $\pi/4$, $\pi/2$, $3\pi/4$, π, though, for both end values, one is helped by recognizing that

$$1 + \frac{1}{3^2} + \frac{1}{5^2} + \frac{1}{7^2} + \cdots = \frac{\pi^2}{8} \qquad [40]$$

No trouble is experienced in checking Eq. 36 for similar values of θ, though one is helped at $\pi/2$ by recognizing that

$$1 - \frac{1}{3} + \frac{1}{5} - \frac{1}{7} + \frac{1}{9} - \cdots = \frac{\pi}{4} \qquad [41]$$

At $\theta = \pi$ because of the discontinuity in $f_1(\theta)$ at this point, the value of the function is midway between $+\pi/2$ and $-\pi/2$. This value is not approached as a limit. However, both Eq. 36 and Eq. 39 describe the same curve between $\theta = 0$ and $\theta = \pi$, though in the region outside they

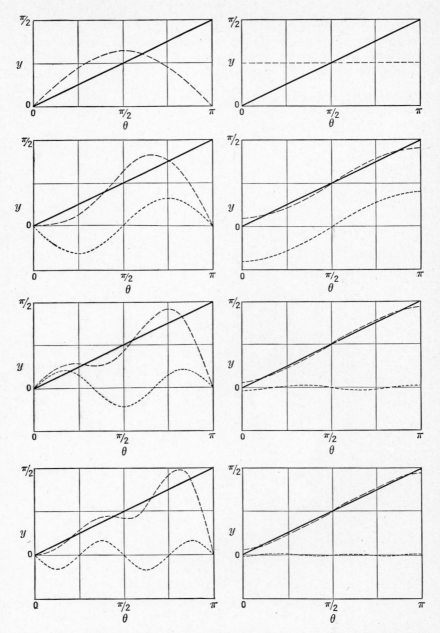

Fig. 4. Showing in downward progression the separate contributions of the successive terms of Eq. 36 (sine series) at the left and Eq. 39 (cosine series) at the right, and the successive approximations to the straight line $y = \theta/2$ in the range $0 < \theta < \pi$. Each new term is represented by - - - and the approximation to the straight line produced by its inclusion by — — —.

118

differ greatly. It is interesting to note the separate contributions of the succeeding terms of Eqs. 36 and 39 as shown in Fig. 4. It is very apparent that the cosine series converges the more rapidly.

9. Series Representing $y = f\left(\dfrac{2\pi}{T}\, t\right)$ **and** $y = f\left(\dfrac{2\pi}{\lambda}\, x\right)$. It is well to repeat that here T represents the period of a simple harmonic motion, that of the fundamental of a vibrating system, and that λ is a wavelength, that of the fundamental of a wave motion. The forms of the whole-range and half-range series are like those for $y = f(\theta)$. Their coefficients may be obtained by procedures exactly like those used in obtaining corresponding values for $f(\theta)$. Thus, for the whole-range sine-cosine series, we have

$$y = f\left(\frac{2\pi}{T}\, t\right) = \frac{b'_0}{2} + \sum_{m=1}^{\infty} a'_m \sin\left(m\,\frac{2\pi}{T}\, t\right) + b'_m \cos\left(m\,\frac{2\pi}{T}\, t\right) \quad [42]$$

$$a'_m = \frac{2}{T} \int_0^T f\left(\frac{2\pi}{T}\, t\right) \sin\left(m\,\frac{2\pi}{T}\, t\right) dt \quad [43]$$

$$b'_0 = \frac{2}{T} \int_0^T f\left(\frac{2\pi}{T}\, t\right) dt \quad [43a]$$

$$b'_m = \frac{2}{T} \int_0^T f\left(\frac{2\pi}{T}\, t\right) \cos\left(m\,\frac{2\pi}{T}\, t\right) dt \quad [44]$$

For the half-range sine series, we have

$$y = f_1\left(\frac{2\pi}{T}\, t\right) = \sum_{m=1}^{\infty} \alpha'_m \sin\left(m\,\frac{2\pi}{T}\, t\right) \quad [45]$$

$$\alpha'_m = \frac{4}{T} \int_0^{T/2} f_1\left(\frac{2\pi}{T}\, t\right) \sin\left(m\,\frac{2\pi}{T}\, t\right) dt \quad [46]$$

For the half-range cosine series, we have

$$y = f_2\left(\frac{2\pi}{T}\, t\right) = \frac{\beta'_0}{2} + \sum_{m=1}^{\infty} \beta'_m \cos\left(m\,\frac{2\pi}{T}\, t\right) \quad [47]$$

$$\beta'_0 = \frac{4}{T} \int_0^{T/2} f_2\left(\frac{2\pi}{T}\, t\right) dt \quad [47a]$$

$$\beta'_m = \frac{4}{T} \int_0^{T/2} f_2\left(\frac{2\pi}{T}\, t\right) \cos\left(m\,\frac{2\pi}{T}\, t\right) dt \quad [48]$$

An analogous equation involving $f\left(\dfrac{2\pi}{\lambda}\, x\right)$ is obtained by substituting

x and λ for t and T of Eq. 42, and the equations for coefficients a''_m, b''_m, α''_m, and β''_m for the (x,λ) series are exactly like Eqs. 42 to 48.

If in Eqs. 17, 19, and 20, one replaces θ by $\dfrac{2\pi}{T} t$ and $\dfrac{2\pi}{\lambda} x$, he obtains for a_m, b_0, and b_m, identically the expressions for the primed and the double primed constants of Eqs. 42 to 48. This indicates that a_m, a'_m, and a''_m, for instance, are the same quantity arising in different connections. That in these expressions we have $2/T$ and $2/\lambda$ where before we had $1/\pi$ is a consequence of the fact that the cycles for the independent variables here end when the values T and λ are reached whereas in the preceding case it ended when 2π not π was reached. Some authors use $0 < t < 2T$ and $0 < x < 2\lambda$ for ranges. In that case the constants preceding the integrals of Eqs. 42 to 48 are reduced to $1/T$, $1/\lambda$, etc.

10. The Limiting Series for the Range $0 < x < \infty$ and Fourier's Integral. With the understanding that λ of the series

$$y = f\left(\frac{2\pi}{\lambda} x\right) = F(x) = \frac{b_0}{2}$$

$$+ \sum_{m=1}^{\infty}\left[a_m \sin\left(m\,\frac{2\pi}{\lambda} x\right) + b_m \cos\left(m\,\frac{2\pi}{\lambda} x\right)\right] \quad [49]$$

will be allowed later to increase indefinitely, recognizing that λ will then no longer represent a wavelength, let us replace it by l. We then have

$$F(x) = \frac{b_0}{2} + \sum_{m=1}^{\infty}\left[a_m \sin\left(m\,\frac{2\pi}{l} x\right) + b_m \cos\left(m\,\frac{2\pi}{l} x\right)\right] \quad [50]$$

in which

$$a_m = \frac{2}{l} \int_0^l F(x) \sin\left(m\,\frac{2\pi}{l} x\right) dx \quad [51]$$

$$b_0 = \frac{2}{l} \int_0^l F(x)\, dx \quad [51a]$$

and

$$b_m = \frac{2}{l} \int_0^l F(x) \cos\left(m\,\frac{2\pi}{l} x\right) dx \quad [52]$$

Substitution in Eq. 50 yields

$$F(x) = \frac{1}{l} \int_0^l F(x)\, dx + \frac{2}{l} \sum_{m=1}^{\infty}\left[\sin\left(m\,\frac{2\pi}{l} x\right) \int_0^l F(x) \sin\left(m\,\frac{2\pi}{l} x\right) dx\right.$$

$$\left. + \cos\left(m\,\frac{2\pi}{l} x\right) \int_0^l F(x) \cos\left(m\,\frac{2\pi}{l} x\right) dx\right] \quad [53]$$

Since definite integrals are functions of their limits, we may, in order to avoid confusion, replace the symbol x where found within such an integral by some other symbol, say μ. Then we may write

$$F(x) = \frac{1}{l} \int_0^l F(\mu)\, d\mu + \frac{2}{l} \sum_{m=1}^{\infty} \left[\int_0^l F(\mu) \sin\left(m\frac{2\pi}{l}\mu \right) \sin\left(m\frac{2\pi}{l}x \right) d\mu \right.$$

$$\left. + \int_0^l F(\mu) \cos\left(m\frac{2\pi}{l}\mu \right) \cos\left(m\frac{2\pi}{l}x \right) d\mu \right] \quad [54]$$

Inspection shows the possibility of replacing a combination of terms such as $\cos\left(m\dfrac{2\pi}{l}\mu \right) \cos\left(m\dfrac{2\pi}{l}x \right) + \sin\left(m\dfrac{2\pi}{l}\mu \right) \sin\left(m\dfrac{2\pi}{l}x \right)$ by $\cos\left[m\dfrac{2\pi}{l}(\mu - x) \right]$. Hence we write

$$F(x) = \frac{1}{l} \int_0^l F(\mu)\, d\mu + \frac{2}{l} \sum_{m=1}^{\infty} \int_0^l F(\mu) \cos\left[m\frac{2\pi}{l}(\mu - x) \right] d\mu \quad [55]$$

Let the summation be now changed so as to extend from $m = -\infty$ to $m = +\infty$. Since the cosines for negative m's are equal to corresponding ones for positive m's, no trouble is experienced. At the same time, the multiplier of the summation changes to $1/l$ and the $\dfrac{1}{l} \displaystyle\int_0^\infty F(\mu)\, d\mu$ now fits into the summation, and we have

$$F(x) = \frac{1}{l} \int_0^l F(\mu)\, d\mu \sum_{m=-\infty}^{\infty} \cos\left[m\frac{2\pi}{l}(\mu - x) \right]$$

$$= \frac{1}{2\pi} \int_0^l F(\mu)\, d\mu \sum_{m=-\infty}^{\infty} \frac{2\pi}{l} \cos\left[m\frac{2\pi}{l}(\mu - x) \right] \quad [56]$$

If now l is increased without limit and $m2\pi/l$ is treated as a new variable, ν say, with its differential $d\nu$ equal to $2\pi/l$, Eq. 56 may be rewritten as follows:

$$\left[F(x) = \frac{1}{2\pi} \int_0^\infty F(\mu)\, d\mu \int_{-\infty}^\infty \cos \nu(\mu - x)\, d\nu \right]_{0 < x < \infty} \quad [57]$$

Though no change in value for the integral occurs when the order of integration is reversed, such reversal is found convenient and necessary in application. Thus reversed Eq. 57 becomes

$$\left[F(x) = \frac{1}{2\pi} \int_{-\infty}^\infty d\nu \int_0^\infty F(\mu) \cos \nu(\mu - x)\, d\mu \right]_{0 < x < \infty} \quad [58]$$

Had we followed the procedure of certain other authors and developed series for the ranges $-\pi < \theta < \pi$, $-T/2 < t < T$, $-\lambda/2 < x < \lambda/2$, instead of $0 < \theta < 2\pi$, $0 < t < T$, $0 < x < \lambda$, the relation obtained in place of Eq. 58 would have satisfied the range $-\infty < \theta < \infty$. Its form, slightly different, is the following:

$$\left[\phi(x) = \frac{1}{\pi} \int_{-\infty}^{+\infty} d\nu \int_{-\infty}^{+\infty} \phi(\mu) \cos \nu(\mu - x) \, d\mu \right]_{-\infty < x < +\infty} \quad [59]$$

The right-hand member of Eq. 59 is known as Fourier's integral. It is more inclusive than Eq. 58, which it includes as a special case. In making the transfer from one form to another, however, one needs to note that the portion of a function which is expanded in the range $0 < x < l$ to yield Eq. 58 is different from that which is expanded in the range $-l/2 < x < l/2$, and that therefore the $F(x)$ of Eq. 58 is not the $\phi(x)$ of Eq. 59.

Eqs. 58 and 59 are found indispensable in the solution of many problems of theoretical and practical physics, involving electricity, magnetism, heat flow, x-ray analysis, etc. To illustrate its use here seems outside the scope of the present work and will not be done.

11. Special Cycles Consisting of a Positive and a Negative Loop. The graphs of many functions met with in practice show cycles consisting of a positive and a negative loop, both of the same extent along the independent variable axis. Because of certain characteristics, many of these permit of simplified treatment. Four cases will be discussed.

Case I. The Area of the Positive Loop Equal to That of the Negative Loop. In this case the term of the whole range sine-cosine series involving b_0 is zero. This is evident from Eq. 19, for the integral $\int_0^{2\pi} f(\theta) \, d\theta$ represents the area enclosed between the loops and the θ-axis; and, if this area is nil, the coefficient is likewise zero. The loops need not be of equal lengths in this instance.

Case II. Positive Loop Asymmetric; Negative Loop a Displaced Image of the Positive Loop. An illustration is given in Fig. 5 at A. It is a cycle that is encountered frequently in electrical engineering. Evidently b_0 is zero. For the further evaluation of coefficients, we have the condition that $f(\theta + \pi)$ shall equal $-f(\theta)$. This is met by both sine and cosine terms when only odd values of m are used since

$$[\sin m\theta = -\sin m(\theta + \pi)]_{m \text{ odd}} \quad [60]$$

$$[\cos m\theta = -\cos m(\theta + \pi)]_{m \text{ odd}} \quad [61]$$

Even values of m do not yield the change of sign. The type of series that satisfies Fig. 5A is therefore the whole range sine-cosine series containing odd terms only, thus

$$y = f(\theta) = a_1 \sin \theta + a_3 \sin 3\theta + a_5 \sin 5\theta + \cdots$$
$$+ b_1 \cos \theta + b_3 \cos 3\theta + \cdots \quad [62]$$

In obtaining values for the coefficients it is evidently not necessary to integrate over more than one loop. In each instance the integral for the whole range will be just twice that for one loop.

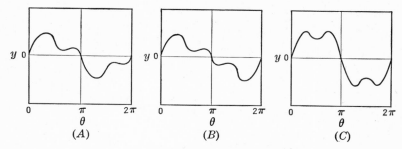

Fig. 5.   Three special cycles with graphs composed of a single positive and a single negative loop of equal extent along the axis of the independent variable.

Case III.   Positive Loop Asymmetric; Negative Loop Possesses Point Symmetry with Respect to the Positive Loop. An illustration is given in Fig. 5B. This type of wave may be met in various fields, in particular in sonics. The function is odd. An evident condition which must be fulfilled by the series is that $f(\pi - \Delta)$ shall equal $-f(\pi + \Delta)$. This is fulfilled by all sine terms whether m is odd or even. All cosine terms fail. Thus

$$\sin (m\pi - \Delta) = -\sin (m\pi + \Delta) \quad [63]$$

while

$$\cos (m\pi - \Delta) = \cos (m\pi + \Delta) \quad [64]$$

It follows that Fig. 5B will be described satisfactorily by a regular half-range sine series.

Case IV.   Positive Loop Symmetrical; Negative Loop Possesses Point Symmetry with Respect to the Positive Loop. An illustration is given in Fig. 5C. This cycle occurs frequently. Obviously in this case, as in case III, the function is odd and a half-range sine series suffices. There is an added condition, however. Here $f(\pi/2 + \Delta)$ equals $f(\pi/2 - \Delta)$.

This condition is fulfilled by sine terms only when m is odd. The series then takes the form

$$y = f(\theta) = a_1 \sin \theta + a_3 \sin 3\theta + a_5 \sin 5\theta + \cdots \qquad [65]$$

While integrating to obtain values for the coefficients, one needs only to integrate over one-half of the first loop. Because of symmetry the integral for the whole loop is twice that for the half.

In this case, were a shift of the origin made to the middle of a loop, the series required would be a half-range cosine series with odd terms only present. The even terms are eliminated by the condition of point symmetry demanded for $\theta' = \pi/2$ in the shifted coordinate system.

12. Tabular Integration Method of Obtaining Series Coefficients.

As the function to be used in illustrating a procedure suitable for such determinations, we make use of an oscillogram [1] (Fig. 6) which is rather similar to the instantaneous power oscillogram of Fig. 1. The cycle involved is of the type described under case II of the preceding section. Our task is that of determining coefficients a_1, a_3, a_5, $\cdots$ b_1, b_3, b_5, $\cdots$. Kerchner and Corcoran in the reference cited give values for the instantaneous current at 5° intervals between 0° and 180° beginning at 0°. To these we shall apply Eqs. 17, 19, and 20, using a tabular trapezoidal method of integration as described in Chapter IV, rather than the slightly different procedure used by the authors. How it is carried out is shown in Table I, where values have been determined for a_1, b_1, a_3, and b_3. Similar procedure will yield values for the a's and b's of higher harmonics. As tabulated, one sees that the same numeric occurs frequently as a sine or a cosine factor. If a slide rule or computing machine is used in making calculations, much time may be saved by setting the rule or computing machine so that successive multiplications involving such a numeric can be carried through conveniently.

Collected values for the desired series are given in Table II. Because of the slightly different procedure mentioned, the constants for the fundamental or first harmonic and for the third harmonic differ slightly from those obtained by Kerchner and Corcoran. Values for the fifth and the seventh harmonics, however, are those which they obtained.

In evaluating the ϵ_m's for a series of the form of Eq. 6, one must choose, in each case, between two supplementary angles with the same value of $\tan \epsilon_m$. Which angle to take depends on the signs of the coefficients a_m and b_m. Referring to Eqs. 7 and 8, it is seen that they may be solved simultaneously for a_m and b_m in terms of A_m and ϵ_m to yield $a_m = A_m \cos \epsilon_m$ and $b_m = A_m \sin \epsilon_m$. With A_m, as defined by Eq. 7, taken as

[1] Kerchner, R. M., and Corcoran, G. F., op. cit., p.139.

essentially positive, it follows that cos ϵ_m has the same sign as a_m and that sin ϵ_m has the same sign as b_m. With this understanding, the ranges for various initial phase angles ϵ_m that correspond to various combinations of positive and negative signs for a_m and b_m are those shown in

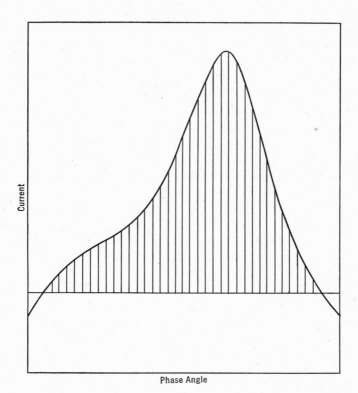

Fig. 6. An oscillogram showing instantaneous current as a function of phase angle for one-half of a cycle. The area between the trace and the phase angle axis has been subdivided into 36 portions by vertical lines drawn at 5 degree intervals. (Kerchner, R. H., and Corcoran, G. F., *Alternating Currents*, p. 139, New York. John Wiley and Sons, Inc., 1938.)

Table III. These relations are also shown graphically in Fig. 7 where a_m and b_m are treated as x and y components of a vector. As is evident, a positive ϵ_m for the range $\pi < \epsilon_m < 2\pi$ may be treated as a negative ϵ_m with a corresponding value between 0 and π.

As a result of the analysis summarized in Table II, and the interpretations of Table III and Fig. 7, we may now write the series to and including the 7th harmonic in the two following equivalent forms, from

TABLE I

ILLUSTRATING THE TRAPEZOIDAL TABULAR METHOD OF DETERMINING COEFFICIENTS FOR THE FOURIER ANALYSIS OF AN OSCILLOGRAM OF INSTANTANEOUS CURRENT (FIG. 6) AS A FUNCTION OF PHASE ANGLE

Values for instantaneous current were obtained from data published by Kerchner and Corcoran.[1] Instead of values for phase angles of 0°, 5°, 10°, etc., as reported by them, the values here reported are those for 2.5°, 7.5°, 12.5°, etc. They have been obtained by averaging and are expressed in arbitrary units. Actually the change is not important.

PART 1. THE FUNDAMENTAL (FIRST HARMONIC)

sin θ	y sin θ +	y sin θ −	θ in degrees	y	cos θ	y cos θ +	y cos θ −
0.0436	0.1		2.5	3.0	0.9990	3.0	
0.1305	1.0		7.5	8.0	0.9914	7.9	
0.2164	2.5		12.5	11.7	0.9763	11.2	
0.3007	4.5		17.5	14.9	0.9537	14.2	
0.3827	5.8		22.5	17.9	0.9239	16.5	
0.4617	9.5		27.5	20.6	0.8870	18.3	
0.5373	12.2		32.5	22.7	0.8434	19.1	
0.6088	15.1		37.5	24.8	0.7934	19.7	
0.6756	18.3		42.5	27.0	0.7373	19.9	
0.7373	21.7		47.5	29.4	0.6756	19.9	
0.7934	25.6		52.5	32.3	0.6088	19.6	
0.8434	30.0		57.5	35.6	0.5373	19.1	
0.8870	35.2		62.5	39.7	0.4617	18.3	
0.9239	41.0		67.5	44.4	0.3827	17.0	
0.9537	47.5		72.5	49.8	0.3007	14.9	
0.9763	55.1		77.5	56.4	0.2164	12.2	

PART 2. THE THIRD HARMONIC

sin 3θ	y sin 3θ +	y sin 3θ −	θ in degrees	y	cos 3θ	y cos 3θ +	y cos 3θ −
0.1305	0.4		2.5	3.0	0.9914	3.0	
0.3827	3.0		7.5	8.0	0.9239	7.4	
0.6088	7.1		12.5	11.7	0.7934	9.3	
0.7934	11.8		17.5	14.9	0.6088	9.1	
0.9234	16.5		22.5	17.9	0.3827	6.9	
0.9914	20.4		27.5	20.6	0.1305	2.7	
0.9914	22.5		32.5	22.7	−0.1305		3.0
0.9239	22.9		37.5	24.8	−0.3827		9.5
0.7934	21.4		42.5	27.0	−0.6088		16.4
0.6088	17.9		47.5	29.4	−0.7934		23.3
0.3827	12.4		52.5	32.3	−0.9239		29.8
0.1305	4.6		57.5	35.6	−0.9914		35.3
−0.1305		5.2	62.5	39.7	−0.9914		39.4
−0.3827		17.0	67.5	44.4	−0.9239		41.0
−0.6088		30.3	72.5	49.8	−0.7934		39.5
−0.7934		44.7	77.5	56.4	−0.6088		34.3

0.9914	63.3		82.5	63.8	0.1305	8.4	
0.9990	71.9		87.5	72.0	0.0436	3.1	
0.9990	81.3		92.5	81.4	−0.0436		3.5
0.9914	90.2		97.5	91.0	−0.1305		11.9
0.9763	97.9		102.5	100.3	−0.2164		21.7
0.9537	104.0		107.5	109.0	−0.3007		32.8
0.9239	106.4		112.5	115.2	−0.3827		44.1
0.8870	104.7		117.5	118.0	−0.4617		54.5
0.8434	98.2		122.5	116.4	−0.5373		62.5
0.7934	87.0		127.5	109.6	−0.6088		66.7
0.7373	72.4		132.5	98.2	−0.6756		66.4
0.6756	57.3		137.5	84.8	−0.7373		62.5
0.6088	43.6		142.5	71.6	−0.7934		56.8
0.5373	31.2		147.5	58.0	−0.8434		48.9
0.4617	21.1		152.5	45.6	−0.8870		40.5
0.3827	13.3		157.5	34.7	−0.9239		32.0
0.3007	7.6		162.5	25.4	−0.9537		24.2
0.2164	3.8		167.5	17.6	−0.9763		17.2
0.1305	1.4		172.5	10.6	−0.9914		10.5
0.0436	0.2		177.5	3.6	−0.9970		3.6
	1481.9					+262.3	−660.3
							−398.0

$$a_1 = \frac{1}{\pi}\left(2 \times 1481.9 \times \frac{\pi}{36}\right) = 82.3$$

$$b_1 = \frac{1}{\pi}\left(2 \times -398.0 \times \frac{\pi}{36}\right) = -22.1$$

$$\sqrt{a_1^2 + b_1^2} = 85.1$$

$$\tan^{-1}\frac{b_1}{a_1} = \tan^{-1} -0.269 = -0.084\,\pi = -15.1°$$

−0.9239		58.9	82.5	63.8	−0.3827		24.4
−0.9914		71.4	87.5	72.0	−0.1305		9.4
−0.9914		80.7	92.5	81.4	0.1305	10.6	
−0.9239		84.1	97.5	91.0	0.3827	34.8	
−0.7934		79.6	102.5	100.3	0.6088	61.1	
−0.6088		66.4	107.5	109.0	0.7934	86.5	
−0.3827		44.1	112.5	115.2	0.9239	106.4	
−0.1305		15.4	117.5	118.0	0.9914	117.0	
0.1305	15.2		122.5	116.4	0.9914	115.4	
0.3827	41.9		127.5	109.6	0.9239	101.3	
0.6088	59.8		132.5	98.2	0.7934	77.9	
0.7934	67.3		137.5	84.8	0.6088	51.6	
0.9239	66.2		142.5	71.6	0.3827	27.4	
0.9914	57.5		147.5	58.0	0.1305	7.6	
0.9914	45.2		152.5	45.6	−0.1305		6.0
0.9239	32.1		157.5	34.7	−0.3827		13.3
0.7934	20.2		162.5	25.4	−0.6088		15.5
0.6088	10.7		167.5	17.6	−0.7934		14.0
0.3827	4.1		172.5	10.6	−0.9239		9.8
0.1305	0.5		177.5	3.6	−0.9914		3.6
	+581.6	−597.8				+836.0	−367.5
		− 16.2				+468.5	

$$a_3 = \frac{1}{\pi}\left(2 \times (-16.2) \times \frac{\pi}{36}\right) = -0.90$$

$$b_3 = \frac{1}{\pi}\left(2 \times 468.5 \times \frac{\pi}{36}\right) = +26.0$$

$$\sqrt{a_3^2 + b_3^2} = 26.0$$

$$\tan^{-1}\frac{b_3}{a_3} = \tan^{-1} -28.9 = -0.489\,\pi = -88°$$

[1] Idem.

which the names of the units accompanying the constants have been omitted.

$$y = 82.3 \sin \theta - 22.1 \cos \theta - 0.90 \sin 3\theta + 26.0 \cos 3\theta$$

$$- 5.38 \sin 5\theta - 3.65 \cos 5\theta + 2.01 \sin 7\theta - 1.29 \cos 7\theta \quad [66]$$

$$y = 85.1 \sin (\theta - 15.1°) + 26.0 \sin (3\theta + 92°)$$

$$+ 6.3 \sin (5\theta - 146°) + 2.4 \sin (7\theta - 33°) \quad [67]$$

TABLE II

COLLECTED VALUES FOR THE CONSTANTS OF SERIES OF THE TYPE OF EQS. 1 AND 6 TO REPRESENT THE INSTANTANEOUS CURRENT OSCILLOGRAM OF FIG. 6, DATA FOR WHICH, TAKEN FROM MEASUREMENTS BY KERCHNER AND CORCORAN,[1] ARE GIVEN IN TABLE I

Values for the fifth and seventh harmonics are those which they computed. Units for a_m, b_m, and $\sqrt{a_m{}^2 + b_m{}^2}$ are arbitrary.

Harmonic	Constant a_m	b_m	A_m or $\sqrt{a_m{}^2 + b_m{}^2}$	$\dfrac{b_m}{a_m}$ or $\tan \epsilon_m$	Quadrant for a Positive ϵ_m	$\tan^{-1} \dfrac{b_m}{a_m}$ or ϵ_m
Fundamental	82.3	−22.1	85.1	− 0.269	4th	− 15.1°
3rd	− 0.90	26.0	26.0	−28.9	2nd	+ 92.0°
5th	− 5.38	− 3.65	6.3	+ 0.679	3rd	−145.9°
7th	2.01	− 1.29	2.4	− 0.640	4th	− 32.6°

TABLE III

SHOWING CONNECTION BETWEEN THE SIGNS OF a_m AND b_m OF THE WHOLE RANGE SINE-COSINE SERIES OF EQ. 1 AND THE RANGE OF THE CORRESPONDING ϵ_m, CONSIDERED POSITIVE, OF EQ. 6 WHEN THE SERIES IS SHIFTED TO THAT FORM

Sign of a_m	Sign of b_m	Range of ϵ_m
+	+	$0 < \epsilon_m < \dfrac{\pi}{2}$
−	+	$\dfrac{\pi}{2} < \epsilon_m < \pi$
−	−	$\pi < \epsilon_m < \dfrac{3\pi}{2}$
+	−	$\dfrac{3\pi}{2} < \epsilon_m < 2\pi$

[1] Op. cit.

Inspection of Eq. 67 shows that the contribution of each harmonic has decreased with the increase in its order. It is probable that the contributions of the harmonics of still higher orders are negligible but such is not certain without further tests, one of which consists in finding the differences between the measured y's and the computed y's, using Eq. 66 or Eq. 67.

With regard to accuracy, it is easily seen that as the order of the harmonic increases, the uncertainty with respect to the magnitudes of the

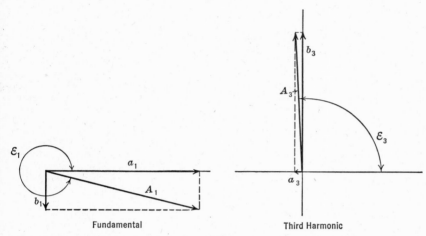

Fundamental   Third Harmonic

FIG. 7. Showing a vector graph useful in determining the range of ϵ_m of Eq. 6 and hence in determining a phase angle when its tangent is known. The graphs represent conditions for the fundamental and the third harmonic shown in Table II.

amplitudes also increases. Referring to the computations for the first and third harmonics as shown in Table I, it is seen that the range of θ for which a given y is assumed to be an average is three times as great for the third as for the first harmonic. For a higher harmonic the range is correspondingly greater, with an uncertainty that is also correspondingly greater.

Certain time-saving, tabular methods [1] have been developed for the determination of the coefficients of a Fourier series. Reference to such shortened methods is recommended for one who is limited by circumstances to the tabular method and has several determinations ahead of him.

[1] Lipka, Joseph, *Graphical and Mechanical Computation*, Chap. VII, New York, John Wiley & Sons, Inc., 1918.

Running, T. R., *Empirical Formulas*, p. 74, New York, John Wiley & Sons, 1917.

H. O. Taylor, *Phys. Rev.*, **6**, 303 (1915).

13. The Rolling Sphere Harmonic Analyzer. The discussion here is based on a description of the construction and operation of an Henrici [1] analyzer by D. C. Miller.[2] In theory it is a device for the mechanical determinations of areas corresponding to the various integrals

$$a_m = \frac{1}{\pi} \int_0^{2\pi} f(\theta) \sin m\theta \, d\theta \qquad [17]$$

and

$$b_m = \frac{1}{\pi} \int_0^{2\pi} f(\theta) \cos m\theta \, d\theta \qquad [20]$$

Obviously, given a certain $f(\theta)$ (Fig. 8A), it is possible to plot various curves (Fig. 8C) corresponding to the various integrands described by

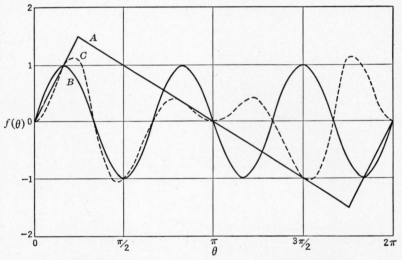

FIG. 8. Graphs illustrating graphical harmonic analysis, using ordinary planimeters. A, Graph of function; B, graph of sine factor of the third harmonic; C, graph of $f(\theta) \sin 3\theta$ as a function of θ.

Eqs. 17 and 20 and then to determine areas with the aid of an ordinary planimeter. Such curve plotting, one for each coefficient, would be very time consuming, and a machine to be of value must eliminate much of such procedure. This the Henrici instrument does.

Integration of the right-hand terms of Eqs. 17 and 20 by the "integration-by-parts" method, replacing $f(\theta)$ by y, yields

[1] Henrici, O., *Phil. Mag.*, **38**, 110 (1894).

[2] Miller, D. C., *J. Franklin Inst.*, **182**, 285 (1916).

$$a_m = \left[-\frac{1}{m\pi} y \cos m\theta \right]_0^{2\pi} + \frac{1}{m\pi} \int_0^{2\pi} \cos m\theta \, dy \qquad [68]$$

and

$$b_m = \left[\frac{1}{m\pi} y \sin m\theta \right]_0^{2\pi} - \frac{1}{m\pi} \int_0^{2\pi} \sin m\theta \, dy \qquad [69]$$

The first member on the right of Eq. 69 is obviously equal to zero. If now, as conditions precedent to the use of the Henrici instrument, conditions are so determined that

$$[y = f(\theta) = 0]_{\substack{\theta = 0 \\ \theta = 2\pi}} \qquad [70]$$

the first member on the right of Eq. 68 also becomes zero. Eqs. 68 and 69 then become

$$a_m = \frac{1}{m\pi} \int_0^{2\pi} \cos m\theta \, dy \qquad [71]$$

and

$$b_m = -\frac{1}{m\pi} \int_0^{2\pi} \sin m\theta \, dy \qquad [72]$$

These are the basic equations governing the construction of Henrici's instrument. Interestingly the sine coefficients now contain a cosine integral and vice versa.

FIG. 9. Photograph of an Henrici harmonic analyzer with a curve in position to be analyzed. (*Miller, D. C., J. Franklin Inst.,* **182**, 285, 1916.)

Fig. 9 shows a photograph of a completed instrument with a curve to be analyzed in position. This curve must be plotted so that a certain linear distance, *s* to *b* in the figure, shall represent the angle 2π radians.

If there are discontinuities, lines perpendicular to the θ-axis are drawn to connect the branches at the point of discontinuity. In operation this curve is traced by the stylus shown with its point at s. During the tracing, the wheels r_1, r_2, r_3 roll backward and forward, carrying the superstructure. Two of these wheels r_1 and r_2 have a common axle shaft that carries five other wheels which, however, do not touch the paper on which the graph has been plotted. Each of these five wheels, of which two are shown in Fig. 10, supports a glass sphere which is

Fig. 10. Photograph of a portion of an Henrici harmonic analyzer showing relation of rolling spheres to the adjacent integrators. (*Miller, D. C., Idem.*)

rotated by it. Their rotation $d\phi$ about an axis (the ϕ-axis) parallel to the line sb of the graph of Fig. 9 corresponding to a change dy on the graph is strictly proportional to dy. Obviously in accord with Eqs. 71 and 72, it is still necessary to multiply each dy by its appropriate $\cos m\theta$ or $\sin m\theta$ and to sum up such products. For this purpose, as shown in Fig. 10 and in plan in Fig. 11, two rolling sphere integrators are kept in contact with each sphere. These integrators in contact with any one sphere are oriented at right angles to each other and contact the sphere at points separated by 90°.

As the stylus (Fig. 9) is moved along the curve, a vertical shaft moves lengthwise of the superstructure and with it a wire is moved which passes around the pulleys at the tops of the frameworks about the glass spheres. The diameters of these pulleys vary as $1 : \frac{1}{2} : \frac{1}{3} : \frac{1}{4} : \frac{1}{5}$ and in size are such that, with the passage of the stylus from s to b, they in turn make just 1, 2, 3, 4, and 5 rotations. With the stylus at s the frameworks about all of the spheres are set for the position $m\theta = 0$. Then, with a slight movement of the stylus, there will be equal slight rotations $d\phi$ of all spheres about the ϕ-axis proportional to the dy of the stylus motion. The integrators for the sine terms s will automatically weight this ϕ according to cos 0° or unity in conformity with Eq. 71 and those for the cosine terms c will similarly weight the $d\phi$ according to sin 0° or zero in conformity with Eq. 72. With further motion of the stylus, however, the frameworks carrying the integrators are shifted to gradually varying orientations about the vertical axes through the spheres. The positions for $m\theta = 0°$ and $m\theta = 30°$ are shown in Fig. 11.

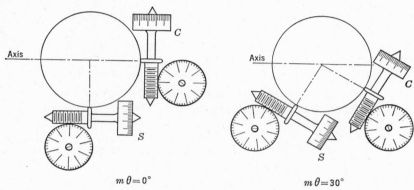

$$m\,\theta = 0°\qquad\qquad m\,\theta = 30°$$

Fig. 11. Diagram showing the positions of the rolling sphere integrators in contact with the mth sphere for positions corresponding to $m\theta = 2n\pi + 0°$ and $m\theta = 2n\pi + 30°$. Integrator S yields the sine component, integrator C the cosine component, of the mth harmonic.

As reflection will show, with the passage of the stylus from s to b (Fig. 9), the framework about the mth sphere will make m complete rotations and the s and the c integrators will give indications proportional to a_m and b_m as given in Eqs. 71 and 72. With dimensions properly chosen the proportionality factor may be made unity.

In use, the changes in the integrator readings with shift of the stylus from s to b (Fig. 9) yield the first five sine and cosine coefficients, not b_0, however. A set of the 6th to 10th coefficients, etc., can be obtained with the aid of other sets of pulleys at the tops of the frameworks carrying the integrators. In anticipation of such changes double pulleys are provided as shown in Fig. 10. Compound pulleys with larger diameters d_4 and d_5 to yield 4 and 5 rotations per change of 2π in θ have also smaller diameters d_9 and d_{10} to yield 9 and 10 rotations for the same change in θ.

Henrici's instrument fails to yield a value for $b_0/2$. Ordinarily for cases treated with an analyzer, this term is of little significance. Should need be felt for obtaining it, one may use an ordinary planimeter to determine the area between the curve and the base line containing the points s and b (Fig. 9) and then divide this area by 2π radians.

By comparing the analyses of known mathematical functions obtained mathematically with those obtained by his Henrici analyzer, Miller demonstrated that the analyzer possessed "an inherent accuracy much greater than can be taken advantage of in graphic work." He stated that "The results are always accurate to a fraction of the width of the line representing the curve, and this precision is maintained uniformly for all the components, even to the thirtieth."

This judgment was based in part on the reconstructions of the original curves which were obtained with the aid of a harmonic synthesizer [1] which he likewise described.

Miller has also compared the speed with which results may be obtained, once data in the form of the required curve are given, with those for obtaining results by tabular methods presumably somewhat like that illustrated above. Of the results of three analyses of the same curve, the sound wave for an organ pipe, he states that the time required for the first ten harmonics by this method was 13 minutes, that the time required by the tabular method involving complete numerical reduction from 36 ordinates was 10 hours, and that the time required by another tabular method with a prepared schedule which used only 18 measured ordinates and yielded only 8 harmonics was 3 hours. Evidently, where much work is to be done in analyzing curves, a harmonic analyzer is a necessary instrument.

14. Other Mechanical Analyzers. Without doubt analyzers of the Henrici type are among the best obtainable. Among purely mechanical instruments, they represent the best. As other instruments in common use, we have the common vibrating reed frequency indicator of electrical power stations, and the Chubb [2] polar analyzer (Fig. 12) which is found in electrical laboratories and power stations. The reed instrument requires a sustained repetition of the $f(\theta)$ but no manual or other graphing of it. It can, however, only give indications of harmonics present and of their relative amplitudes. It cannot, at least as constructed at present, show phase relations. The Chubb polar instrument requires a graph on polar paper, which is mounted in use on a circular gear-driven table. Each sine and cosine term requires a separate adjustment of gears. There are two motions, one of the table forward and back along a straight track, the other a rotation of the table with m cyclic trips on the straight track for each rotation. The tracer arm which moves only perpendicular to the straight track has the tracer

[1] Miller, D. C., *J. Franklin Inst.*, **181**, 51 and 285 (1916).
[2] Chubb, L. W., *Elec. J.*, **11**, 91 (1914).

point of an ordinary polar planimeter inserted in a hole at one end. The area swept out by this tracer point during a cycle, in any particular instance, is proportional to the corresponding a_m or b_m. From the series of values obtained, an analysis for $f(\theta)$ similar to that represented in Eq. 1 is obtained.

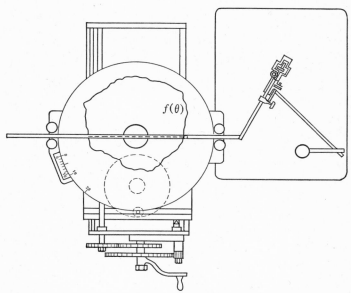

FIG. 12. A diagram showing the principles of operation of the Chubb polar harmonic analyzer.

15. Nonmechanical Harmonic Analyzers. Although the Henrici analyzer method saves much time in comparison with the straight tabular method, it is still time consuming. Other methods for specific purposes may be much superior through not requiring the plotting of a curve or by virtue of employing automatic integrating devices. Generally, however, these improvements have been at the expense of precision in the analyses obtained. Where, as is often true, time and expense are important factors, some one of these methods may be more desirable.

In a sense these methods are also mechanical because of the mechanical devices employed, but they are here classed as nonmechanical because their important features depend upon photoelectric, electronic, electromagnetic, etc., effects.

The basic theories for all analyzers start with Eqs. 17 and 20 and are necessarily much alike. It is necessary in all instances to multiply in effect an $f(\theta)$ by a $\cos m\theta$ and by a $\sin m\theta$ where ordinarily a separate

operation must be performed for each value chosen for m and sometimes
for each cosine or sine multiplication. Further, phase relations must
be controllable with precision.

A simple harmonic analyzer dependent on photoelectric and electronic effects was patented in 1933 by Marrison,[1] of the Bell Telephone

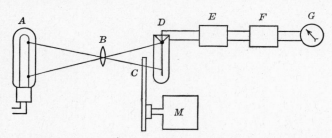

FIG. 13. A diagram to show the principles of operation of the Marrison photoelectric
harmonic analyzer for the case where only the amplitudes of the harmonics are to
be determined.

Laboratories. The main features of the method are shown in Fig. 13.
The function $f(\theta)$ is conveniently laid out in polar coordinates either by
the appropriate blackening of a transparent circular plate disc or by
cutting each disc to form a template as shown in Fig. 14. The dotted
line is the axis of zero amplitude. Whichever way prepared, the $f(\theta)$
disc is mounted on a motor whose speed of operation may be varied

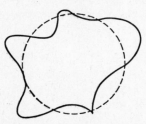

FIG. 14. An $f(\theta)$ set up in
polar coordinates for use
with the Marrison har-
monic analyzer.

conveniently and precisely as desired. Thus
mounted as shown at C in Fig. 13, it is
rotated in the plane of the image of a line
source of light A, formed by a simple
convex lens, B. Back of this image plane,
the light beam modified by the rotating
$f(\theta)$ enters a photoelectric cell, D, the output current of which passes to an amplifier,
E. The output of E in turn passes to a
filter, F, selective at a fixed frequency, and
to a current meter, G, of the desired sensitivity.

Let the characteristic frequency of the selective filter be arbitrarily
fixed at 100 cycles/sec. In accord with this choice, the procedure for an
harmonic analysis follows. The motor M is driven first at a speed of
100 rps and the indication of meter G is read. Obviously, with all frequencies but 100 per second eliminated by F, the reading of G is a meas-

[1] Marrison, W. A., U. S. Patent 1,901,400.

ure of the amplitude of the first harmonic or fundamental of $f(\theta)$. Next the speed of M is reduced to 50 rps and the indication of G is read once more. At this speed a component of $f(\theta)$ whose frequency is twice that of the fundamental will be repeated 100 times per second in the output of the photoelectric cell D and will have its amplitude recorded at G. Similarly the amplitudes of succeeding harmonics may be obtained by operating the motor at speeds of $\frac{1}{3}$, $\frac{1}{4}$, $\frac{1}{5}$, etc., of 100 rps. Once $f(\theta)$ has been properly transferred to the motor-driven disc, the time required for the amplitude analysis is very brief.

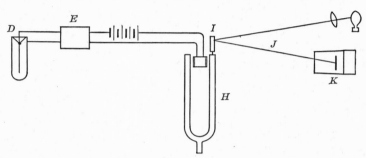

Fig. 15. A diagram to show the principles of operation of the Marrison photoelectric harmonic analyzer for the case where amplitudes and phase relations are both determined.

Unfortunately the analysis just described gives no indications of phase relations. For this Marrison proposes, as shown in Fig. 15, the substitution of an electrically driven tuning fork—with mirror I attached, a light beam J, and a moving photographic film K to replace the filter F and the meter G shown in Fig. 13. Obviously a harmonic being analyzed will be shown drawn out as a sine curve with an amplitude proportional to that of the harmonic. For the phase determination, a straight-line trace on the same moving film is produced by light reflected from a mirror which is stationary except for a small jog produced once each rotation of the motor by an appropriate contact mechanism. Fig. 16 is given by Marrison as the analysis of the $f(\theta)$ of Fig. 14. Obviously the three components agree precisely in their phases for one particular value of θ and differ in amplitudes.

Another optical analyzer using photoelectric effects for its integrations has been constructed by Wente [1] and described by Montgomery.[2] In the instrument described, the $f(\theta)$ is represented by a variable area record or by a variable density record such as are found on photographic

[1] Wente, E. C., U. S. Patent No. 2,098,326.

[2] Montgomery, H. C., *Bell System Tech. J.*, **17**, 406 (1938).

films for sound reproduction, while the cos $m\theta$ and the sin $m\theta$ factors are represented by similar records of the variable density type only. The $f(\theta)$ record may vary from 1/16 inch to 5/16 inch in length and must not be higher than long. The sine and cosine factor records are about 1 inch by 2 inches. In operation the $f(\theta)$ and a cosine or a sine record

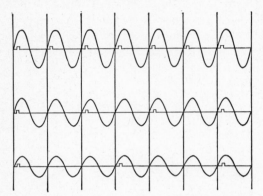

FIG. 16.   The graphical analysis of the $f(\theta)$ of Fig. 14, according to Marrison.

are mounted in an optical system (Fig. 17), and light from an incandescent lamp is passed through to a collecting photoelectric cell whose response is an integrated product of the transmittances of the two records.   By successive substitutions of the various sine and cosine records other corresponding photoelectric responses are obtained.   Certain corrections must necessarily be taken into account.   Although negative

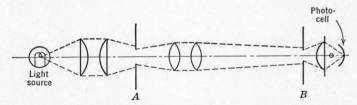

FIG. 17.   A diagram showing the optical arrangements for an analysis using Wente's optical harmonic analyzer.   (*Montgomery, H. C., Bell System Tech. J.*, **17**, 406, 1938.)

values for $f(\theta)$, cos $m\theta$ and sin $m\theta$ will always occur, negative values for light flux are not possible.   This difficulty is eliminated by combining the variable light flux with a constant flux of appropriate magnitude, so that the light flux may be positive at all points of passage through the system.   Also 100% transmission as is indicated by sin $m\theta$ for $m\theta$

equal to 90° is an evident physical impossibility, and a modulating factor is necessary on this account.

An analysis made with Wente's instrument when compared with one made with an Henrici instrument showed certain discrepancies in magnitude of amplitudes. (See Fig. 18, which shows comparative analysis of the sound "ou" as in out.) On the basis of time of operation, however, this method proved greatly superior. Thirty harmonics using an Henrici instrument is said to require from five to six hours, whereas the same results are obtainable by the optical instrument in about 1½ minutes.

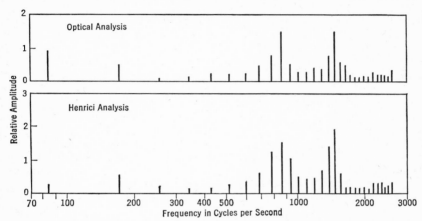

Fig. 18. Comparative analyses of the sound *ou* in *out* as determined by Henrici mechanical and Wente optical harmonic analyzers. (*Montgomery, H. C., Bell System Tech. J.*, **17**, 406, 1938.)

A combined optical and electronic analyzer is the cathode-ray instrument devised by V. O. Johnson[1] of the Westinghouse Electric & Manufacturing Co. In operation, the waveform to be analyzed and the sine and cosine factors are supplied electrically, the former from the source under study, the latter from a good quality, variable frequency oscillator. The function $f(\theta)$ is supplied to one pair of plates of a cathode-ray oscillograph. The cos $m\theta$ or the sin $m\theta$ factor in effect is supplied to the other pair. Properly adjusted, the trace on the face of the cathode-ray tube is a Lissajous figure whose complexity (Fig. 19) reveals visually which particular harmonic is under consideration. From the areas enclosed within two traces, one can determine the amplitude of a harmonic and its phase with regard to the fundamental. When determining these areas, one must recognize that portions traced counterclockwise are positive and that those traced oppositely are negative, or

[1] Johnson, V. O., *Trans. Am. Inst. Elec. Engrs.*, **60**, 1032 (1941).

vice versa. The results obtained by this method are said to check well with the tabular method.

A more definitely electronic device is that manufactured by the General Radio Co. It is described as a heterodyne type of vacuum-tube

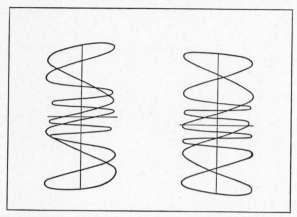

FIG. 19. A pair of Lissajous figures for determining a seventh harmonic as obtained by V. O. Johnson, using his cathode-ray method. (*Johnson, V. O., Trans. Am. Inst. Elec. Engrs.*, **60**, 1032, 1941.)

voltmeter (Fig. 20). The manufacturer states, "The output of the local oscillator and the whole of the complex waveform to be examined are fed to a balanced modulator where their combination produces both the sum and the difference frequencies, or side bands, in the output. The original of the complex waveform is not passed by the modulator intermediate-frequency output transformer, and the local carrier frequency is suppressed in the output because of the two-tube balanced

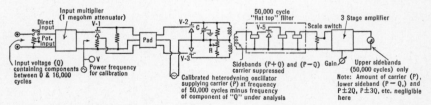

FIG. 20. Simplified diagram of the General Radio Co. electronic harmonic analyzer.

modulator employed. The 50-kilocycle component of the upper side band, proportional to the voltage of that frequency present in the original wave to which the main dial is set, is selected and amplified by the intermediate stages." The current thus amplified is read in a meter.

An analysis requires dial adjustments one by one to the harmonic frequencies in the waveform under examination, adjustment with each new component to a standard sensitivity for the fundamental, and recording of the meter readings. Only component frequencies and their amplitudes are obtained. No phase relations can be determined. The voltage uncertainty is said to be within $\pm 5\%$ on all ranges. This method is particularly suitable where the complex waveform is available as a continuously repeated emf in an electrical circuit. The analysis is then but a matter of a few minutes.

Many other harmonic analyzers are described in the literature.[1]

16. Bettering the Approximation Involved When Only a Finite Number of Terms of a Fourier Series Are Used. In harmonic analyses, such as that carried out above, one makes determinations of coefficients as though coefficients for an infinite number of terms were to be used when applications were to be made, and then in fact stops with a finite, usually rather small, number of terms. A question naturally arises. Considering that only a few terms are to be used, would not somewhat changed values for the computed coefficients fit the data better? The answer involving least-squares procedure (Chap. XI) states that, given that the series is to be a harmonic series even though possessing a finite number of terms, the equation yielding the best fit has exactly the coefficients given by the standard Fourier analysis. Even if but one sine or cosine term is to be used in representing a given function, the best coefficient for that term is that specified by Fourier analysis. To illustrate, if one should attempt to represent the instantaneous power curve of Fig. 6 by a single term such as $a_5 \sin 5\theta$, the best value for a_5 would be -5.38, the best equation, should both $\sin 5\theta$ and $\cos 5\theta$ be determined, would be

$$y = 6.3 \sin (5\theta - 146°) \tag{68}$$

Obviously, a trigonometric series, containing a finite number of terms whose coefficients have been obtained by the Fourier method, can be bettered only by increasing the number of terms.

17. Summary. It is shown in this chapter that any cyclic function of an independent variable which is finite, single valued, and possesses only a finite number of finite discontinuities, may be represented by an infinite trigonometric series known as a Fourier series. It has been shown that these series are always convergent. Series of this type when integrated term by term are always convergent, though it cannot be said generally that the series obtained by differentiation will also converge.

[1] Hall, Harry H., *J. Acoustics Soc. Am.*, **8**, 257 (1938). A general discussion of various types of analyzers is given.

With the angle θ as the independent variable and $0 < \theta < 2\pi$ as the range, we have as the most general of Fourier series the whole range sine-cosine series

$$y = f(\theta) = \frac{b_0}{2} + \sum_{m=1}^{\infty} (a_m \sin m\theta + b_m \cos m\theta) \qquad [1]$$

Values for the coefficients are given by

$$a_m = \frac{1}{\pi} \int_0^{2\pi} y \sin m\theta \, d\theta \qquad [17]$$

$$b_0 = \frac{1}{\pi} \int_0^{2\pi} y \, d\theta \qquad [19]$$

and

$$b_m = \frac{1}{\pi} \int_0^{2\pi} y \cos m\theta \, d\theta \qquad [20]$$

Eq. 1 with coefficients evaluated may be changed to a form which is generally more useful for practical purposes, namely

$$y = f(\theta) = \frac{b_0}{2} + \sum_{m=1}^{\infty} A_m \sin (m\theta + \epsilon_m)$$

$$= \frac{b_0}{2} + \sum_{m=1}^{\infty} A_m \cos \left(m\theta + \epsilon_m - \frac{\pi}{2} \right) \qquad [6]$$

where

$$A_m = \sqrt{a_m{}^2 + b_m{}^2} \qquad [7]$$

and

$$\epsilon_m = \tan^{-1} \frac{b_m}{a_m} \qquad [8]$$

Still another form, containing the imaginary i, useful in theoretical physics, to which Eq. 1 may be converted is

$$y = f(\theta) = \frac{b_0}{2} + \frac{1}{2} \sum_{m=1}^{\infty} [(b_m - ia_m)e^{im\theta} + (b_m + ia_m)e^{-im\theta}] \qquad [11]$$

There are two half-range series. With point symmetry for the cyclical function about points on the θ-axis at $\theta = 0$, π, 2π, etc., the coefficients of the cosine terms of Eq. 1 including b_0 become zero and the series reduces to the half-range sine series

$$y = f_1(\theta) = \sum_{m=1}^{\infty} \alpha_m \sin m\theta \qquad [29]$$

where

$$\alpha_m = \frac{2}{\pi} \int_0^\pi f_1(\theta) \sin m\theta \, d\theta \qquad [30]$$

With line symmetry for the cyclical functions about lines perpendicular to the θ-axis at $\theta = 0$, π, 2π, etc., the coefficients of the sine terms of Eq. 1 become zero and the series reduces to the half-range cosine series

$$y = f_2(\theta) = \frac{\beta_0}{2} + \sum_{m=1}^\infty \beta_m \cos m\theta \qquad [31]$$

of which

$$\beta_0 = \frac{2}{\pi} \int_0^\pi f_2(\theta) \, d\theta \qquad [32]$$

and

$$\beta_m = \frac{2}{\pi} \int_0^\pi f_2(\theta) \cos m\theta \, d\theta \qquad [33]$$

Series representing $y = f(\theta)$ may be transformed at once into series representing $y = f\left(\frac{2\pi}{T} t\right)$ or $y = f\left(\frac{2\pi}{\lambda} x\right)$, of which T is a period of vibration and λ a wavelength, by substituting for θ, $(2\pi/T)t$ in one case and $(2\pi/\lambda)x$ in the other case.

Thus for the former case corresponding to Eqs. 1, 17, 19, 20, 29, 30, 31, 32, and 33 we have

$$y = f\left(\frac{2\pi}{T} t\right) = \frac{b_0}{2} + \sum_{m=1}^\infty a'_m \sin\left(m \frac{2\pi}{T} t\right) + b'_m \cos\left(m \frac{2\pi}{T} t\right) \qquad [42]$$

$$a'_m = \frac{2}{T} \int_0^T f\left(\frac{2\pi}{T} t\right) \sin\left(m \frac{2\pi}{T} t\right) dt \qquad [43]$$

$$b'_0 = \frac{2}{T} \int_0^T f\left(\frac{2\pi}{T} t\right) dt \qquad [43a]$$

$$b'_m = \frac{2}{T} \int_0^T f\left(\frac{2\pi}{T} t\right) \cos\left(m \frac{2\pi}{T} t\right) dt \qquad [44]$$

$$y = f_1\left(\frac{2\pi}{T} t\right) = \sum_{m=1}^\infty \alpha'_m \sin\left(m \frac{2\pi}{T} t\right) \qquad [45]$$

$$\alpha'_m = \frac{4}{T} \int_0^{T/2} f_1\left(\frac{2\pi}{T} t\right) \sin\left(m \frac{2\pi}{T} t\right) dt \qquad [46]$$

$$y = f_2\left(\frac{2\pi}{T}\,t\right) = \frac{\beta'_0}{2} + \sum_{m=1}^{\infty} \beta'_m \cos\left(m\,\frac{2\pi}{T}\,t\right) \qquad [47]$$

$$\beta'_0 = \frac{4}{T} \int_0^{T/2} f_2\left(\frac{2\pi}{T}\,t\right) dt \qquad [47a]$$

$$\beta'_m = \frac{4}{T} \int_0^{T/2} f_2\left(\frac{2\pi}{T}\,t\right) \cos\left(m\,\frac{2\pi}{T}\,t\right) dt \qquad [48]$$

Equations exactly like Eqs. 42 to 48 are obtained when θ in Eq. 1 is similarly replaced by $\left(\dfrac{2\pi}{\lambda}\,x\right)$, λ and x replacing T and t.

For the case of a noncyclical function in which in effect the wavelength λ extends from $x = 0$ to $x = \infty$, the whole-range sine-cosine series transforms into the Fourier integral

$$\left[F(x) = \frac{1}{2\pi} \int_{-\infty}^{+\infty} d\nu \int_0^{\infty} F(\mu) \cos \nu(\mu - x)\, d\mu \right]_{0\,<\,x\,<\,\infty} \qquad [58]$$

Where the function extends indefinitely in both directions, we have

$$\left[F(x) = \frac{1}{\pi} \int_{-\infty}^{\infty} d\nu \int_{-\infty}^{\infty} F(\mu) \cos \nu(\mu - x)\, d\mu \right]_{-\infty\,<\,x\,<\,\infty} \qquad [59]$$

the right-hand member of which is known as Fourier's integral.

Four frequently occurring special cycles consisting of a positive and a negative loop yield simplified series. Case I. If the areas of the two loops add up to zero the b_0, β_0, or b'_0 term is zero. Case II. If the positive loop is asymmetric and the negative loop is a displaced image of the positive loop, the series satisfying the function is a whole-range sine-cosine series containing odd terms only. Case III. If the positive loop is asymmetric and the negative loop possesses point symmetry with respect to the positive loop, the series satisfying the function is a regular half-range sine series. Case IV. If the positive loop is symmetrical and the negative loop possesses point symmetry with respect to the positive loop, the series satisfying the function is a half-range sine series containing odd terms only. Cosine series may be obtained for Cases III and IV if, in effect, the origin is shifted along the θ-axis by $\pi/2$.

The coefficients for the series terms involve integrations. Often the function to be integrated is not expressed mathematically and it is necessary to resort to tabular or mechanical integrations. Tabular integrations as illustrated in Table I are usually time consuming. Further, the coefficients for the higher harmonics tend to become progressively more and more uncertain. Mechanical integration, however, once the function is properly graphed, becomes a simple matter for a device such as Henrici's rolling sphere harmonic analyzer. The time required is very much shorter than for the tabular method. Further, it yields coefficients for the higher harmonics with approximately the accuracy attained for the fundamental. Other devices generally less accurate but much more rapid in operation are available.

Least-squares treatment shows that, if a finite number of terms of a Fourier series only are to be used in representing a function, the best values for the coefficients are just those occurring in the solution for an infinite series.

PROBLEMS

1. Determine the whole-range sine-cosine series to represent $y = \theta^2$ for the range $0 < \theta < 2\pi$.

2. Express the result of Problem 1 as a harmonic series in which relative phases of the various harmonics are shown.

3. In certain amplifications of photoelectric currents the light beam is "chopped" regularly to give an illumination E for the time interval $T/2$ and no illumination for an equal time interval and then an illumination E once more for the interval $T/2$, etc. What is the harmonic series that represents the illumination?

4. What is the harmonic series that represents a "chopped" illumination such as described in the preceding problem except that the illumination, and no illumination intervals are $2T/3$ and $T/3$?

5. Find the half-range sine series for the broken line $y = \theta$ for the range $0 < \theta < \pi/2$, $y = \pi - \theta$ for the range $\pi/2 < \theta < 3\pi/2$, and $y = -2\pi + \theta$ for the range $3\theta/2 < \theta < 2\pi$.

6. Find the half-range cosine series for the broken line $y = \theta$ for the range $0 < \theta < \pi/2$, $y = \pi/2$ for the range $\pi/2 < \theta < 3\pi/2$, and $y = 2\pi - \theta$ for the range $3\pi/2 < \theta < 2\pi$.

7. Assuming the portion of Fig. 5A for the region $0 < \theta < 2\pi$ to consist of two right-angled triangles with 30° as the smallest angle, compute and compare the two Fourier series obtained first when the origin is located as shown and second when the origin is located instead at $\theta = \pi$.

8. The cycle of the graph of displacement of a point on a vibrating string shows two self symmetrical loops which are symmetrical with respect to a point on the time axis. Measurements of displacement at the indicated phase angles give the following values:

Phase angles in degrees	5	15	25	35	45	55	65	75	85
Displacements in cm	+0.041	−0.013	+0.054	−0.017	−0.023	+0.125	+0.424	+0.771	+1.001

Graph the function and make a harmonic analysis.

9. Compute the fifth harmonic for the data of Table I.

10. Find the half-range sine series to represent Fig. 2. Follow the suggestion in the text by assuming $\phi = 2\theta$.

CHAPTER VI

THE NORMAL FREQUENCY DISTRIBUTION

1. Introduction. The basic problem of every quantitative experiment is that of determining directly or indirectly what we call the "true value" of a quantity—the period of a pendulum, the normality of a solution, etc. Strictly speaking, we can never measure the true value of any quantity; we can obtain only an approximation thereto. By refining our methods of measurement, we can obtain closer and closer approximations, but there is always a limit beyond which refinements have not or cannot be made. It is thus desirable to know in any particular case just what relation the measured value bears to the true value. For obtaining this information, a knowledge of the law of frequency distribution of measurements is of great value.

Consider, for example, the measurement of the prism angle, X, of a 60° prism on a spectrometer with a scale which can be read to 0.001'. It will be found that, though all readings are taken with equal care, successive measurements will not agree with one another. In a particular case, assume values of

60° 0.320'	60° 0.320'
.318	.319
.317	.322
.320	.320
.321	.319
.319	.321

to be obtained. Given only this list of values, the question arises, what value shall be taken as being probably nearest to the true value. We may take the arithmetic mean, $\overline{X} = \Sigma X/n$; the geometric mean, $\overline{X}_G = \sqrt[n]{X_1 \times X_2 \cdots X_n}$; the root mean square mean, $\overline{X}_{RMS} = \sqrt[2]{(X_1{}^2 + X_2{}^2 + \cdots X_n{}^2)/n}$; the median, M_e, the middlemost value when listed in order of magnitude; the mode, M_0, the value of X which occurs most frequently; or any one of a number of other such values. Or, with perhaps some slight justification, we might reason that since in the past our measurements have usually been higher than those obtained by others, we should regard the smallest value as the best approximation to the true value.

Consider now the frequency distribution of the above series of angle measurements, showing how often, relatively, the various actual values occur. The plot of Fig. 1 is a very convenient method of presenting an over-all view of the spread of values and the general nature of the distribution. It shows, among other things, that the reading 60° 0.320′, representing the angular interval 60° 0.3195′ to 60° 0.3205′, is obtained four times; and, as indicated by the ratio of the area of the rectangle

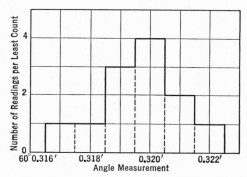

Fig. 1.   The frequency distribution for twelve readings of a certain prism angle. The least count, the smallest amount by which two measurements can vary and still be detected as unequal, is 0.001′ in this case.

centering at 60° 0.320′ to the total area under the curve, that the relative frequency of occurrence of this reading is $\frac{1}{3}$.

If the number of measurements were increased indefinitely and the least count made as small as possible, the distribution curve would appear less steplike and in the limit would become smooth. This smooth curve is the infinite parent distribution of the measurements. The observed set of twelve measurements may be thought of as a sample set from the indefinitely large number of measurements which make up the parent distribution. The equation of the parent frequency distribution curve is referred to as the law governing the distribution of the observed measurements. Knowing this law, it is possible to arrive at a value for the measured quantity which, except for instrumental errors and personal idiosyncrasies of the observer, we can justly declare to be the most probable value.

Depending on the assumptions made, several forms of frequency distribution laws have been obtained. Which is most likely to govern the distribution of a proposed set of measurements is generally impossible of prediction in advance. However, the normal distribution law, or, as it is sometimes called, the law of errors, seems to fit observed distributions in a great number of cases. Further, the normal law is one of the simplest, containing only one arbitrary constant; and many of the other distribution laws reduce to the normal law under suitable limiting conditions. Because of our desire for this simplicity, we often mistakenly assume that the normal law governs all distributions of measurements. For many distributions, however, this assumption is obviously impossible.

In this chapter we first present Hagen's derivation of the normal distribution law and then explain its physical interpretation. The procedure of normalization of the law is carried through, and its significance in describing probabilities is discussed. The precision indexes associated with the normal distribution are then defined and explained. Finally, we derive the criterion of least squares, and show that for a distribution governed by the normal law, the mean is the most probable value.

2. Hagen's Derivation of the Law of Normal Frequency Distribution. The normal law may be derived, using various sets of basic assumptions. The assumptions used by Hagen seem to simulate physical conditions moderately well and to permit of a simple derivation. The derivation follows. Hagen assumed (1) that errors unavoidably enter in each of a series of measurements of a quantity, (2) that each of these errors may be thought of as being composed of a great number of very small equal elementary errors, and (3) that in any measurement, an elementary error is as likely to enter in a positive as in a negative sense.

To illustrate these assumptions, we shall assume that the arithmetic mean, 60° 0.3197′, of the measurements reported above is the true value, though we shall see that this is not at all necessarily the case. The deviation of the first reading from the assumed true value—i.e., the assumed error of the first reading—then becomes 0.0003′; that of the second reading, 0.0017′; etc. The frequency of occurrence of these errors for the group as a whole is shown in Fig. 2. The distribution is identical in form with that given in Fig. 1. Each error, in view of the assumptions, is to be thought of as due to many minute errors which may be associated with the temperatures of the various parts of the spectrometer, irregularities of instrumental calibration, uncertainties of position of the eye when reading, peculiar tendencies of the reader, and a host of other causes which one may conjure up if so inclined. Each of these minute errors, if one is so minded, may be broken up into a number of smaller elementary errors. For the purpose of the derivation it is necessary, as stated, to assume that these elementary errors are all of the same magnitude and that each occurs as often negatively as positively.

The way in which any particular elementary error enters in a particular measurement would be, of course, quite beyond our power to control or to predict.

Let δ be the magnitude of one of the assumed equal elementary errors entering a measurement. The probability that any δ will enter positively is $\frac{1}{2}$; the probability that it will enter negatively is also $\frac{1}{2}$. If there are m of them, the probability that all the δ's will be

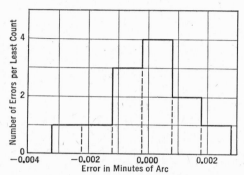

Fig. 2. The frequency distribution of the errors of twelve readings of a certain prism angle, assuming the arithmetic mean to be the true value.

positive, thus yielding an error of $+m\delta$, is evidently $\left(\dfrac{1}{2}\right)^m$. The probability that all δ's but one will be positive, and that the resultant error is $+(m-2)\delta$, is $m\left[\left(\dfrac{1}{2}\right)^{m-1} \times \left(\dfrac{1}{2}\right)^{1}\right]$. The factor m appears here because there are m ways in which the combination of errors under consideration can take place. Similarly, the probability that only $(m-2)$ δ's will be positive, giving a resultant error of $+(m-4)\delta$ is $\dfrac{m(m-1)}{2!}\left[\left(\dfrac{1}{2}\right)^{m-2} \times \left(\dfrac{1}{2}\right)^{2}\right]$, or, $\dfrac{m(m-1)}{2!}\left(\dfrac{1}{2}\right)^{m}$. The coefficients of the term $\left(\dfrac{1}{2}\right)^m$ are seen thus to be the coefficients in the binomial expansion of $(a+b)^m$. Table I follows.

In Fig. 3, the computed probabilities, dP, are shown as small rectangles, each 2δ wide. In the limit, as $\delta \to 0$, the height of a rectangle becomes the ordinate of a point on a smooth curve. This ordinate is called a probability coefficient and is defined by

$$y = \frac{dP}{dx} \qquad\qquad [1]$$

TABLE I

THE RELATION BETWEEN THE COMPONENT ELEMENTARY ERRORS AND THE RESULTANT ERRORS OCCURRING IN MEASUREMENTS, AND THEIR PROBABILITIES OF OCCURRENCE ACCORDING TO HAGEN'S TREATMENT

Number of Elementary Errors		The Resultant Error, x	Its Probability dP
Positive	Negative		
m	0	$m\delta$	$\left(\dfrac{1}{2}\right)^m$
$m - 1$	1	$(m - 2)\delta$	$m\left(\dfrac{1}{2}\right)^m$
$m - 2$	2	$(m - 4)\delta$	$\dfrac{m(m - 1)}{2!}\left(\dfrac{1}{2}\right)^m$
$m - 3$	3	$(m - 6)\delta$	$\dfrac{m(m - 1)(m - 2)}{3!}\left(\dfrac{1}{2}\right)^m$
.			
.			
.			
$m - n$	n	$(m - 2n)\delta$	$\dfrac{m(m - 1)\cdots(m - n + 1)}{n!}\left(\dfrac{1}{2}\right)^m$
$m - n - 1$	$n + 1$	$(m - 2n - 2)\delta$	$\dfrac{m(m - 1)\cdots(m - n)}{(n + 1)!}\left(\dfrac{1}{2}\right)^m$

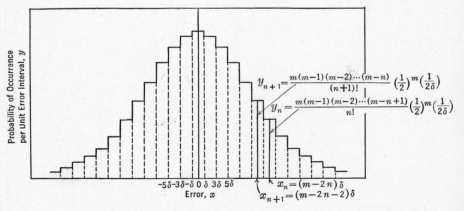

$$y_{n+1} = \frac{m(m-1)(m-2)\cdots(m-n)}{(n+1)!}\left(\frac{1}{2}\right)^m\left(\frac{1}{2\delta}\right)$$

$$y_n = \frac{m(m-1)(m-2)\cdots(m-n+1)}{n!}\left(\frac{1}{2}\right)^m\left(\frac{1}{2\delta}\right)$$

$$x_n = (m - 2n)\delta$$

$$x_{n+1} = (m - 2n - 2)\delta$$

FIG. 3.   The probability of an error occurring in measurements as a function of the error, according to Hagen's treatment.

where dP represents the probability of an error lying between $x - \frac{1}{2}dx$ and $x + \frac{1}{2}dx$. Physically, y is related to P and to x just as a velocity is related to distance traversed and to time.

We seek the equation of a continuous curve which represents the case where the elementary error, δ, becomes indefinitely small, and the number of elementary errors, m, increases without limit. This may be obtained by (1) determining the $\Delta y/\Delta x$ between the tops of adjacent elementary rectangles of Fig. 3; (2) obtaining the corresponding $\lim\limits_{x \to 0} \left(\dfrac{\Delta y}{\Delta x}\right)$, or, dy/dx; and, (3) integrating dy/dx with respect to x to obtain $y = f(x)$. Following this plan and using the points of Fig. 3 corresponding to the errors $x_{n+1} = (m - 2n - 2)\delta$ and $x_n = (m - 2n)\delta$, we have

$$\frac{\Delta y}{\Delta x} = \frac{y_n - y_{n+1}}{x_n - x_{n+1}} = \frac{y_n - \dfrac{m - n}{n + 1} y_n}{2\delta} = -\frac{y_n}{2\delta} \frac{m - 2n - 1}{n + 1} \qquad [2]$$

Taking account of the fact that $n \gg 1$, and that for the error x_n

$$2n = m - \frac{x_n}{\delta} \qquad [3]$$

we may write, in the limit, for the region where the errors are small in comparison with the maximum possible error, i.e., where $x \ll m \; \delta$

$$\frac{dy}{dx} = -\frac{y}{2\delta} \frac{\dfrac{x}{\delta}}{\dfrac{m}{2} - \dfrac{x}{2\delta}} = -\frac{yx}{m\delta^2} \qquad [4]$$

The error $m\delta$, that occurring when the elementary errors are either all positive or all negative, is relatively very large; δ, on the other hand, is one-half the minimum variation in errors, and is infinitesimal in comparison. The product $m\delta^2$ is finite, however, and is of importance in the discussion of the law. Customarily the fraction $1/m\delta^2$ is replaced by $2h^2$. The significance of h, which is called the "modulus of precision" will be given later. The differential form of Eq. 4 then becomes

$$\frac{dy}{dx} = -2h^2yx \qquad [5]$$

whence, finally,

$$y = ke^{-h^2x^2} \qquad [6]$$

This is the standard form for the normal law of errors, or more appropriately and more generally, as will soon appear, the law of the normal frequency distribution.

A plot of Eq. 6 in which x stands for an accidental error [1] of measurement is shown in Fig. 4. In conformity with Fig. 3, the curve has a maximum at $x = 0$, is symmetrical with respect to the y-axis, and approaches the x-axis asymptotically at both extremes. Actually, because of the manner of derivation, it occurs that Eq. 6 is only an approximation to what is called the binomial distribution law in which an

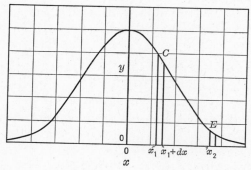

Fig. 4. A graph of the equation $y = ke^{-h^2x^2}$.

infinite number of infinitesimal elementary errors occur. The two distributions differ most in the regions that are referred to as tails. On a percentage basis, the failure to check increases with the magnitude of the error.

Another method of derivation, due to Gauss, starts with the assumption that the most probable approximation to the true value of a quantity of which many determinations have been made with equal precision, is the arithmetic mean of those determinations. His procedure leads finally to the result obtained by Hagen, namely, Eq. 6. As is to be expected, and as will be shown, granted Eq. 6 as a conclusion of Hagen's reasoning, we may deduce Gauss's assumption as a consequence.

Although here derived on the basis of errors occurring in a number of measurements of a single physical quantity, Eq. 6 is often useful for representing other types of frequency distributions. Thus, the frequency distribution of the weights of a large number of apples, picked at random,

---

[1] We refer here only to such errors as may be classed as accidental. None of the types that may be classed as systematic errors, or that are due to theoretical considerations, enter into the law of normal frequency distribution.

can also be represented rather closely by it. It is meaningless, of course, to speak here of a "true value" for the weight of an apple or of the combined influence of a great number of "elementary errors." It is proper, however, to speak of deviations from a mean weight or some similar value, caused by variations in such elementary factors as the age of the tree, the cultivation it receives, the type of soil, the climate, the size and health of the branch, the location of the apple on the branch, the amount of surrounding foliage which may cut off sunlight, etc. In the discussion to follow, therefore, we refer to x-values sometimes as "errors," but more often as deviations.

Frequency distributions are often desired for other purposes than those of obtaining "best" values from groups of measurements. A knowledge of the distribution of the sizes of a sample group of manufactured products tells whether the batch from which the sample came is sufficiently close to the size specified, whether proper manufacturing conditions are being maintained, etc. A shoe manufacturer would want to know the distribution of foot sizes in the population in which his products are sold in order to properly apportion his production. A botanist would obtain the distribution of sizes of a number of samples of a certain plant grown under special conditions and compare it with the distribution of sizes obtained under ordinary conditions to see whether or not the special conditions produce a significant change in the size of the plant.

In general, as will be shown in the following chapter, a randomly chosen distribution will not follow the normal law. Nevertheless, so many distributions do approximate this law, within the limits of experimental or sampling error, that the concept of the normal law is of great value. We should think of the normal distribution law not as one which all types of measurements must obey, but as a simple and convenient law applicable to many distributions whose graphs have the general shape shown in Fig. 4.

3. Galton's Quincunx. Of interest here is Galton's quincunx, a piece of apparatus which is based on Hagen's assumption that a very large number of small elementary errors enter to determine an actual resultant error in a measurement. Once set in motion, the quincunx automatically yields a binomial frequency distribution which resembles the normal distribution and lends plausibility to Hagen's method of derivation. In design (Fig. 5), as suggested by its name, it is based on an arrangement of five pegs, four of which are at the corners of a square, with the fifth at the center. Small shot, falling down through the small hole in the hopper at the top, receive small sidewise impulses directed with equal probability to the right and to the left as they impinge upon the quincunx array of pegs, and are finally collected in bins at the bottom. The upper boundary of the collected shot approximates a curve of the form of Eq. 6.

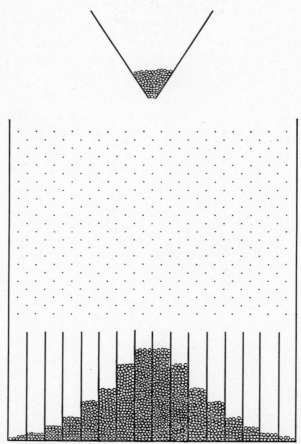

FIG. 5. Galton's quincunx, a device for illustrating the physical basis of the normal frequency distribution law.

4. The Constants h and k of the Equation $y = ke^{-h^2x^2}$. As shown in Fig. 6A, varying the constant h, keeping k constant, results when graphed in a series of curves which differ only in their lateral spreads. Similarly, varying k only results in a series of curves which differ, as shown in Fig. 6B, only in their vertical extents. Any one curve may be obtained from any other by appropriate expansions and contractions laterally and vertically. Since a large value for h corresponds to a small spread of measurements, h is appropriately a modulus of precision. The significance and the evaluation of k, however, are less evident. Instead of considering k itself, consider the significance of Eq. 6 as a whole. Assume a group of measurements with least count Δx, whose deviations from their mean obey the law of Eq. 6. Then the probability that a randomly chosen measurement has the deviation x_1 is $y_1\Delta x$; the probability that it has the deviation x_2 is $y_2\Delta x$; etc. Further, the probability that its deviation is either x_1 or x_2 is $(y_1 + y_2)\Delta x$. Thus, the probability that its deviation lies between $-\infty$ and $+\infty$ is $\Sigma y\Delta x$. This sum contains the y's corresponding to all possible x's between $-\infty$ and

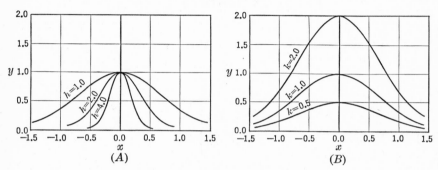

Fig. 6. Graphs of $y = ke^{-h^2x^2}$ for varying values of h and k. In A the common value for k is 1.00. In B the common value for h is 1.00.

$+\infty$. Since it is certain that the random deviation concerned lies between $-\infty$ and $+\infty$, $\Sigma y\Delta x$, represented graphically by the area under the curve of Fig. 4, must equal unity. As $\Delta x \to 0$, we have

$$\int_{-\infty}^{+\infty} y\,dx = 1 \qquad [7]$$

Fig. 6 shows that for each h a k may be determined to satisfy Eq. 7. The procedure follows.

5. Normalization of the Equation $y = ke^{-h^2x^2}$. Here, the procedure is based upon analytical geometry considerations, though such is not a necessity. In Fig. 7 is shown the solid generated by rotating about the y-axis the curve representing the positive half of the equation $y = ke^{-h^2x^2}$. Let $A/2$ represent the area in the x–y plane which is bounded by the curve and the x- and y-axes, hence also the corresponding area in the y–z plane. Then

$$A = 2k \int_0^\infty e^{-h^2x^2}\,dx = 2k \int_0^\infty e^{-h^2z^2}\,dz \qquad [8]$$

Further, since x and z are independent variables, we may write

$$A^2 = 4k^2 \int_0^\infty e^{-h^2 x^2} \, dx \int_0^\infty e^{-h^2 z^2} \, dz$$

$$= 4k^2 \int_0^\infty \int_0^\infty e^{-h^2(x^2+z^2)} \, dx \, dz \qquad [9]$$

Viewed geometrically with the aid of Fig. 7, evaluating the double integral corresponds to determining the volume of the solid which is bounded

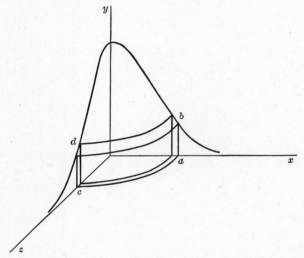

FIG. 7. A convenient diagram for use in normalizing the equation $y = ke^{-h^2 x^2}$.

by the x–z, the x–y, and the y–z planes and the surface obtained by the rotation about the y-axis. For the element of volume indicated by $abcd$, the common ordinate is $ke^{-h^2 r^2}$, where $r^2 = x^2 + z^2$, and the area of its projection on the x–z plane, dS, is $(\pi/2)r \, dr$. For the volume, V, there follows

$$V = \int y \, dS = k \int_0^\infty \int_0^\infty e^{-h^2(x^2+z^2)} \, dx \, dz$$

$$= \frac{k\pi}{2} \int_0^\infty e^{-h^2 r^2} r \, dr \qquad [10]$$

The integration is simple. There follow

$$V = \frac{k\pi}{4h^2}$$

$$A^2 = 4kV = \frac{k^2\pi}{h^2}$$

and

$$A = \frac{k\sqrt{\pi}}{h} \qquad [11]$$

Since A is to represent unit probability, we have

$$k = \frac{h}{\sqrt{\pi}} \qquad [12]$$

and for the normalized equation of the law of normal frequency distribution

$$y_x = \frac{h}{\sqrt{\pi}} e^{-h^2x^2} \qquad [13]$$

Here y_x is to be viewed as a probability coefficient which, when properly expressed, has a unit attached. In case x is measured in seconds, h and y will be expressed in reciprocal seconds, and $y_x\, dx$, an element of probability, will be a numeric. The subscript x in Eq. 13 has been added to distinguish the probability coefficient there considered from other different but similar coefficients that will be considered later.

Whenever it is desired to have the area under the curve represent a number of observations, n, we need only set $k = nh/\sqrt{\pi}$ so that

$$y_n = ny_x = \frac{nh}{\sqrt{\pi}} e^{-h^2x^2} \qquad [14]$$

Although its units are the same as those for y_x, y_n itself is to be regarded as a frequency coefficient. Obviously, to fit the normal law to an observed set of measurements, it is necessary to find the proper value of h.

6. Special Values of x Associated with the Curve $y = (h/\sqrt{\pi})\, e^{-h^2x^2}$ **—Precision Indexes.** Four x-values of special significance, usually referred to as a group by the name *precision indexes*, are (1) $1/h$, the reciprocal of the modulus of precision; (2) a, the average deviation; (3) σ, the standard deviation; and (4) p, the probable error. They are defined with respect to Eq. 13 as follows:

1. The quantity $1/h$ is that value of x for which the corresponding y-value is $1/e$ times the maximum y-value; i.e.

$$(y_x)_{1/h} = \frac{y_0}{e} = \frac{h}{e\sqrt{\pi}} \qquad [15]\ ^1$$

It is seen that high values for y_0 and narrow spreads go with high values for h. Since precise measurements yield distributions of this shape, h is appropriately a modulus of precision as already noted.

2. The average deviation, a, is defined as the mean deviation without regard to sign. Mathematically

$$a = \frac{2\displaystyle\int_0^\infty xy_x\,dx}{\displaystyle\int_{-\infty}^\infty y_x\,dx} = \frac{2h}{\sqrt{\pi}}\int_0^\infty xe^{-h^2x^2}\,dx = \frac{1}{\sqrt{\pi}}\frac{1}{h} \qquad [16]$$

3. The standard deviation, σ, is defined as the square root of the mean squared deviation. In terms of Eq. 13,

$$\sigma = \left[\frac{\displaystyle\int_{-\infty}^\infty x^2 y_x\,dx}{\displaystyle\int_{-\infty}^\infty y_x\,dx}\right]^{1/2} = \frac{2h}{\sqrt{\pi}}\left[\int_0^\infty x^2 e^{-h^2x^2}\,dx\right]^{1/2} = \frac{1}{\sqrt{2}}\frac{1}{h} \qquad [17]$$

4. The probable error, p, is that value of x which satisfies the relation

$$\frac{h}{\sqrt{\pi}}\int_{-p}^{+p} e^{-h^2x^2}\,dx = \frac{1}{2} \qquad [18]$$

The area under the normal curve between the limits p and $-p$ is one-half the total area; and the probability of a deviation less than p in absolute value is equal to the probability of a deviation greater than p. By means of tables we find $p = 0.477/h$.

The relations of the precision indexes to one another for a strictly normal distribution are given by

$$p : a : \sigma : \frac{1}{h} = 0.477 : 0.564 : 0.707 : 1.000 \qquad [19]$$

and approximately by

$$p : a : \sigma : \frac{1}{h} = 3\tfrac{1}{2} : 4 : 5 : 7 \qquad [20]$$

---

[1] It would be more logical to represent the second member of this equation as $(y_x)_0/e$; but no other value such as $(y_{hx})_0$ is being used, hence the simplification.

The relative positions of the precision indexes on the curve of Eq. 13 are shown in Fig. 8. The values of the ordinates corresponding to these special values of x are also indicated in terms of the maximum ordinate, y_0.

It is customary to indicate by a subscript the quantity to which a precision index applies. Where, as above, the indexes are obtained for

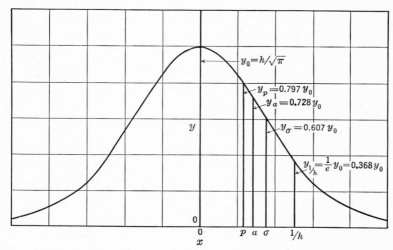

FIG. 8. A graph of the law of normal frequency distribution, showing the relative positions of the precision indexes p, a, σ, and $1/h$.

a distribution of x-values, it is proper to write them as p_x, a_x, σ_x, and $(1/h)_x$, and to consider them as applying to the individual x-values comprising the distribution.

7. Tabular Representations for the Normal Curve. The calculation of y-values corresponding to given x-values in Eq. 13 is somewhat involved. Obviously, a table of corresponding x- and y-values would eliminate much computation. However, since the physical nature of x and the value of h both change from one distribution to another, such a table would, in general, be valid for only one particular distribution. If, however, instead of x, we use hx, or x/σ, or x/p as the independent variable, a single table will cover all cases. Recognizing that for a given distribution regardless of whether deviations are expressed in terms of x, hx, x/σ, x/p or otherwise, the probabilities associated with given ranges of measured values must remain invariant, we may write at once

$$y_x \, dx = y_{hx} \, d(hx) = y_{x/\sigma} \, d\left(\frac{x}{\sigma}\right) = y_{x/p} \, d\left(\frac{x}{p}\right) \qquad [21]$$

of which y_{hx}, $y_{x/\sigma}$ etc., like y_x, represent probability coefficients. For the case involving hx as the independent variable, we have, as is evident

$$y_x = y_{hx} \frac{d(hx)}{dx} = h y_{hx} \tag{22}$$

With the aid of Eq. 22, one may easily obtain a distribution of $y_x = f(x)$, once given tabulated values of

$$y_{hx} = f(hx) = \frac{1}{h} y_x = \frac{1}{\sqrt{\pi}} e^{-h^2 x^2} \tag{23}$$

as in Table I of Appendix 2. To illustrate, the y_x corresponding to $h = 5.0$ cm^{-1} and $x = 0.10$ cm, is obtained as follows. From the table, the value of y_{hx} for $hx = 0.50$ is seen to be 0.439. Multiplied by h, there results 2.20 cm^{-1}, the desired y_x.

Frequently a normal frequency distribution curve is fitted to observed data in order to find the expected probability of occurrence of a deviation lying between x_1 and x_2. For this purpose we desire a convenient method for obtaining the probability, P_x, of a deviation lying between $-x$ and $+x$, for we may then express the probability of a deviation lying between x_1 and x_2 by one-half of the difference $P_{x_2} - P_{x_1}$. The value of P_x is represented graphically by the area under the normal curve between the limits $-x$ and $+x$, or mathematically, by

$$P_x = \frac{h}{\sqrt{\pi}} \int_{-x}^{x} e^{-h^2 x^2} \, dx \tag{24}$$

To evaluate P_x we may (1) draw the normal curve and measure the designated area with a planimeter; (2) calculate or obtain from Table I of Appendix 2 a series of ordinates between 0 and x and apply a quadrature formula; (3) express $e^{-h^2 x^2}$ in series form and perform the integration indicated by Eq. 24 for each term; or, preferably, (4) make use of tables giving probability summations. The results obtained for each of the first three procedures, showing P_x as a function of x, are valid for only one distribution. Obviously, a probability table is desired whose values are independent of both the nature of x and the value of h. One such is obtained when hx is used as the independent variable. The evaluation for the normal law may then be written

$$P_x = P_{hx} = \frac{2}{\sqrt{\pi}} \int_{0}^{hx} e^{-(hx)^2} \, d(hx) \tag{25}$$

A table showing P_{hx} as a function of hx such as is found in Table II of Appendix 2 applies to all normal distributions. If, for example, for a distribution where $h = 5 \text{ cm}^{-1}$, we wish to know the probability of a positive deviation less than 0.1 cm, we first note that $hx = 0.5$, and then read the desired probability from the table as one-half of $P_{0.1 \text{ cm}} = P_{(hx=0.5)}$ $= 0.520$ or 0.260. On the other hand, the probability of occurrence of a deviation, either positive or negative, less than 0.1 cm is $P_{(hx=0.5)}$, or 0.520.

In practice, σ and p are used much more often as precision indexes than is $1/h$. In consequence, values for $P_{x/\sigma}$ and $P_{x/p}$ as functions of $x/\sigma (= hx/0.707)$ and of $x/p (= hx/0.477)$ are often desired. Such values are readily obtainable from the table just referred to.

Illustrating the use of Table II of Appendix 2 with respect to $P_{x/\sigma}$, consider the following. Given that the standard deviation for the lateral deviations of target hits from a central vertical line is 15 inches, and that the frequency distribution is normal, what is the expected percentage of hits falling within the 15-inch range? What range of deviation will probably include 90% of the hits? Replying to the first question, it is apparent that we seek the value of $P_{(x/\sigma=1)}$. We first find the value of $hx (= x/\sqrt{2}\,\sigma)$ that corresponds to $x/\sigma = 1$. It is 0.707. In the table we find the corresponding P_{hx} to be 0.683. Obviously this is also the desired $P_{(x/\sigma=1)}$ and the percentage is 68.3%. Replying to the next question, we seek first the hx which yields 90% for the corresponding P_{hx}, and then the corresponding x/σ and x. These values in turn are found to be 1.16, 1.64, and 25 inches.

Similarly, illustrating the use of Table II of Appendix 2 with respect to $P_{x/p}$, consider the following questions. Given that the probable error for the masses of bearing balls of a certain group is 15 mg and that the distribution is normal, what is the expected percentage of balls whose deviations are at least 30 mg or $2p$? What is the minimum deviation from the mean mass that will include 99% of the balls? The procedure here is very similar to that used just above. Replying to the first question, we seek the value of $P_{(x/p=2)}$. The corresponding $hx (= 0.477x/p)$ is 0.954. The corresponding P_{hx} is 0.823. This is the desired $P_{x/p}$ and the answer is unity less 82.3% or 17.7%. Replying to the second question, for a P_{hx} of 99%, the table indicates an hx of 1.82. The corresponding x/p and x are 3.81 and 57 mg.

8. The Arithmetic Mean of a Set of Measurements. We return now to the question raised at the beginning of this chapter: given n measurements of a quantity, $X_1, X_2, \cdots X_n$, all taken with equal care, what, on the basis of the normal frequency distribution, is the most probable value of the quantity? As an aid in finding this value, we introduce $\overline{X}''$, an arbitrary function of all the measurements. It may be conveniently thought of as a variable pseudo-mean whose value depends on the method of formation. We may, if we wish, define it by

$$\overline{X}'' = \left(\frac{\Sigma X^m}{n}\right)^{1/m} \tag{26}$$

where m, as a variable, may have any value ranging from 0 to ∞. Let $x''_1, x''_2, \cdots x''_n$ be the deviations of $X_1, X_2, \cdots X_n$ from $\overline{X}''$. On the basis of the previous discussion of the nature and the distribution of errors, it is now assumed that the preferred value of $\overline{X}''$ is that for which the corresponding combined probability of simultaneous occurrence of $x''_1, x''_2, \cdots x''_n$ is a maximum. If the set of measurements obeys the normal law, the probability of occurrence of the deviation x''_1, i.e., the deviation lying between x''_1 and $x''_1 + \Delta x''$ where $\Delta x''$ is the least count of the set of measurements, is given by

$$\Delta P_{x''_1} = P_{(x''_1 + \Delta x'')} - P_{x''_1} = y_{x''_1} \Delta x'' \tag{27}$$

Similarly,

$$\Delta P_{x''_2} = y_{x''_2} \Delta x'', \text{ etc.} \tag{28}$$

The combined probability of the deviations x''_1 and x''_2 both occurring in the order specified is then given by

$$(\Delta^2 P)_{x''_1, x''_2} = \Delta P_{x''_1} \Delta P_{x''_2} = y_{x''_1} y_{x''_2} (\Delta x'')^2 \tag{29}$$

$$= \left(\frac{h}{\sqrt{\pi}}\right)^2 e^{-h^2(x''^2_1 + x''^2_2)} (\Delta x'')^2 \tag{30}$$

Hence, the condition that the combined probability of occurrence of $x''_1, x''_2, \cdots x''_n$ should be a maximum may be written as

$$(\Delta^n P)_{x''_1, \cdots x''_n} = \left(\frac{h}{\sqrt{\pi}}\right)^n e^{-h^2 \Sigma x''^2} (\Delta x'')^n = a \text{ maximum} \tag{31}$$

or, in logarithmic form, as

$$\ln(\Delta^n P)_{x''_1, \cdots x''_n} = \ln\left(\frac{h \Delta x''}{\sqrt{\pi}}\right)^n - h^2 \Sigma x''^2 = a \text{ maximum} \tag{32}$$

The conditions which must be fulfilled in order that Eq. 32 may be true are

$$\frac{d}{d\overline{X}''} \left[\ln(\Delta^n P)_{x''_1, \cdots x''_n}\right] = 0 \tag{33}$$

and

$$\frac{d^2}{d\overline{X}''^2} \left[\ln(\Delta^n P)_{x''_1, \cdots x''_n}\right] < 0 \tag{34}$$

As the first derivative, we have

$$\frac{d}{d\overline{X}''}[\ln(\Delta^n P)_{x''_1, \cdots x''_n}] = -h^2 \frac{d(\Sigma x''^2)}{d\overline{X}''}$$

$$= -h^2\left(2x''_1 \frac{dx''_1}{d\overline{X}''} + 2x''_2 \frac{dx''_2}{d\overline{X}''} + \cdots 2x''_n \frac{dx''_n}{d\overline{X}''}\right)$$

$$= -2h^2(x''_1 + x''_2 + \cdots x''_n) \qquad [35]$$

The step eliminating the derivatives is a consequence of the definition of an x''_k, namely that $x''_k = \overline{X}'' - X_k$ and that accordingly

$$\frac{dx''_k}{d\overline{X}''} = 1 \qquad [36]$$

As the second derivative, we have

$$\frac{d^2}{d\overline{X}''^2}[\ln(\Delta^n P)_{x''_1, \cdots x''_n}]$$

$$= \frac{d}{d\overline{X}''}[-2h^2(x''_1 + x''_2 + \cdots x''_n)] = -2nh^2 \qquad [37]$$

Applying the condition of Eqs. 33 and 34 requires that

$$x''_1 + x''_2 + \cdots x''_n = 0 \qquad [38]$$

and

$$-2nh^2 < 0 \qquad [39]$$

It is at once evident that the latter of these two equations is true and that the former fulfills the condition that $\overline{X}''$ shall be the arithmetic mean of the given n measurements.

The conclusion just derived with the aid of the normal frequency distribution law, as noted above, was used by Gauss as the fundamental assumption on which his derivation of the law was based.

Rearrangement of Eq. 32 yields

$$\Sigma x^2 = \frac{1}{h^2}\ln\left(\frac{h\,\Delta x}{\sqrt{\pi}}\right)^n - a \text{ maximum} = a \text{ minimum} \qquad [40]$$

where now an x represents the deviation of an individual measurement, X, from the mean, $\overline{X}$. In this form one sees that the assumptions (1) that the measurements follow the normal distribution law and (2) that the combined probability of occurrence of the observed deviations from the mean is a maximum lead to a least value for Σx^2. This is the basis of the well-known principle of least squares.

9. Summary. A knowledge of the law of frequency distribution governing a set of data is often valuable as a means to an end, e.g., in finding the best value of a series of angle measurements, or as an end in itself, e.g., in helping a shoe manufacturer to decide how to apportion his production. A great number of such laws have been derived. One of the simplest and most applicable is the normal distribution law

$$y_n = \frac{nh}{\sqrt{\pi}} e^{-h^2 x^2} \qquad [14]$$

Here x represents the deviations of the observed values from their arithmetic mean; h, the modulus of precision, is a constant whose value depends on the precision of the data, i.e., the spread of the observed values about their mean; n is an arbitrary constant usually set equal to 1 or to the total number of observed x-values; and y has the nature of a frequency coefficient or a probability coefficient, depending on whether n equals the number of observed values or unity.

Special values of x of interest are (1) the arithmetic mean of the x-values, for which the corresponding y_x has its maximum value, y_0; (2) the reciprocal of the modulus of precision, $1/h$, whose corresponding y-value is y_0/e; (3) the average deviation, a, for which $y_a = 0.728y_0$; (4) the standard deviation, σ, for which $y_\sigma = 0.607y_0$; and (5) the probable error, p, for which $y_p = 0.797y_0$. The quantities $1/h$, a, σ, and p are called precision indexes and are related by the equation

$$p : a : \sigma : \frac{1}{h} = 0.477 : 0.564 : 0.707 : 1.000 \qquad [19]$$

The quantity P_x, defined by

$$P_x = \frac{h}{\sqrt{\pi}} \int_{-x}^{x} e^{-h^2 x^2}\, dx \qquad [24]$$

represents the probability of occurrence of a deviation not greater than x in magnitude. The probability of a deviation between x_1 and x_2 in value is then $P_{x_2} - P_{x_1}$. The probable error is that value of x for which $P_p = \frac{1}{2}$.

Values of y_n in Eq. 14 corresponding to specific x-values are most conveniently obtained from Table I, Appendix 2, showing

$$y_{hx} = \frac{1}{\sqrt{\pi}} e^{-h^2 x^2} \qquad [23]$$

Values of P_x in Eq. 24 corresponding to specific x-values are similarly best obtained from Table II, Appendix 2, showing

$$P_{hx} = \frac{2}{\sqrt{\pi}} \int_0^{hx} e^{-h^2x^2} \, d(hx) \qquad [25]$$

The assumptions (1) that measurements obey the normal distribution law and (2) that the combined probability of occurrence of observed deviations from the best value is a maximum leads to the conclusions (1) that the arithmetic mean of a set of measurements is the best approximation to the true value of the quantity measured and (2) that the sum of the squares of the deviations of the observed values is a minimum when the deviations are taken from the mean. Conclusion (2) is the basis of the principle of least squares.

PROBLEMS

1. Plot, on the same set of coordinate axes, binomial distributions whose succeeding ordinates correspond to succeeding coefficients of $(\frac{1}{2} + \frac{1}{2})^5$ and $(\frac{1}{2} + \frac{1}{2})^{11}$. Make the total widths and the areas included under the two curves the same.

2. Plot to scale, on the same set of coordinate axes, two normalized curves such that the modulus of precision of one is twice that of the other.

3. With the aid of tables, find, for one of the curves of Problem 2, the values of hx for which $2P_x$ has in succession the values 0.2, 0.4, 0.6, and 0.8. Draw vertical lines on the plot at the appropriate abscissas.

4. What are the values for y_0 that correspond to values of $1/h$ of (a) 2 sec, (b) 150 cm/sec, (c) 40 in., (d) 3 sec/day?

5. Where $1/h$ is 2 ft and the least count is 1 in., what is the probability that three randomly chosen measurements, regardless of the order of their taking, will have deviations of 8 in., 16 in., and −4 in.? What, if the order is specified?

6. Show that the curve of the normal distribution law has inflection points at $x = \pm \sigma$.

7. A value which has been quoted for the rest mass of the electron m_0 is $9.1154 \times 10^{-28}(1 \pm 0.00018)$ gm, of which ± 0.00018 has the significance of a fractional probable error and is equal to p_{m_0}/m_0. On the basis of the above statement, determine the probability that the value given is correct (1) to within 0.0005×10^{-28} gm, (2) to within 0.00010×10^{-28} gm.

8. A value quoted for the calcite grating space at 20° C is $3.03560 \, (1 \pm 0.00002)$ A (see Problem 7). On the basis of the above, determine the standard deviation and the modulus of precision for the quantity and the probability that the result is correct to within 2.57σ.

CHAPTER VII

THE NORMAL FREQUENCY DISTRIBUTION (*continued*)

1. Introduction. In the preceding chapter we discussed the derivation and the interpretation of a theoretical frequency distribution, the so-called normal distribution

$$y_x = \frac{h}{\sqrt{\pi}} e^{-h^2 x^2} \qquad [1]$$

It was there noted that any observed set of values, assumed normally distributed, is to be considered as a sample set from an infinitely large parent group of measurements whose frequency distribution has the form of Eq. 1.

In this chapter we shall describe the relation between the sample and the parent distributions in greater detail. With this purpose in mind, we discuss first the procedure of fitting the best normal curve to a given distribution, and then we develop short methods of finding the mean and the precision indexes. Some uses of the precision indexes are described, and criteria are obtained for the rejection of observations possessing unduly large deviations from the mean. Limitations of the normal law are then presented, and certain tests for goodness of fit of the normal law to an observed distribution are described.

2. Quantitative Evaluation of Precision Indexes. The process of fitting the best normal curve to an observed distribution is, in effect, that of determining the most probable distribution of the infinite parent group. For this purpose, the calculation of only one constant, the modulus of precision, h, is required.

Given n equally precise measurements of a quantity $X_1, X_2, \cdots X_n$, with deviations $x_1, x_2, \cdots x_n$ from the mean $\overline{X}$, the assumption is made that the desired modulus of precision is the modulus which ascribes to the observed data a maximum of probability of occurrence. Assuming the normal law, the probability that the readings will occur in the order given is

$$(\Delta^n P)_{x_1, x_2, \cdots x_n} = \Delta P_{x_1} \times \Delta P_{x_2} \times \cdots \Delta P_{x_n} \qquad [2]$$

$$= \left(\frac{h}{\sqrt{\pi}}\right)^n e^{-h^2 \Sigma x^2} (\Delta x)^n = \text{a maximum}$$

or in logarithmic form

$$\ln (\Delta^n P)_{x_1 \cdots x_n} = n \ln h - \frac{n}{2} \ln \pi - h^2 \Sigma x^2 + n \ln (\Delta x) = \text{a maximum} \quad [3]$$

Differentiating with respect to h, to obtain the modulus associated with the maximum probability of occurrence, yields

$$\frac{d}{dh} [\ln (\Delta^n P)_{x_1 \cdots x_n}] = \frac{n}{h} - 2h\Sigma x^2 = 0 \quad [4]$$

whence

$$h^2 = \frac{n}{2\Sigma x^2} \quad [5]$$

or

$$\frac{1}{h} = \sqrt{\frac{2\Sigma x^2}{n}} \quad [6] \text{ }^1$$

A second differentiation of Eq. 3 with respect to h yields $-n/h^2 - 2\Sigma x^2$, a quantity which is essentially negative and indicates that the relation expressed in Eq. 6 corresponds to a condition of maximum probability for the given measurements.

In view of Eq. 6, the most probable values of the precision indexes for an individual observation are given by

$$\sigma = \frac{1}{\sqrt{2h}} = \sqrt{\frac{\Sigma x^2}{n}} \quad [7] \text{ }^1$$

$$p = 0.6745\sigma = 0.6745 \sqrt{\frac{\Sigma x^2}{n}} \quad [8] \text{ }^1$$

and

$$a = \frac{\Sigma |x|}{n} \quad [9]$$

[1] Many authors differentiate between the precision indexes $1/h$, σ, and p computed for the individual readings of the sample group and the corresponding precision indexes for the infinite parent group. These latter values are assumed to be more worth while. That the mean of this latter group shall coincide with that of the former group is not to be expected. Consequently the deviations x which have been treated above are not deviations from the *true value* of the quantity measured, i.e., the mean of the infinite group. Obviously, could deviations from this unknown mean be used in computing for our sample group the values of $1/h$, σ, and p, the term Σx^2 would be greater than that actually found. Statistical theory gives for its most probable value $n\Sigma x^2/(n-1)$. It follows that the precision indexes then obtained are greater than those represented in Eqs. 6, 7, and 8. They are obtained, in fact, by replacing the n of those equations by $n-1$, and are so found in many texts. The present authors, however, are deviating from this policy. There are three reasons. First, by keeping the forms of Eqs. 6, 7, and 8 as they are, the cor-

As precision indexes, p and σ are used more often than a. That this should be the case, despite the evident greater ease of determining an a, seems to be largely due to a discovery by Gauss. He found that p and σ, as defined above, were 14% more effective than a, and 9% more effective than $(\Sigma x^3)^{\frac{1}{3}}$, another possible precision index. Expressed otherwise, the p or σ from 100 observations is as precise, relatively, as the a from 114 similar observations. (See page 196.) Because of the foregoing, we shall, for the most part, from now on, ignore a as a precision index. Further, when describing precision indexes for quantities, following custom, we shall ignore $1/h$ also and emphasize only p and σ.

To fit the normal curve, we need only calculate h and substitute in

$$y_x = \frac{h}{\sqrt{\pi}} e^{-h^2 x^2} \qquad [1]$$

if a probability coefficient is desired, or in

$$y_n = \frac{nh}{\sqrt{\pi}} e^{-h^2 x^2} \qquad [10]$$

if a frequency distribution is desired. In calculating h and the precision indexes where n is small, we may conveniently use Eqs. 6 to 9 as they stand. Usually, however, Σx^2 will involve lengthy computations, especially if $\overline{X}$ is carried out to more significant figures than are contained in the original X-readings. Hence, the use of some short method such as that of the following section is advisable as a time saver and as an aid in eliminating computational errors.

3. A Short Method of Computing Means and Precision Indexes. To find the mean and σ, say, of the measurements $X_1, X_2, \cdots X_n$, we first assume an approximate mean, $\overline{X}'$, having a convenient rounded value near that of the true mean, and then deal with the differences

responding equations relating to the more important precision indexes of means are kept simpler. Instead of involving $\sqrt{n(n-1)}$, the simpler relations involve n only. The second reason is that in practice seldom, if ever, as will be indicated later in this chapter, are truly normal frequency distributions encountered, even in the infinite parent groups. At the best, then, the precision indexes sought can only be approximations, and it appears that in reality the expressions involving n only may be as significant as those involving $\sqrt{n(n-1)}$ instead. The third reason is that even for parent groups whose distributions approximate the normal very closely, the uncertainties in the precision indexes themselves often exceed the assumed error due to approximating $(n-1)/n$ by unity.

Nevertheless, for the sake of those who differ, the authors will attempt, throughout this book, to make reference to this footnote wherever the above simplification has been made.

$X_1 - \overline{X}'$, $X_2 - \overline{X}', \cdots X_n - \overline{X}'$. The associated numerics are usually small and more or less evenly divided between positive and negative values. Procedure is based on the following basic relations:

$$\overline{X} = \frac{\Sigma X}{n} = \frac{\Sigma[\overline{X}' + (X - \overline{X}')]}{n} = \overline{X}' + \frac{\Sigma(X - \overline{X}')}{n} = \overline{X}' + \Delta \quad [11]$$

and

$$\sigma^2 = \frac{\Sigma x^2}{n} = \frac{\Sigma(X - \overline{X})^2}{n} = \frac{\Sigma(X - \overline{X}' - \Delta)^2}{n}$$

$$= \frac{\Sigma(X - \overline{X}')^2 - 2\Delta\Sigma(X - \overline{X}') + n\Delta^2}{n}$$

$$= \frac{\Sigma(X - \overline{X}')^2}{n} - \left[\frac{\Sigma(X - \overline{X}')}{n}\right]^2 = \frac{\Sigma(X - \overline{X}')^2}{n} - \Delta^2 \quad [12]$$

The necessary computations, together with a check to be discussed later, are carried through in Table I. To one who has done much computing, the smallness of the numbers dealt with makes a considerable appeal.

Where computed results are matters of concern, it is desirable to have checks as insurance against errors. There are two checks possible for the mean, $\overline{X}$. One consists in determining actual values for the deviations $X - \overline{X}$ and then noting whether or not the sum of the positive deviations equals the sum of the negative deviations. The other consists in selecting a new $\overline{X}'$ and proceeding according to Eq. 11, taking care not to use computations made use of in the original calculation. The second method is likely to be the shorter if the value of the mean is carried to a greater number of significant figures than the original measured values. Neither of these checks need be made in case one has determined the σ and wishes to insure against error there also, since certain checks for σ involve a simultaneous check for $\overline{X}$.

Two procedures for checking σ will be cited. One is based on the defining relation, Eq. 12, which by simple expansion yields

$$\sigma^2 = \frac{\Sigma(X - \overline{X})^2}{n} = \frac{\Sigma X^2}{n} - \frac{2\overline{X}\Sigma X}{n} + \overline{X}^2 = \frac{\Sigma X^2}{n} - \overline{X}^2 \quad [13]$$

This equation does not involve summations previously made, and therefore can satisfy as a check. The summation ΣX^2 will, however, generally involve uncomfortably large numbers. Procedure for the second check consists in selecting a new convenient $\overline{X}'$ and proceeding as in Eq. 12. This method, which is illustrated in Table I, is likely to prove much the shorter. The reader who doubts this assertion is invited to make the test, using Eq. 13.

When calculating σ for a set of positive and negative values whose mean is nearly zero, the advantages of using Eq. 12 rather than Eq. 13 generally disappear. Note that if $\overline{X}'$ is taken as zero Eqs. 12 and 13 become identical, so that only the second of the two checks for σ mentioned above can be used.

TABLE I

ILLUSTRATING A SHORT METHOD FOR COMPUTING $\overline{X}$ AND σ, TOGETHER WITH A CONVENIENT CHECK. THE FREQUENCY OF OCCURRENCE OF THE OBSERVED VALUES OF X IS GIVEN BY f

X	f	$\overline{X}' = 128$			$\overline{X}' = 129$		
		$X - \overline{X}'$	$f(X - \overline{X}')$	$f(X - \overline{X}')^2$	$X - \overline{X}'$	$f(X - \overline{X}')$	$f(X - \overline{X}')^2$
125	2	-3	-6	18	-4	-8	32
126	3	-2	-6	12	-3	-9	27
127	9	-1	-9	9	-2	-18	36
128	15	0	0	0	-1	-15	15
129	11	1	11	11	0	0	0
130	7	2	14	28	1	7	7
131	2	3	6	18	2	4	8
132	1	4	4	16	3	3	9
	50		14	112		-36	134

$$\Delta = \tfrac{14}{50} = 0.28$$
$$\overline{X} = 128 + 0.28 = 128.28$$
$$\sigma^2 = \tfrac{112}{50} - (0.28)^2 = 2.16$$
$$\sigma = 1.47$$
$$p = 0.675 \times 1.47 = 0.99$$

$$\Delta = -\tfrac{36}{50} = -0.72$$
$$\overline{X} = 129 - 0.72 = 128.28$$
$$\sigma^2 = \tfrac{134}{50} - (0.72)^2 = 2.16$$
$$\sigma = 1.47$$
$$p = 0.675 \times 1.47 = 0.99$$

Accepted values: $\overline{X} = 128.3$; $\sigma = 1.5$; $p = 1.0$.

4. Chauvenet's Criterion. Occasionally, in a series of readings, one or two values occur which differ considerably from the series as a whole. Though we might normally expect such widely divergent values to occur once, say, on the average in 100 readings, it is quite possible for that once to occur in a group of 10 or of only 5 measurements. In such a case, the influence of this divergent reading on the magnitude of the mean is disproportionately large, and it is generally conceded that the mean obtained would be closer to the true value if this reading were rejected. There is no suggestion in the criterion that a gross error has been made in taking a reading which it rejects, although it is very possible that such is the explanation for the deviation.

Rejection of a given reading of a series on the basis of a hunch is not satisfactory, and a criterion of rejection is desirable. Of the several which have been developed, that due to Chauvenet seems most generally accepted. In words, this criterion states that any reading of a series of n readings shall be rejected when the magnitude of its deviation from the mean of the series is such that the probability of occurrence of all deviations that large or larger does not exceed $1/2n$. Expressed partly in equation form, it states that if the deviation x of a reading from the mean is greater than the deviation $\tilde{x}$, where $\tilde{x}$ is defined by

$$1 - P_{\tilde{x}} = 1 - \frac{h}{\sqrt{\pi}} \int_{-\tilde{x}}^{+\tilde{x}} e^{-h^2 x^2}\, dx = \frac{1}{2n} \qquad [14]$$

the reading shall be rejected. To illustrate, in a series of ten readings whose probable error is $p_x(= 0.477/h_x)$, a reading shall be rejected if its deviation from the mean is greater than $2.91 p_x$ (see Table III, Appendix 2). The probability of occurrence of all deviations as great or greater is then less than $1/20$. For 20 readings, the value of $\tilde{x}$ is $3.32 p_x$. The variation of $\tilde{x}$ with n is shown in Table III, Appendix 2.

If, after a reading has been rejected in accordance with Chauvenet's criterion, it is felt that a second reading is also too divergent to retain, it too should be subjected to the criterion, with the understanding that the reading already rejected is no longer a member of the series and the new mean concerns the $n - 1$ remaining measurements. This procedure may be repeated until it is found that no values lie outside the limits set by Eq. 14.

5. Limitations of the Normal Law. It is blindly assumed by many that the vast majority of frequency distributions obey the normal law. There are many reasons why such should not be the case. We shall discuss certain of them in some detail.

1. The normal distribution is symmetrical—equal positive and negative deviations between limits from the mean are equally likely to occur. Few observed distributions are perfectly symmetrical, however, and numerous distributions show a decided preponderance of values either greater or less than the mean (Fig. 1). Such distributions are called skewed—negatively if the majority of the observations exceed the mean, and positively for the opposite condition.

2. The normal law permits variations from $-\infty$ to $+\infty$; i.e., it assigns a probability greater than zero to every finite deviation from

the mean.   Hence, such distributions as that of the speeds of molecules of a gas at a given temperature (Fig. 1) cannot be represented
by the normal law since it is meaningless to speak of negative speeds.

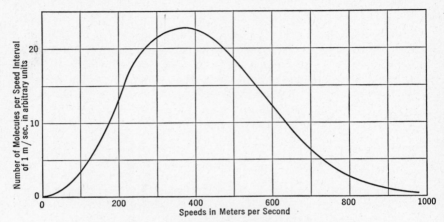

FIG. 1.   The non-normal distribution of the speeds of oxygen molecules at 0° C.

3. The normal curve has only one maximum ordinate, at the mean
value.   Some distributions, however, have more than one maximum
(Fig. 2) and cannot be normal.

4. Let us assume, despite the three limitations stated, that a particular distribution, say that of the diameters, d, of a group of bearing

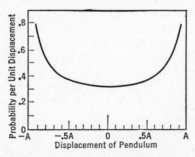

FIG. 2.   A non-normal distribution with more than one maximum ordinate, showing
the probability of finding a pendulum bob at different displacements from its equilibrium position for a given amplitude of vibration.   (*University of Pittsburgh.*
Atomic Physics, 2nd Ed., p. 165, New York, John Wiley & Sons, Inc., 1937.)

balls, obeys the normal law, at least to the extent of the balls whose
diameters fall between $d + 5p_d$ and $d - 5p_d$.   Then it necessarily
follows that if all the balls are truly spherical and of equal density,

the distributions of their masses, i.e., of the (d^3) of the bearing balls cannot obey the law. Consider three hypothetical balls, A, B, and C, with diameters equal to the mean diameter, $\bar{d}$, the mean diameter minus the probable error of the distribution, $\bar{d} - p_d$, and the mean diameter plus the probable error, $\bar{d} + p_d$, respectively (Fig. 3A). Since the diameter distribution of the group of balls is assumed normal, A, B, and C divide them into four equal subgroups—those having diameters less than B, those having diameters between A and B, etc. Assuming equal density and truly spherical shape for all, A, B, and C again divide them into the same four equal subgroups on

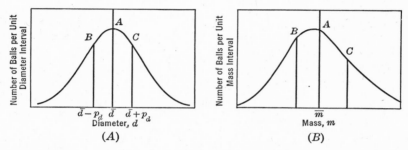

Fig. 3. Distributions of (A) the diameters and (B) the masses of a group of bearing balls. If A is assumed normal, B is necessarily skewed.

the basis of mass also; i.e., all balls having diameters less than B also have masses less than B, etc. Hence, if the mass distribution is to be normal, ball A should have the mean mass, and B and C should have masses respectively less than and greater than the mean by an amount equal to the probable error of the mass distribution. However, the masses of A, B, and C are $b\bar{d}^3$, $b(\bar{d} - p_d)^3$, and $b(\bar{d} + p_d)^3$, respectively, where b is an appropriate constant, and it is seen that the mass difference between A and B is not equal to the mass difference between A and C (Fig. 3B). Thus, if the diameter distribution is normal, the mass distribution is skewed and hence nonnormal.

By similar reasoning it is seen that distributions of the surface areas involving d^2, the moments of inertia involving d^5, the values of $1/d$, $1/d^2$, etc., for the group are also nonnormal if the d-distribution is assumed normal. Since the a priori probability of normality for the distribution of d is equal to that for d^2, d^3, $d^{\frac{1}{2}}$, etc., the probability of any one obeying the normal law strictly is effectively zero.

Further evidence as to the nonuniversality of the normal law even for ordinary distributions is furnished by the large number of statistical distribution laws in use for different purposes. Fry [1] lists eight types, some of which cover several subtypes. Those named in addition to the Normal law are the Poisson law, the Binomial law, Pearson Types I, II, III, and IV, and the Gram Charlier series.

As such nonnormal distributions of considerable interest in present-day research, we have the Poisson distribution, its integral, and its derivative. The equation for the law itself is

$$P_{n,x} = \frac{\left(\dfrac{k}{\alpha}\right)^n}{n!}\, e^{-x/\alpha} \qquad [15]$$

of which $P_{n,x}$ represents, for a random distribution of events in a limited range of the variable x, the probability that n events will occur in the interval x, α the average interval of x between events, and accordingly x/α the expected number of events in the interval x. For the case of $n = 0$, or no events occurring in the interval, Eq. 15 reduces to

$$P_{0,x}dx = e^{-x/\alpha}dx \qquad [16]$$

and, the rate of change of $P_{0,x}$ with respect to x, to

$$\frac{dP_{0,x}}{dx} = -\frac{1}{\alpha}e^{-x/\alpha} \qquad [17]$$

For the probability, however, that n or more events will occur in the interval x, $P_{>n,x}$, we have the summation

$$P_{>n,x} = \sum_{m=n}^{\infty} P_{m,x} \qquad [18]$$

The last equation represents, for example, the probability distribution of concern when one tries to correlate the visual responses with the quanta of radiant energy that are absorbed by the visual fluid of the retina during brief flashes of light received by the eye. It has been used by Hecht [2] and his co-workers in a study of the operation of visual mechanisms at the threshold of vision. (See Fig. 14, Chap. II.)

Similarly, $-dP_{0,x}/dx$ of Eq. 17 represents, for the emission of α-particles from a radioactive specimen, for example, the frequency distribution for time intervals between successive α-particle emissions. Fig. 4 represents data of this nature obtained by Halliday.[3] Offhand,

[1] Fry, Thornton C., *Probability and Its Engineering Uses*, New York, D. Van Nostrand Company, Inc., 1928.

[2] Hecht, S., Shaler, S., Pirenne, M. H., *Science*, **93**, 585 (1941).

[3] Halliday, D., Ph.D. thesis, University of Pittsburgh, 1941.

on the mere basis of randomness, one might be inclined to assume that the normal frequency distribution or a close approximation to it would apply there. Such, however, is far from the case.

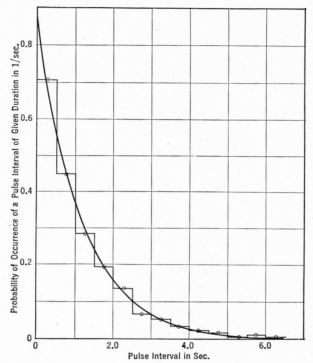

FIG. 4. The Poisson distribution of Eq. 17 as represented by the frequency distribution of time intervals between successive receptions of α-particles from a radioactive source, as obtained by D. Halliday, who measured 3133 pulse intervals. The horizontal portions of the broken line represent observed probabilities for half-second intervals expressed in terms of reciprocal seconds. The unbroken line represents the expectation according to Eq. 17 for a mean interval of 1.169 sec.

6. Justification for Assuming the Normal Law. In view of the above limitations, one must consider a new situation carefully before ever assuming that the normal distribution law applies to a series of measured values that has been obtained. But now, having concluded in a particular case that the normal distribution law or a close approximation is reasonable, what shall be done? Let us examine more closely what is meant by the statement that the normal law governs a given distribution. We mean by this statement that as the number of observations included in the sample distribution increases, the probabilities of occurrence of deviations from the mean approach ever more closely the values predicted by Eq. 1. An actual sample distribution with a finite number of observations never indicates such predicted probabilities. Instead, it may be quite skewed, or even two-peaked, and still the infinite parent distribution might conform with the normal law. In such cases the deviations from normality would disappear if it were possible or practical to add a sufficiently great number of values.

Referring to limitation 1 above, a distribution of a finite number of readings need not be perfectly symmetrical to be considered normal.

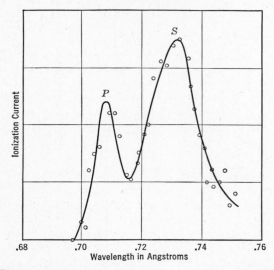

FIG. 5. The Compton effect, an illustration of a two-maximum distribution resulting from the inclusions of two physically separate, but not separated, photon distributions. Graph shows unmodified, P, and shifted, S, Mo $K\alpha$ radiation scattered by carbon. (*Compton, A. H., Phys. Rev.*, **21**, 715, and **22**, 409, 1923.)

Conversely, it is admitted that the infinite parent distribution corresponding to an observed apparently normal distribution may be non-normal. The same argument applies to limitation 4. It happens, especially when the precision indexes are relatively small, that the distributions of such related things as the diameters, areas, masses, etc., of a group of bearing balls say, may all be effectively normal, even though each distribution is somewhat skewed, and even though only one of the related infinite parent distributions can possibly be normal, even for a restricted range.

Limitation 3 is not an important one, since relatively few distributions have more than one maximum ordinate, and, as stated above, some two-peaked distributions may actually be samples from infinite parent distributions that are normal. However, when the parent distribution follows a nonnormal law, proper tests, such as the chi-square test to be discussed later, may disclose this fact and thus prevent drawing false conclusions by assuming normality. It is interesting that in some cases two maxima are obtained as a result of the inclusion in a single distribution of two sets of dissimilar values, each of which yields a distribution with one peak normally when taken alone (Fig. 5).

Despite its limitations, the normal law, in addition to being capable of representing distributions that are believed to be normal, is also capable of representing sufficiently well many distributions which, from a priori consideration, are known to be nonnormal. Adding to this the fact that the normal curve is the simplest to fit, we feel justified in adopting the normal law where skewness, flatness, and other characteristics do not cause too serious deviations from the normal distribution.

At any rate, for one reason or another, it is customary to assume that the measurements of a quantity follow the normal distribution law when the least count is small in comparison with the variations from the mean and the distribution is not too obviously nonnormal. On this basis, a considerable superstructure of treatment of data has been founded, including that in the succeeding chapters of this book.

7. Qualitative Tests for the Normal Distribution. Tests for applicability of the normal law may be classed as either quantitative or qualitative. The former are the more definite in their interpretations, but they are rather involved and tedious to carry through. The qualitative tests are simple, but often difficult to interpret. They are of value, however, in exposing distributions which deviate greatly from the normal. Two tests will be described: (1) superposing the normal curve, and (2) plotting on probability paper.

(*a*) *Superposing the Normal Curve.* A good idea of the normality of a distribution may be obtained by superposing on the graph of observed values the computed normal distribution which best fits. For the demonstration of how this may be done, we use data by Birge.[1] See Table II and Fig. 6.

Normal procedure, described earlier in this chapter, leads to

$$\sigma = 3.60 \times 10^{-3} \, m\mu \qquad [19]$$

$$\frac{1}{h} = 5.09 \times 10^{-3} \, m\mu \qquad [20]$$

[1] Birge, R. J., *Phys. Rev.*, **40**, 207 (1932). The data of the table were reported to the authors by private correspondence.

and for the 500 observations

$$y_n = 500 \text{ residuals} \times y_x = 55.4 \frac{\text{residuals}}{10^{-3} \text{ m}\mu} e^{-\frac{0.0386}{(10^{-3}\text{ m}\mu)^2} x^2} \qquad [21]$$

TABLE II

DATA BY BIRGE [1] SHOWING, FOR 500 OBSERVATIONS OF A SPECTRAL LINE, THE
FREQUENCY OF OCCURRENCE OF VARIOUS RESIDUALS, x

By chance the mean was such that all residuals could be expressed precisely in terms
of a tenth of the least count, 0.0010 mμ, of his instrument.

Observed						Computed	
x in 10^{-3} mμ	No. of residuals	x in 10^{-3} mμ	No. of residuals	hx	y_{hx}	x in 10^{-3} mμ	y_n in residuals $\frac{}{10^{-3} \text{ m}\mu}$
+0.1	62	− 0.9	53	0.0	0.5642	0.00	55.4
1.1	41	− 1.9	52	0.2	.5420	1.02	53.2
2.1	45	− 2.9	30	0.4	.4818	2.04	47.2
3.1	44	− 3.9	31	0.6	.3936	3.05	38.6
4.1	34	− 4.9	22	0.8	.2975	4.07	29.2
5.1	20	− 5.9	21	1.0	.2076	5.09	20.4
6.1	16	− 6.9	11	1.2	.1336	6.11	13.1
7.1	3	− 7.9	1	1.4	.0794	7.13	7.8
8.1	4	− 8.9	4	1.6	.0436	8.14	4.3
9.1	3	− 9.9	1	1.8	.0221	9.16	2.2
10.1	1	−10.9	0	2.0	.0104	10.18	1.0
11.1	1	−11.9	0	2.2	.0044	11.20	0.4

Continuing, we may compute values directly, using Eq. 21 or make
use of Table I of Appendix 2, for whose use residuals must be expressed
in terms of $1/h$ or as hx. For $hx = 1$, i.e., for x equal to $1/h$ or $5.09 \times$
10^{-3} mμ, we obtain for the relative probability coefficient, y_{hx}, the value
0.2076. From this in accord with Eq. 22 of Chapter VI, namely

$$y_x = y_{hx} \frac{d(hx)}{dx} = hy_{hx} \qquad [22]$$

we obtain, as a corresponding value for y_n,

$$y_n = ny_x = \frac{500 \text{ residuals}}{5.09 \times 10^{-3} \text{ m}\mu} 0.2076$$

$$= 98.2 \frac{\text{residuals}}{10^{-3} \text{ m}\mu} 0.2076 = 20.4 \frac{\text{residuals}}{10^{-3} \text{ m}\mu} \qquad [23]$$

[1] Idem.

This value plotted in Fig. 6 at $x = +5.09 \times 10^{-3}$ mμ and $x = -5.09$ $\times 10^{-3}$ mμ yields two points of the desired superposed normal frequency curve for that graph.   Other points may be obtained by seeking similarly (the last half of Table II) values of y_{hx} corresponding to hx values, such as 0.0, 0.2, 0.4$\cdots$1.2, 1.4, etc.   In all cases the factor 98.2 residuals/10^{-3} mμ serves in obtaining the appropriate y_n.

That the superposed curve of Fig. 6 fits well is evident.   The ensemble of data, as shown by figure and data, is thought, in comparison with

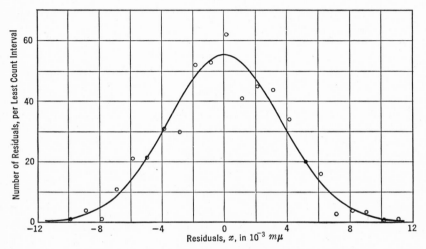

FIG. 6.   Graph showing the frequency distribution of the residuals for 500 observations of a spectral line as obtained by Birge (Table II), and the superposition of the best fitting normal frequency curve.

other experimental data, to conform to an unusually high degree with the normal distribution curve.

(b) *Plotting the Ogive Curve.*   An alternate method of plotting a distribution curve, Galton's ogive curve, is shown in Fig. 7.   In this curve, the number (or percentage) of occurrences of magnitudes either less or greater than x is shown as a function of x.   Plotting the normal curve in this manner would be equivalent to plotting, as a function of x, the integral Y_1, where

$$Y_1 = \int_{-\infty}^{x} y_x \, dx = \frac{h}{\sqrt{\pi}} \int_{-\infty}^{x} e^{-h^2 x^2} \, dx \qquad [24]$$

or, of course, Y_2 where

$$Y_2 = \int_{x}^{\infty} y_x \, dx = 1 - Y_1 \qquad [25]$$

Distribution data, however, are frequently presented in the form of finite values of ΔY to correspond to finite increments of range of x, Δx, which are usually constant throughout. For such cases instead of Eqs. 24 and 25, we therefore use the summations

$$Y_{1n} = \sum_{m=1}^{n} y_m \, \Delta x \tag{26}$$

and

$$Y_{2n} = \sum_{m=n+1}^{N} y_m \, \Delta x \tag{27}$$

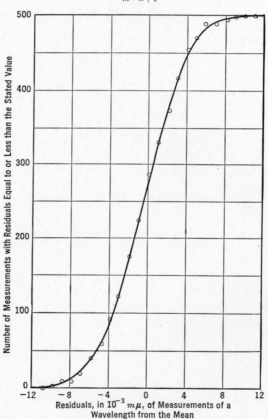

FIG. 7. Galton's ogive curve for the distribution of Table II.

in which Y_{1n} and Y_{2n} represent numbers of readings. They are usually plotted as functions of x_m, or $m\Delta x$. Often in tabulations, the values listed for the independent variable are central values for the succeeding least-count intervals. To secure passage of the curve through the zero-residual 50%-frequency point for a normal distribution, Y_{1n} and Y_{2n} may be plotted as functions of $x + \Delta x/2$ and $x - \Delta x/2$.

Though the ogive curve possesses some advantages over the ordinary method of plotting distributions, it is much less suitable as a test for

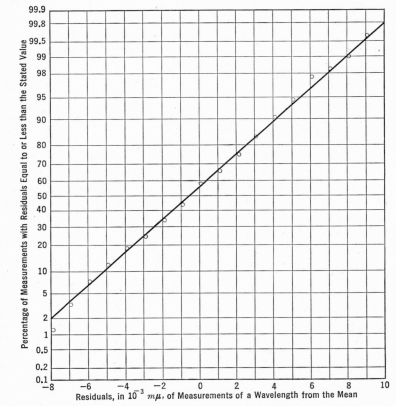

FIG. 8. Graph of frequency distribution of Table II plotted on probability paper.

normality of data, since generally departures from normality are concealed rather than exposed. If, however, the ogive curve data are plotted on so-called probability paper rather than on rectangular coordinate paper, the resultant curve possesses all the advantages of the ogive curve and in addition provides a convenient test for normality.

On probability paper the scale showing the number of occurrences, expressed as a percentage of the total number of occurrences, is distorted so that the distances from 50% to all other percentages are proportional to the corresponding values of x/σ. The scale is symmetrical about the 50% coordinate line, and the integrals Y_1 and Y_2 or the summations Y_{1n} and Y_{2n}, in case the data follow the normal distribution law, plotted as functions of x on such coordinates yield straight lines. Hence, a plot showing the relative numbers of observations having values less than (or greater than) x, as a function of x, will deviate from a straight line if the distribution deviates from the normal. Fig. 8 shows the application of this test for normality to the data of Table II. Deviations from normality are revealed though perhaps not as clearly as in Fig. 6. However, insofar as ease and time of construction are concerned, this method of testing is much the superior.

8. Quantitative Tests for Deviations from Assumed Distributions. When a distribution of data is believed, for theoretical reasons or otherwise, to follow some recognized law of which there are many, it may be judged by its closeness of fit to an equation following that law. Often, however, many distributions are without theoretical or even empirical backing. Then particularly the deviation from an assumed normal distribution may be sought. There are two tests known as skewness, represented in magnitude by $\sqrt{\beta_1}$, and flatness, represented in magnitude by β_2, which are used to indicate deviations from the normal frequency curve. One test, the chi square, χ^2, may be used whatever the distribution. The chi-square test is much more important and much more used than the other tests.

Skewness, or asymmetry with respect to the distribution about the mean of the observed values, obviously cannot be revealed by the sum of the deviations from the mean, for that is zero by definition, nor by the sum of the squares of such deviations or of such deviations raised to an even power since in such squares or even powers there are no distinctions between positive and negative deviations. The sums of odd powers, however, do make such distinctions and will indicate asymmetries. Arbitrarily, the sum of the third powers of deviations expressed in terms of the standard deviation σ in each instance is used. The defining equation used is

$$\sqrt{\beta_1} = \frac{\Sigma (X - \overline{X})^3}{n\sigma^3}$$ [28]

In case the data are represented by a curve which has been drawn, the following equation may be used instead.

$$\sqrt{\beta_1} = \frac{\displaystyle\int_{-\infty}^{+\infty} yx^3 dx}{\sigma^3 \displaystyle\int_{-\infty}^{+\infty} ydx}$$ [29]

Obviously $\sqrt{\beta_1}$ is zero for a strictly normal distribution. How significant any particular computed value may be is only comprehended by determining values for various asymmetric distributions. That for the distribution of Table I is $+0.013$; that for the molecular speeds of the molecules of a gas (Fig. 1) is about 21.

Flatness, the distortion represented in Fig. 9, on the other hand obviously cannot be represented quantitatively by any odd power summation. Nor will a second power summation of deviations expressed in terms of the standard deviation suffice since when so expressed all such summations, however flat or skewed, yield σ by definition. A fourth power summation will nevertheless show up such characteristics. In accordance therewith, flatness β_2 is defined by

$$\beta_2 = \frac{\Sigma(X - \overline{X})^4}{n\sigma^4} \qquad [30]$$

for ungraphed data, and by

$$\beta_2 = \frac{\displaystyle\int_{-\infty}^{+\infty} yx^4dx}{\sigma^4 \displaystyle\int_{-\infty}^{+\infty} ydx} \qquad [31]$$

for graphed data.

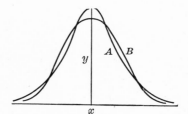

FIG. 9. Illustrating the distortion called flatness. A represents the normal distribution curve; B, that possessing flatness.

For a normal distribution β_2 is 3. Evidently distributions may be more flat or less flat than that which is normal. Owing to the increased effectiveness of large values of y accompanying large values for x in yielding large values for a fourth power summation, it is evident that the β_2 for curve B of Fig. 9 will be less than 3.

Differing, as already noted from the two tests just described, the chi-square test may be applied to determine the deviation of an actual distribution from any assumed law for the infinite parent distribution. In this case, one considers the probability that a random sample, taken from the infinite parent, shall differ from the assumed law by the amount found. Though some prefer 0.05 as the limiting probability, it is generally held that a sample is satisfactory if the probability of its occurrence is 0.01 or greater.

The function χ^2, as defined by Pearson, the originator of the test, is based on a comparison of observed, f_o, with expected, f_c, frequencies of occurrence of individual readings, and is given by

$$\chi^2 = \sum \frac{(f_o - f_c)^2}{f_c} \qquad [32]$$

In the application of Eq. 32, it is usual to array the observed measurements in groups, to each of which a certain specified range is assigned. Thus arranged, the number included in any one group is taken as the observed frequency of occurrence for the corresponding group range. The ranges for the various groups of a distribution need not be the same.

Once χ^2 has been obtained for a particular set of data, it remains to determine what the probability of its occurrence shall be. For this

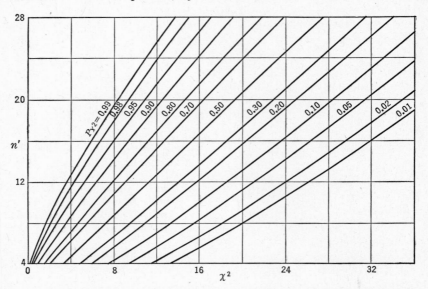

Fig. 10. Showing chi-square probability, P_{χ^2}, for goodness of fit of a sample distribution as a function of χ^2 and of n', the number of groups of data less the number of imposed conditions.

purpose Pearson [1] has computed extended tables of probability of occurrence, which depend not only on χ^2 but also on n', the number of groups selected less the number of imposed conditions.[2] One imposed condition is that the total number of items entering χ^2 must equal the number entering the various groups. Other conditions sometimes imposed are those ascribing to the infinite parent a distribution described by constants, in the normal case, the $\overline{X}$ and σ determined from the sample. In this case n' becomes three less than the number of groups. Sometimes still other conditions are specified and should be taken into account. A graph giving chi-square probabilities as a function of χ^2 and n' is given

[1] Pearson, K., *Trans. Am. Math. Soc.*, **31**, 133 (1929).

[2] Fry, Thornton C., *Probability and Its Engineering Uses*, p. 294, New York, D. Van Nostrand Company, Inc., 1928.

in Fig. 10. (See also Table IV of Appendix 2.) Application to the velocity of light measurements of Michelson, Pease, and Pearson [1] is shown in Table III. On the assumption that the infinite parent distribution is

TABLE III

APPLICATION OF THE CHI-SQUARE TEST TO THE VELOCITY OF LIGHT MEASUREMENTS OF MICHELSON, PEASE, AND PEARSON

From 233 determinations a weighted average velocity of light of 299,773.85 km/sec was obtained; c' represents the excess of a measured velocity over 299,000 km/sec. A frequency, f_o, for a specified range represents the number of determinations falling within the range, and f_c represents the number expected on the basis of the given $\overline{X}$ and of a σ of 14.7 km/sec. (The present authors are greatly indebted to Dr. E. Q. Adams who pointed out that the procedure of the first printing, wherein f_o was taken as a sum of weights, was in error, and who has supplied the material here presented).

Range of c' in km/sec.	f_o	f_c	$(f_c - f_o)$	$\dfrac{(f_c - f_o)^2}{f_c}$
<741	3 ⎫	2.25 ⎫	− 0.75 ⎫	0.25 ⎫
741–45	7 ⎬ 14	3.04 ⎬ 11.24	− 3.96 ⎬ −2.76	5.15 ⎬ 0.68
46–50	4 ⎭	5.95 ⎭	+ 1.95 ⎭	0.64 ⎭
51–55	8	10.42	+ 2.42	0.56
56–60	17	16.24	− 0.76	0.04
61–65	23	22.60	− 0.40	0.01
66–70	29	28.06	− 0.94	0.03
71–75	45	31.09	−13.91	6.23
76–80	40	30.73	− 9.27	2.80
81–85	17	27.11	+10.11	3.78
86–90	16	21.37	+ 5.37	1.35
91–95	10	14.99	+ 4.99	1.66
96–00	5 ⎫	9.39 ⎫	+ 4.39 ⎫	2.06 ⎫
801–05	2 ⎬ 14	5.27 ⎬ 19.14	+ 3.27 ⎬ +5.14	2.03 ⎬ 1.38
06–10	3	2.62	− 0.38	0.05
>810	4 ⎭	1.86 ⎭	− 2.14 ⎭	2.46 ⎭
	233	233		$\chi^2 = 29.10$ 18.52

For $\chi^2 = 29.10$ and $n' = 13$, $P\chi^2 = 0.005$. For $\chi^2 = 18.52$ and $n' = 8$, $P\chi^2 = 0.018$.

normal, the value computed for P_{χ^2} indicates a rather small probability, 0.005, that another similar set taken at random would deviate as much or more from a normal distribution. However, if the grouping, which is entirely arbitrary, is changed by collecting the three lowest and the four highest groups of the table into two larger groups, as indicated by

[1] Michelson, A. A., Pease, F. G., Pearson, F., *Astrophys. J.*, **82**, 56 (1935).

the brackets, a recognized procedure where the n's of adjacent groups are small, the computed value for P_{χ^2} is larger, about 0.018. On the other hand, Fig. 11, in which summations of weights rather than numbers of determinations are graphed, suggests that these low probabilities may indicate that the present distribution has a flatness (kurtosis), β_2, less than 3, as has Pearsons' Type VII distribution. Obviously, these measurements are much less normally distributed than are Birge's spectral line measurements. (Fig. 6 and Table II.)

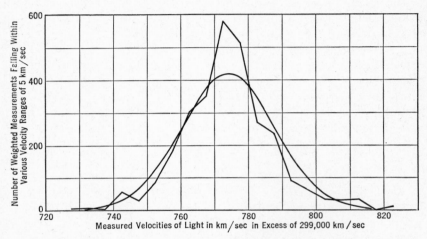

FIG. 11. Distribution of measurements of the velocity of light made by Michelson, Pease, and Pearson (see Table III) grouped for velocity intervals of 5 km/sec. The broken line represents actual measurements. The smooth curve represents the distribution expected had the measurements followed the normal law.

9. Summary. The methods for the quantitative evaluations of h, σ, p, and a are described in Eqs. 6 to 9.

A short method for computing a mean $\overline{X}$ and the precision index σ for a set of n readings consists in assuming an approximate mean, $\overline{X}'$, and then applying the two following equations:

$$\overline{X} = \overline{X}' + \frac{\Sigma(X - \overline{X}')}{n} \qquad [11]$$

$$\sigma^2 = \frac{\Sigma(X - \overline{X}')^2}{n} - \left[\frac{\Sigma(X - \overline{X}')}{n}\right]^2 \qquad [12]$$

Chauvenet's criterion, intended to eliminate from a set of readings the effect due to single readings exerting unduly large effects on the means, states that a reading should be rejected when it yields a deviation from the mean such that the probability of occurrence of deviations of that magnitude and greater is less than $1/2n$, where n is the number of readings. With $\tilde{x}$ as the limiting minimum deviation for rejection, the criterion takes the form

$$1 - P_{\tilde{x}} = 1 - \frac{h}{\sqrt{\pi}} \int_{-\tilde{x}}^{+\tilde{x}} e^{-h^2 x^2} \, dx = \frac{1}{2n} \qquad [14]$$

The limitation of the normal distribution law is discussed in some detail, but it is indicated that it is customary to assume that most sets of measurements follow that law and that a considerable superstructure of precision treatment of data has been built upon it.

Qualitative and quantitative tests for the goodness of fit of the normal distribution law are described. These included (1) superposing the best normal distribution curve, (2) plotting the ogive curve on ordinary cross-section and on probability paper, (3) computing skewness and flatness, and (4) applying the chi-square test. Chi square, χ^2, is given by

$$\chi^2 = \sum \frac{(f_o - f_c)^2}{f_c} \qquad [32]$$

of which f_o and f_c are observed and expected frequencies of occurrence of values as grouped about arbitrarily chosen mean values. With χ^2 computed, one seeks, from a table or from Fig. 10, a probability of occurrence, P_{χ^2}, of the given set of readings as a function of χ^2 and n' the number of groups of readings less the number of imposed conditions. A P_{χ^2} of 0.01 or more is usually considered satisfactory as a probability.

PROBLEMS

1. Find approximate values of p, a, σ, and $1/h$ for the data of Fig. 1, Chapter VI.

2. Given that the times recorded by 36 observers as the interval for a certain phenomenon were distributed as follows:

3 observers recorded 32.0 sec
7 " " 32.2 "
12 " " 32.3 "
6 " " 32.4 "
6 " " 32.5 "
1 " " 32.6 "
1 " " 33.0 "

Compute the mean, p, a, σ, and $1/h$. Should the last recorded observation be eliminated?

3. Plot the data of Problem 2 and draw on the same sheet the curve of the normal distribution law which has the same modulus of precision as that computed from the data.

4. Given that the distribution of diameters, D, about their mean, D_0, for a set of bearing balls, all of the same density, is

$$y_D = \frac{h_D}{\sqrt{\pi}} e^{-h_D{}^2(D-D_0)^2}$$

show that the distribution of their volumes, V, about the volume, V_0 of a ball whose diameter is D_0 is given to a first approximation by

$$y_V = \frac{h_V}{\sqrt{\pi}} \left(1 - \frac{2}{3}\frac{V-V_0}{V_0}\right) e^{-h_V{}^2(V-V_0)^2} \left(1 - \frac{2}{3}\frac{V-V_0}{V_0}\right)$$

of which h_V is defined by

$$h_V = \left[\frac{2}{9\pi V_0{}^2}\right]^{1/3} h_D$$

5. Plot curves like those of Figs. 6, 7, and 8 to represent the distribution of data given in Table I. What is your conclusion regarding the sensitivity of the various methods of plotting in showing variations of distribution curves from normal?

6. The mean annual temperatures of Pittsburgh reported by the U. S. Weather Bureau for the 71 years, 1872–1942, are

Ranges of Mean Annual Temperature in °F	Number of Years of Occurrence of Means Within the Specified Ranges
48.8–49.2	1
49.3–49.7	2
49.8–50.2	1
50.3–50.7	3
50.8–51.2	6
51.3–51.7	8
51.8–52.2	8
52.3–52.7	9
52.8–53.2	10
53.3–53.7	10
53.8–54.2	7
54.3–54.7	5
54.8–55.2	0
55.3–55.7	1

Make graphs of the data similar to those of Figs. 6 and 7. Determine values for the mean annual temperature and for p, σ, and $1/h$. Judged from the distribution given, what is the probability that the mean temperature of Pittsburgh for the coming year will fall between 49.5° F and 50.5° F? What are the limits of the smallest range of temperature within which that temperature has a 50% chance of occurring?

7. Using Fig. 10 and Birge's data as recorded in Table II, determine the values of σ and P_{χ^2} which apply.

CHAPTER VIII

MEANS AND PRECISION INDEXES OF UNEQUALLY WEIGHTED MEASUREMENTS

1. Introduction. In the preceding chapter, we derived expressions for the precision indexes, $(1/h)_x$, σ_x, a_x, and p_x, of a single X-reading chosen at random from a series of equally precise readings assumed to obey the normal distribution law. We found, among other things, that these indexes tell us the likelihood that a single reading will deviate from the mean of the series by a certain amount. Granted this, it now becomes desirable to know the precision indexes of the mean itself, i.e., the likelihood that the mean will deviate by a certain amount from the so-called grand mean, the mean of a series of similarly determined means. To know that an individual reading of a specified length has a probable error of 0.05 mm is worth while; to know that the mean of a series of length readings has a probable error of 0.002 mm is generally more important.

Some readings of a series may, because of conditions, be more reliable than others. It is then customary to assign weights to the individual readings. Usually such assigned weights are arbitrary, though not without reason. Often the assignments are in accord with some plan. If one reading is considered, roughly speaking, twice as reliable as a second, respective weights having the ratio 2 : 1 may be assigned; e.g., weights of 4 and 2, or of 1 and ½, etc. For a group of such readings, as for one of equally reliable readings, it is desirable to obtain the most probable mean and its precision indexes.

In this chapter we first derive an expression for the mean of a series of weighted measurements. The precision indexes of the individual weighted readings are then obtained, and their relationship to the arbitrary weights is pointed out. We next consider the mean, whether obtained from equally or unequally weighted readings, as a particular kind of weighted reading, and derive its precision indexes. A short method for computing means and precision indexes from unequally weighted readings is then presented. Finally, we consider the problem of combining several mean values of a quantity into a grand mean and its precision indexes, first for the case where the intermediate means are consistent, and then for the case where they are inconsistent.

189

2. The Mean of Weighted Single Observations of a Quantity. In what follows, we assume that a reading X_1 having a weight w_1 is equivalent to w_1 readings of unit weight whose mean is X_1. This does not exclude fractional weights, since weights are only relative; the question of what might be meant by 0.1 reading of unit weight is irrelevant. As will be shown, it is important to recognize that these w_1 readings are not individually assumed equal to X_1 and that only their average possesses that value.

Let X_1, X_2, $\cdots X_n$ be a series of measurements having weights w_1, w_2, $\cdots w_n$, respectively. By our assumption, this series is equivalent to a particular series having $(w_1 + w_2 + \cdots w_n)$ readings of equal precision. The mean of this new series, and hence also of the unequally weighted series is evidently

$$\overline{X} = \frac{w_1 X_1 + w_2 X_2 + \cdots w_n X_n}{w_1 + w_2 + \cdots w_n} = \frac{\Sigma w X}{\Sigma w} \qquad [1]$$

3. Precision Indexes of Weighted Single Observations. Let X_1, X_2, $\cdots X_n$ be a series of observations having known weights, w_1, w_2, $\cdots w_n$, but unknown moduli of precision, h_1, h_2, $\cdots h_n$. We again obtain an expression for the mean of this series, but this time by the method discussed on page 161, making use of the variable pseudo-mean, $\overline{X}''$. As in Chapter VI, we seek the $\overline{X}''$ possessing a maximum probability of occurrence for the observed data. Assuming a normal distribution wherein x_1, x_2, $\cdots x_n$ are the deviations from $\overline{X}''$ of X_1, X_2, $\cdots X_n$, measurements having least counts of Δx, we have

$$(\Delta^n P)_{1,2,3,\cdots n} = \Delta P_{x_1} \times \Delta P_{x_2} \times \cdots \Delta P_{x_n}$$

$$= \left(\frac{1}{\sqrt{\pi}}\right)^n (h_1 \times h_2 \times \cdots h_n) e^{-(h_1^2 x_1^2 + \cdots h_n^2 x_n^2)} (\Delta x)^n \quad [2]$$

$$= \text{a maximum}$$

or in logarithmic form

$$\ln (\Delta^n P)_{1,2,3,\cdots n} = -n \ln (\sqrt{\pi}) + \Sigma \ln h - (h_1^2 x_1^2 + \cdots h_n^2 x_n^2)$$

$$+ n \ln (\Delta x) \quad [3]$$

$$= \text{a maximum}$$

Differentiating with respect to $\overline{X}''$, we write

$$\frac{d}{d\overline{X}''} [\ln (\Delta^n P)] = -2 \left(h_1^2 x_1 \frac{dx_1}{d\overline{X}''} + \cdots h_n^2 x_n \frac{dx_n}{d\overline{X}''}\right) = 0 \qquad [4]$$

Since

$$\frac{dx_1}{d\overline{X}''} = \frac{dx_2}{d\overline{X}''} = \cdots = 1 \qquad [5]$$

we have as the condition for the maximum [1] probability of occurrence of the observations

$$h_1^2 x_1 + h_2^2 x_2 + \cdots h_n^2 x_n = 0 \qquad [6]$$

Representing the value of $\overline{X}''$, computed in accord with Eq. 6, by $\overline{X}$, we write

$$\Sigma h^2 x = \Sigma h^2 (X - \overline{X}) = \Sigma h^2 X - \overline{X} \Sigma h^2 = 0 \qquad [7]$$

or

$$\overline{X} = \frac{\Sigma h^2 X}{\Sigma h^2} \qquad [8]$$

Comparing Eqs. 1 and 8, remembering that the values of h are independent of each other, we find h^2 proportional to w, or

$$\frac{h_1}{h_2} = \sqrt{\frac{w_1}{w_2}} \qquad [9]$$

The relative precision indexes for the unequally weighted readings are therefore given by

$$\frac{\dfrac{1}{h_1}}{\dfrac{1}{h_2}} = \frac{p_1}{p_2} = \frac{a_1}{a_2} = \frac{\sigma_1}{\sigma_2} = \sqrt{\frac{w_2}{w_1}} \qquad [10]$$

The precision indexes of weighted single observations of a quantity vary inversely as the square roots of their weights. Letting h, in the further discussion, represent the modulus of precision for an observation arbitrarily assumed to have unit weight, we obtain from Eq. 9

$$\frac{1}{h_1} = \frac{\dfrac{1}{h}}{\sqrt{w_1}} \qquad [11]$$

$$\sigma_1 = \frac{\sigma}{\sqrt{w_1}} \qquad [12]$$

$$p_1 = \frac{p}{\sqrt{w_1}} \qquad [13]$$

[1] That Eq. 6 represents a maximum rather than a minimum is shown by the standard procedure of differentiating Eq. 4 to obtain $d^2/(d\overline{X}'')^2$, a quantity which is found to be essentially negative.

We may now assign absolute values to the precision indexes of the unequally weighted observations X_1, X_2, $\cdots X_n$. We merely replace the various h's of Eq. 3 by their equals as given by Eq. 11. There follow

$$\ln (\Delta^n P)_{1,2,\cdots n} = \tfrac{1}{2} \ln \frac{w_1 w_2 \cdots w_n}{\pi^n} + n \ln h - h^2 \Sigma w x^2 + n \ln (\Delta x) \quad [14]$$

$$= \text{a maximum}$$

$$\frac{d}{dh} [\ln (\Delta^n P)_{1,2,\cdots n}] = \frac{n}{h} - 2h\Sigma w x^2 = 0 \quad [15]$$

$$h^2 = \frac{n}{2\Sigma w x^2} \quad [16]$$

Hence, for the observation having unit weight,

$$\frac{1}{h_X} = \sqrt{\frac{2\Sigma w x^2}{n}} \quad [17]\,[1]$$

$$\sigma_X = \frac{1}{\sqrt{2}h} = \sqrt{\frac{\Sigma w x^2}{n}} \quad [18]\,[1]$$

and

$$p_X = 0.67\sigma = 0.67 \sqrt{\frac{\Sigma w x^2}{n}} \quad [19]\,[1]$$

By substitution in Eqs. 11 to 13, similar expressions follow for the precision indexes of other observations of different weight. Eqs. 17 to 19 differ significantly from the corresponding expressions derived in Chapter VII for observations all of which are of equal weight. In place of the Σw that one might offhand expect in the denominators of these equations, theory shows the presence of n. This is the evidence for the caution given above when stating that a reading X_1 with weight w_1 is not equivalent to w_1 identical readings X_1 all of unit weight. We may now illustrate the statement that reading X_1 with weight w_1 cannot be so considered. In Table I are presented three groups of readings. The first reading, 43, of group 1, with a weight of 5 is replaced in group 2, in accord with the faulty assumption, by five readings of 43, each with unit weight, and in group 3, in accord with the probable correct assumption, by five readings, each of unit weight, whose mean is 43. It is to be noted that these five vary among themselves to about the same extent as the remaining five which are assumed throughout to have unit weight. It is seen that the computed values for σ for groups 1 and 2

[1] See footnote on page 167.

are necessarily different, whereas those for groups 1 and 3 are essentially alike, in conformity with what theory suggests.

4. Precision Indexes of Means. If the reading X_1 with weight w_1 is equivalent to w_1 readings whose mean is X_1, then the inverse is also true: n readings of unit weight whose mean is $\overline{X}$ are equivalent to a

TABLE I

SHOWING THAT A READING X_1 WITH WEIGHT w_1 IS NOT EQUIVALENT TO w_1 READINGS EACH HAVING THE VALUE X_1

Group 1				Group 2				Group 3			
X	w	x	wx^2	X	w	x	wx^2	X	w	x	wx^2
				43	1	0.5	0.25	40	1	2.5	6.25
				43	1	0.5	0.25	43	1	0.5	0.25
43	5	0.5	1.25	43	1	0.5	0.25	45	1	2.5	6.25
				43	1	0.5	0.25	44	1	1.5	2.25
				43	1	0.5	0.25	43	1	0.5	0.25
39	1	3.5	12.25	39	1	3.5	12.25	39	1	3.5	12.25
44	1	1.5	2.25	44	1	1.5	2.25	44	1	1.5	2.25
42	1	0.5	0.25	42	1	0.5	0.25	42	1	0.5	0.25
45	1	2.5	6.25	45	1	2.5	6.25	45	1	2.5	6.25
40	1	2.5	6.25	40	1	2.5	6.25	40	1	2.5	6.25
$\Sigma wx^2 = 28.50$				28.50				42.50			
$\overline{X} = 42.5$				42.5				42.5			
$\sqrt{\dfrac{\Sigma wx^2}{n}} = \sigma = 2.2$				1.7				2.1			

single reading $\overline{X}$ whose weight is n. Hence, in view of Eqs. 18 and 19, the precision indexes of a mean obtained from n equally weighted readings are given by

$$\left(\frac{1}{h}\right)_{\overline{X}} = \frac{\left(\frac{1}{h}\right)_X}{\sqrt{n}} \qquad [20]\,[1]$$

$$\sigma_{\overline{X}} = \frac{\sigma_X}{\sqrt{n}} = \frac{\sqrt{\Sigma x^2}}{n} \qquad [21]\,[1]$$

$$p_{\overline{X}} = \frac{p_X}{\sqrt{n}} = 0.67\sigma_{\overline{X}} = 0.67\frac{\sqrt{\Sigma x^2}}{n}, \text{ etc.} \qquad [22]\,[1]$$

[1] See footnote on page 167.

where $(1/h)_X$, σ_X, etc., represent the precision indexes of an individual reading of unit weight.

For a mean, $\overline{X}$, obtained from unequally weighted readings, similar reasoning allows us to consider $\overline{X}$ as a single reading with the weight Σw.   Hence for this case,

$$\sigma_{\overline{X}} = \frac{\sigma_X}{\sqrt{\Sigma w}} = \sqrt{\frac{\Sigma wx^2}{n\Sigma w}} \qquad [23]\,{}^1$$

$$p_{\overline{X}} = \frac{p_X}{\sqrt{\Sigma w}} = 0.67\sigma_{\overline{X}} = 0.67\sqrt{\frac{\Sigma wx^2}{n\Sigma w}}\,,\text{ etc.} \qquad [24]\,{}^1$$

The probable error of the mean, $p_{\overline{X}}$, is the quantity which physicists generally accept as a measure of the accuracy of a reported result.   It predicts that of a great number of similarly determined means, just one-half should normally deviate from the grand mean by an amount greater than $p_{\overline{X}}$.

With weights assigned according to Eq. 10, it usually happens that the numbers taken proportional to $(1/p)^2$ turn out to be awkward.   In such cases, one uses rounded values for the w's with seldom more than two significant digits.   For example, with $p_1 : p_2 : p_3 : \cdots$ varying as $3 : 40 : 8 : \cdots$, we might well use $w_1 : w_2 : w_3 : \cdots$ varying as $1100 : 6 : 160 : \cdots$ rather than $1111.11 : 6.25 : 156.25$.   The departures from theory introduced thereby are not only very small but are quite justifiable in view of the general theory itself.

5. A Short Method for Computing Means and Precision Indexes from Weighted Observations.   Just as in equally precise measurements, much time and labor may be saved by using a short method for computing $\overline{X}$, $\sigma_{\overline{X}}$, etc., for weighted measurements.   Proceeding as on page 168, selecting $\overline{X}'$ as a convenient approximate mean, and representing $\overline{X} - \overline{X}'$ by Δ, we obtain

$$\overline{X} = \overline{X}' + \Delta = \overline{X}' + \frac{\Sigma w(X - \overline{X}')}{\Sigma w} \qquad [25]$$

and

$$\sigma_{\overline{X}}{}^2 = \frac{\Sigma wx^2}{n\Sigma w} = \frac{\Sigma w(X - \overline{X}')^2 - \Delta^2\Sigma w}{n\Sigma w} \qquad [26]$$

The computations are conveniently carried through in tabular form as in Table II.   As a check, the calculation of $\overline{X}$ and $\sigma_{\overline{X}}$ may be repeated, using a different value of $\overline{X}'$.

{}^1 See footnote on page 167.

TABLE II

ILLUSTRATING A SHORT METHOD FOR COMPUTING $\overline{X}$ AND $\sigma_{\overline{X}}$ FROM WEIGHTED DATA, TOGETHER WITH A CONVENIENT CHECK

X	f	Σw_x	$\overline{X}' = 128$			$\overline{X}' = 129$		
			$X - \overline{X}'$	$\Sigma w_x(X - \overline{X}')$	$\Sigma w_x(X - \overline{X}')^2$	$X - \overline{X}'$	$\Sigma w_x(X - \overline{X}')$	$\Sigma w_x(X - \overline{X}')^2$
125	2	2	-3	-6	18	-4	-8	32
126	3	5	-2	-10	20	-3	-15	45
127	9	18	-1	-18	18	-2	-36	72
128	15	45	0	0	0	-1	-45	45
129	11	35	1	35	35	0	0	0
130	7	12	2	24	48	1	12	12
131	2	2	3	6	18	2	4	8
132	1	1	4	4	16	3	3	9
	50	120		35	173		-85	223

$$\Delta = \tfrac{35}{120} = 0.29 \qquad\qquad \Delta = -\tfrac{85}{120} = -0.71$$
$$\overline{X} = 128 + 0.29 = 128.29 \qquad \overline{X} = 129 - 0.71 = 128.29$$
$$\sigma_{\overline{X}} = \sqrt{\frac{173 - 120(0.29)^2}{50 \times 120}} \qquad \sigma_{\overline{X}} = \sqrt{\frac{223 - 120(-0.71)^2}{50 \times 120}}$$
$$= 0.16 \qquad\qquad\qquad = 0.16$$
$$p_{\overline{X}} = 0.67 \times 0.16 = 0.11 \qquad p_{\overline{X}} = 0.11$$

The data of Table II are those of Table I, page 170, with arbitrarily assigned weights. For the equally weighted data, $\overline{X}$ and $\sigma_{\overline{X}}$ are found to be 128.3 and 0.21. Comparing these with the values from Table II, we note that the means are nearly identical but that the $\sigma_{\overline{X}}$ is appreciably smaller for the weighted data. This is a consequence of the arbitrarily greater weightings of measurements near the mean.

6. The Grand Mean and Its Precision Indexes. The concept of a grand mean arises when one wishes to combine, for instance, various determinations of the velocity of light, c, such as Michelson made with 8-sided, 12-sided, and 16-sided rotating mirrors of glass and of steel, in an attempt to determine the best value for c, and the probable error, p_c.

Let $\overline{X}_1, \overline{X}_2, \cdots \overline{X}_n$ be a set of intermediate means, corresponding in the above example to determinations of c made with (1) an 8-sided glass mirror, (2) a 12-sided steel mirror, etc. Let $p_{\overline{X}_1}, p_{\overline{X}_2}, \cdots p_{\overline{X}_n}$ be their probable errors. It is assumed that these intermediate means differ because of accidental errors only. As has been shown, the weights of these means vary inversely as the squares of their probable errors, and we may assign to them the arbitrary weights $k^2/p_{\bar{X}_1}^2$, $k^2/p_{\bar{X}_2}^2, \cdots$ $k^2/p_{\bar{X}_n}^2$, where k is a constant and may be interpreted as the probable error of a mean of unit weight. Further, as also shown above, $\bar{X}_1$, $\bar{X}_2, \cdots \bar{X}_n$ may be viewed as the means of $k^2/p_{\bar{X}_1}^2$, $k^2/p_{\bar{X}_2}^2, \cdots k^2/p_{\bar{X}_n}^2$ individual measurements, all of the same precision. With this understanding, Eqs. 1 and 24 may be used to obtain the desired mean and its probable error. They yield

$$\bar{\bar{X}} = \frac{\Sigma w \bar{X}}{\Sigma w} = \frac{\Sigma \left(\bar{X} \dfrac{k^2}{p_{\bar{X}}^2} \right)}{\Sigma \dfrac{k^2}{p_{\bar{X}}^2}} \qquad [27]$$

and

$$p_{\bar{\bar{X}}} = \frac{p_{\bar{X}}}{\sqrt{\Sigma w}} = \frac{k}{\sqrt{\Sigma \dfrac{k^2}{p_{\bar{X}}^2}}} = \frac{1}{\sqrt{\Sigma \dfrac{1}{p_{\bar{X}}^2}}} \qquad [28]$$

It is seen that $p_{\bar{\bar{X}}}$ is smaller than the probable error of any of the intermediate means.

In illustration, where (10.0 ± 0.2) gm, (10.2 ± 0.5) gm, and (9.9 ± 0.4) gm are the intermediate means, we have, corresponding to an arbitrary selection of 4 gm^2 for k^2, the following results:

$\bar{X}$	$p_{\bar{X}}$	$\dfrac{k^2}{p_{\bar{X}}^2}$	$\bar{X}\dfrac{k^2}{p_{\bar{X}}^2}$
10.0 gm	0.2 gm	100	1000.0 gm
10.2	0.5	16	163.2
9.9	0.4	25	247.5
		141	1410.7 gm

$$\bar{\bar{X}} = \frac{1410.7 \text{ gm}}{141} = 10.00 \text{ gm}$$

$$p_{\bar{\bar{X}}} = \frac{2 \text{ gm}}{\sqrt{141}} = 0.17 \text{ gm}$$

7. The Precision Index of a Precision Index. In reporting a precision index, a question of concern is that of the extent to which it should be expressed. Should the number of significant digits be one, two, three, or more, or should it vary with the case at hand? A common-sense answer will usually suffice, and without doubt the number of digits depends on the case at hand. Obviously when n is large, more confidence may be given to derived values for p and σ than when n is small, but this rule is only roughly comparative. It would be highly gratifying, however, to have a rule based on theoretical considerations if possible which is universally applicable.

One rule [1] states that the standard deviation of σ itself is given approximately by

$$\sigma_\sigma = \frac{\sigma}{\sqrt{2(n-1)}} \qquad [29]$$

For example, if $n = 9$, $1/\sqrt{2(n-1)} = \frac{1}{4}$ and therefore one need record not more than two figures in σ and, at that, the second figure is barely significant. With $n = 9$ and the first digit 8 or 9, not more than one digit is needed. Similarly for probable errors, the rule states that the probable error of p is approximately given by

$$p_p = \frac{2p}{3\sqrt{2(n-1)}} \qquad [30]$$

More than two significant digits are rarely needed for the proper expression of a probable error. Where $n = 100$, $2/3\sqrt{2(n-1)}$ approximates $1/14$. Depending, in this instance, on whether the first digit of p is greater than or less than 2, we may well limit the expression of p to only two or to only three digits with the last rounded to 0 or to 5; e.g., $p = 0.42$ or $p = 0.115$.

8. Internal versus External Consistency. It has been mentioned, but should be emphasized here, that when we consider the mean to be the most probable value obtainable from a set of measurements, we make the principal assumptions (1) that the measurements are normally distributed, and (2) that they deviate from the true value because of accidental errors only. The first assumption is generally fulfilled to a moderate degree and in any case can be tested. The second, however, is often invalid; a constant error in theory, apparatus, procedure, etc., may cause the mean to deviate from the true value by many times its probable error. It is impossible to detect such a constant error from the frequency distribution of a single set of measurements, or of a set of means of measurements taken under essentially identical conditions.

For the cases thus far discussed, we can proceed only as we have and consider all errors accidental. When, however, we wish to combine or compare the results of several workers, using different methods, apparatus, etc., we frequently find evidence for the occurrence of constant

[1] Rossini and Deming, *J. Wash. Acad. Sci.*, **29**, 416 (1939).

errors. Such discrepancies, for example, are shown in Bleakney's [1] tabulation, presented in part in Table III, of the ionization potentials of molecular hydrogen as determined by various observers.

TABLE III

A SET OF INCONSISTENT MEAN VALUES FOR THE H_2 IONIZATION POTENTIAL AS MEASURED BY VARIOUS OBSERVERS

(16.5 ± 0.5) volts	(15.4 ± 0.1) volts
(17.1 ± 0.2)	(15.6 ± 0.1)
(15.6 ± 0.1)	(15.37 ± 0.03)

These values differ from each other much more than their probable errors indicate that they should. Constant errors must have entered into some or possibly all of the determinations. It would be incorrect to combine these means into a grand mean and compute its probable error by Eqs. 27 and 28. We are thus faced with two problems: (1) How may inconsistent means be combined best into a grand mean and its probable error determined? (2) When is a set of means to be considered inconsistent rather than consistent?

9. Testing Intermediate Means for Consistency. Several tests for consistency of means have been proposed, some more arbitrary than others. Thus, for thermochemical measurements, Rossini and Deming [2] propose that two means be considered inconsistent when they differ by more than twice the sum of their standard deviations. A second test for inconsistency compares the difference between two means, $\overline{X}_2 - \overline{X}_1$, with the standard deviation, σ, of that difference; and if the probability of occurrence of a difference as great as $\overline{X}_2 - \overline{X}_1$ on the basis of the computed σ is found to be less than 0.01, the means are declared inconsistent. The procedure follows. It can be shown (Chap. IX) that the standard deviation of the difference of two means of normally distributed sets of measurements is related to the standard deviations of the means by the equation

$$\sigma_{(\overline{X}_2 - \overline{X}_1)} = \sqrt{\sigma_{\overline{X}_1}{}^2 + \sigma_{\overline{X}_2}{}^2} \qquad [31]$$

With the $\sigma_{(\overline{X}_2 - \overline{X}_1)}$ determined, the corresponding hx is then obtained using the relation

$$hx = \frac{\overline{X}_2 - \overline{X}_1}{\sqrt{2}\sigma_{(\overline{X}_2 - \overline{X}_1)}} = \frac{\overline{X}_2 - \overline{X}_1}{\sqrt{2(\sigma_{\overline{X}_1}{}^2 + \sigma_{\overline{X}_2}{}^2)}} \qquad [32]$$

Next in Table II, Appendix 2, one seeks the probability of occurrence of an hx as great as that just computed or greater. The decision follows.

---

[1] Bleakney, W., *Phys. Rev.*, **40**, 497 (1932).

[2] Rossini and Deming, op. cit., p. 416.

If the computed hx turns out to be greater than 1.83, the means are to be declared inconsistent on this basis.

A third criterion of inconsistency, proposed by Birge,[1] consists in assigning the arbitrary weights $k^2/p_{\overline{X}_1}{}^2$, $k^2/p_{\overline{X}_2}{}^2$, etc., to the set of n means and calculating the grand mean by Eq. 27. Then, on the basis of internal consistency, the probable error of a mean of unit weight is

$$p_{\text{internal}} = k \qquad [33]$$

and on the basis of external consistency, applying Eq. 19, it is

$$p_{\text{external}} = 0.67 \sqrt{\frac{\Sigma w(X - \overline{\overline{X}})^2}{n}} \qquad [34]\,^2$$

Hence, if the set of means is consistent, the ratio

$$\frac{p_{\text{external}}}{p_{\text{internal}}} = 0.67 \sqrt{\frac{\Sigma w(X - \overline{\overline{X}})^2}{nk^2}} \qquad [35]$$

should equal unity except for statistical fluctuations. Birge assumes that the ratio $p_{\text{external}}/p_{\text{internal}}$ is normally distributed about the mean value, 1, with the modulus of precision $\sqrt{n}$. The probability of occurrence of an observed deviation from unity may then be found by calculating the corresponding value of hx

$$hx = \sqrt{n}\left(\frac{p_{\text{external}}}{p_{\text{internal}}} - 1\right) \qquad [36]$$

and using Table II, Appendix 2. If this probability is less than 0.01, i.e., $hx > 1.83$, the means are considered inconsistent.

Because of the assumptions made in deriving Eqs. 32 and 36, the probability values obtained do not have the exact significance that has been given them. Nevertheless the tests are useful for detecting inconsistencies in values obtained by different observers.

10. Combining Inconsistent Means. When a set of means is not consistent, we may assume, for lack of anything better, that the constant errors which enter to cause the means to deviate from the true value are distributed normally. We then have as alternate methods for finding $\overline{\overline{X}}$: (1) averaging the intermediate means without regard to weights or probable errors; (2) assigning arbitrary weights to the intermediate means, perhaps on the basis of experience with the customary accuracy of the observers involved, and finding $\overline{\overline{X}}$ by applying Eq. 1; or (3)

[1] Birge, R. T., *Phys. Rev.*, **40**, 213–224 (1932).
[2] See footnote on page 167.

assigning weights proportional to the inverse squares of the reported probable errors and calculating $\overline{X}$ by Eq. 27. This is equivalent to assuming that a worker who obtains a great number of values, or very consistent ones, is more likely to eliminate constant errors than a worker whose values are fewer or less consistent. Generally method (2) or (3) is preferable to (1).

Regardless of which of the three methods above is used for calculating $\overline{X}$, Eq. 28 should not be used for finding $p_{\overline{X}}$, since, because of constant errors, $\overline{\overline{X}}$ is not as accurate as this result would indicate. Instead, we should consider the intermediate means to be elementary observations, weighted in accord with the method used in obtaining $\overline{\overline{X}}$, and calculate $p_{\overline{X}}$ by applying Eq. 24. Calculating the grand mean and probable error for the values of Table III by Eqs. 27 and 24 yields (15.44 ± 0.07) volts. This indicates the accuracy with which we know the H_2 ionization potential better than the value obtained by using Eqs. 27 and 28, namely (15.437 ± 0.027) volts.

11. Why Inconsistent Means? Several reasons for inconsistent means may be mentioned. In what follows we shall ignore errors that are purely computational.

(*a*) *Errors of Construction of Instruments.* These errors are numerous. Consider the spectrometer. The angle scale may be irregular, it may be mounted eccentrically with respect to the main vertical axis, it may be mounted with its normal at an angle with the main vertical axis. The collimator and the telescope may not point perpendicular to or toward the main axis. Other constructional faults are more or less obvious.

(*b*) *Errors of Experimental Procedure.* Readings may not be taken in a truly chance order. Particularly, if *y*-values are determined for a sequence of *x*-values increasing or decreasing consistently in magnitude, possibilities for a gradual instrumental or other drift may not be observed though observable. A one-sided scale illumination may be used. Where cross-hair settings are made, this may be a source of considerable error. Readings may be taken under conditions where an observer making settings is cognizant of the general trend of the readings taken. Under such conditions succeeding settings will not be independent. It is rather difficult for one making settings to follow a setting that he believes low, for instance, in consequence of readings reported, with a setting that is not biased in the opposite direction. A maker's scale may be assumed correct. Temperature variations may be ignored. Faulty instrumental construction may be ignored. Where small electrical emf's and small variations are important, constructional materials and designs become vital. Other procedure errors are more or less obvious.

(c) *Errors of Statistical Treatment.* One may attempt to determine a precision index for a case where the least count is of the same order of magnitude as the precision index to be determined. One may easily obtain an exalted view of one's own precision under these circumstances. One may assume an erroneous distribution of variations of observed values from the mean. Generally the apparent inconsistencies between means will be lessened rather than increased on this score. One may fail to assign weights properly to the various readings forming a group. A single reading whose weight is given as zero by the application of Chauvenet's criterion may, if included, yield a mean to which but little weight may be given. One may ignore or treat incorrectly the contributions of certain factors in determining a precision index for a mean. See Chapter IX, which concerns the propagation of precision indexes.

(d) *Errors of Theory.* Difficulties arise here particularly when some one or more constants enter in the production of widely differing phenomena. The case is well illustrated in Chapter X in the discussion of the present dilemma with regard to the constants of atomic physics. Errors of theory are not always easy to correct.

(e) *Errors of Unsuspected Sources.* These are the errors that remain after all other imagined probable sources of error are given consideration. With discovery, an error belonging to this group is transferred at once to one of the above groups.

12. Summary. When combining readings certain of which are believed more reliable than others, the resultant mean is believed improved if relative weights are assigned to the individual readings. Specifically, if p_1 and p_2 are the probable errors of two observations, X_1 and X_2, the relative weights are given by

$$\frac{w_1}{w_2} = \frac{p_2^{\,2}}{p_1^{\,2}} \qquad [10]$$

and the mean of the series of observations is found to be

$$\overline{X} = \frac{\Sigma wX}{\Sigma w} \qquad [1]$$

The probable error of the mean of n observations is given by

$$p_{\overline{X}} = \frac{p_X}{\sqrt{n}} \qquad [22]$$

if all the observations are equally precise, or by

$$p_{\bar{X}} = \frac{p_X}{\sqrt{\Sigma w}} = 0.67 \sqrt{\frac{\Sigma w x^2}{n \Sigma w}} \qquad [24]\,{}^{1}$$

where $x = X - \bar{X}$, if the observations are unequal in weight.

Generally it is more convenient to calculate $\bar{X}$ and $\sigma_{\bar{X}}$ by the equations

$$\bar{X} = \bar{X}' + \Delta = \frac{\Sigma w(X - \bar{X}')}{\Sigma w} \qquad [25]$$

and

$$\sigma_{\bar{X}}{}^2 = \frac{\Sigma w(X - \bar{X}')^2 - \Delta^2 \Sigma w}{n \Sigma w} \qquad [26]$$

where $\bar{X}'$ is a convenient, assumed, approximate mean and $\Delta = \bar{X} - \bar{X}'$, than it is to use the defining equations.

The probable error of a calculated probable error is approximately

$$p_p = \frac{2p}{3\sqrt{2(n-1)}} \qquad [30]$$

A group of means with known probable errors may be combined into a grand mean, $\bar{\bar{X}}$, and its probable error computed by the equations

$$\bar{\bar{X}} = \frac{\Sigma\left(\bar{X}\,\dfrac{k^2}{p_{\bar{X}}{}^2}\right)}{\displaystyle\sum \frac{k^2}{p_{\bar{X}}{}^2}} \qquad [27]$$

and

$$p_{\bar{X}} = \frac{k}{\sqrt{\displaystyle\sum \frac{k^2}{p_{\bar{X}}{}^2}}} = \frac{1}{\sqrt{\displaystyle\sum \frac{1}{p_{\bar{X}}{}^2}}} \qquad [28]$$

where k is an arbitrary constant, if the intermediate means are consistent with each other. If they are inconsistent, $\bar{X}$ may be obtained by averaging without regard to probable errors or, preferably, by weighting arbitrarily or inversely as the squares of the probable errors and using Eq. 1 or Eq. 27. The probable error of the grand mean of a set of inconsistent means should be obtained by applying Eq. 24.

To test two independently obtained means for consistency, we may calculate h_x by Eq. 32 or Eq. 36. If, roughly, $h_x > 1.83$, the means may be considered inconsistent.

---

[1] See footnote on page 167.

PROBLEMS

1. Given the intermediate means:

10.01 ± 0.25 gm	9.98 ± 0.04 gm
10.00 ± 0.12	9.97 ± 0.06
9.99 ± 0.05	9.96 ± 0.15

Find the best grand mean and its probable error.

2. Show that if 400 measurements of equal precision are divided into five groups, of say 40, 60, 80, 100, and 120 readings, selected at random, to yield intermediate means with varying probable errors, and these are then combined to yield a grand mean for the whole group with a probable error determined by the method outlined, the results will be the same as those obtained by treating the 400 measurements as a single group.

3. Beattie,[1] summarizing the values obtained for the ice point on the Kelvin scale, gives the following for the measurements reported in 1937 and before. On the basis of these data, what is the expected value of the ice point? First treat all as belonging to a single group and then second as belonging to two separate groups.

Gas Used	Method	No. of Points	T
He	α_v	21	$273.176°$ K
He	α_p	10	.157
H_2	α_v	19	.139
H_2	α_p	8	.131
N_2	α_v	27	.138
N_2	α_p	15	.143
Ne	α_v	4	.212
Ne	α_p	4	.129

4. In Bearden's paper "A Determination of e/m from the Refraction of X-Rays in a Diamond Prism" (*Phys. Rev.*, **54**, 698 (1938)), there is given, in Table I, a set of experimental values for δ, i.e., $1 - \mu$, where μ is the index of refraction. In Fig. 4 of that paper there are given the weighted mean values of e/m as obtained by various workers, together with their probable errors. Find (1) the mean of the δ's given in Table I, together with its precision indexes, and (2) the weighted mean value of e/m, taking into account all values plotted in Fig. 4 of the paper, together with its probable error.

[1] Beattie, James A., in *Temperature—Its Measurement and Control in Science and Industry*, p. 83, New York, Reinhold Publishing Corporation, 1941.

5. Dunnington [1] has given the following summary of e/m_0 measurements for the electron. Compute the weighted mean and its probable error.

Experimenter	Date	Method	$10^{-7} e/m_0$ emu	$10^{-3} p$ emu
BOUND ELECTRON OR SPECTROSCOPIC GROUP				
Houston	1927	Fine structure H^1—He^4	1.7607	10
Kinsler and Houston	1934	Zeeman effect	1.7571	7
Shane and Spedding	1935	Fine structure H^1—H^2	1.7582	4
Williams	1938	"	1.7580	4
Houston	1938	"	1.7593	5
FREE ELECTRON GROUP				
Perry and Chaffee	1930	Linear acceleration	1.7610	10
Kirchner	1932	"	1.7590	9
Dunnington	1937	Magnetic deflection	1.7597	4
Shaw	1938	Crossed fields	1.7581	13
Bearden	1938	X-ray refraction	1.7600	3

[1] Dunnington, F. G., *Rev. Modern Phys.*, **11**, 65 (1939).

CHAPTER IX

THE PROPAGATION OF PRECISION INDEXES

1. Introduction. In Chapter VI it was shown that the arithmetic mean of a series of measurements is the "best" value of the quantity measured, and in Chapters VII and VIII methods of obtaining the precision indexes of such measurements and means were described. In a great number of cases, however, the quantity sought cannot be measured directly but must be calculated from the means of two or more other directly measured quantities. Thus, we have

(a) a length which is obtained by subtracting one position reading from another;

(b) the specific heat, c, of the material of a body which cools by radiation only, in vacuo, in accord with the equation

$$c = \frac{dQ/dt}{mdT/dt} \qquad [1]$$

where m, dQ/dt, and dT/dt are, in order, the mass of the body, its rate of loss of energy by radiation, and its rate of cooling;

(c) the computed first radiation constant, σ (often called the Stefan-Boltzmann constant), as obtained from the equation

$$\sigma = \frac{2\pi^5 k^4}{15h^3 c^2} \qquad [2]$$

where k, h, and c are, in order, the Boltzmann atomic constant, the Planck constant, and the velocity of light in free space; and

(d) the index of refraction, n, of the glass of a prism for a particular wavelength of light, obtained with the aid of a spectrometer, using the equation

$$n = \frac{\sin\dfrac{A + D}{2}}{\sin\dfrac{A}{2}} \qquad [3]$$

where A and D are the angle of the prism and the minimum deviation produced by the prism for the particular wavelength of light used.

205

It is, of course, just as desirable to know the reliability of such indirectly measured quantities as of the directly measured ones previously discussed.

Evidently the precision indexes of a calculated quantity depend on the indexes of the measured quantities of which it is a function. Their calculation, given the means and the precision indexes of the measured quantities, is based on the following theory of the propagation of precision indexes.

In this chapter we shall consider how to determine the precision indexes of an indirectly measured quantity, U, in terms of the directly measured quantities $\bar{X}$ and $\bar{Y}$ and their indexes, first for special cases such as those involving sums, products, etc., and finally for the general case where U is any function of $\bar{X}$ and $\bar{Y}$. The application of the principle of the propagation of precision indexes to the problem of designing experiments is also discussed.

2. Cases Involving a Sum or Difference. Let

$$U = \bar{X} + \bar{Y} \tag{4}$$

where $\bar{X}$ and $\bar{Y}$ are the means of two separate sets of readings, with probable errors $p_{\bar{X}}$ and $p_{\bar{Y}}$. We assume that each of the two sets involved the same number of readings, say 20 or 50, with precisions such as to give the resultant values of $p_{\bar{X}}$ and $p_{\bar{Y}}$. Whether or not the actual sets of observations involved equal numbers of readings is immaterial. All that is necessary is to be assured that the assumed sets are equivalent to the actual sets.

With the pairing done at random, let the assumed individual X and Y readings be paired off to give (X_1, Y_1), (X_2, Y_2), etc. We may then write, where u_1, x_1, y_1, etc., are deviations from the means U, $\bar{X}$, and $\bar{Y}$

$$U_1 = \bar{U} + u_1 = X_1 + Y_1 = \bar{X} + x_1 + \bar{Y} + y_1$$
$$U_2 = \bar{U} + u_2 = X_2 + Y_2 = \bar{X} + x_2 + \bar{Y} + y_2, \text{ etc.} \tag{5}$$

In view of Eq. 4, these may be rewritten as

$$u_1 = x_1 + y_1$$
$$u_2 = x_2 + y_2, \text{ etc.} \tag{6}$$

By definition

$$\sigma_U{}^2 = \sum \frac{u^2}{n^2} \tag{7}^1$$

However,

$$\Sigma u^2 = \Sigma x^2 + 2\Sigma xy + \Sigma y^2 \tag{8}$$

---

[1] See footnote on page 167.

of which for the normal case we set

$$2\Sigma xy = 0 \tag{9}$$

because any particular product xy is as likely to be positive as negative and the summation on that account will tend toward zero. It follows that

$$\sigma_{\bar{U}} = \sqrt{\sigma_{\bar{X}}^2 + \sigma_{\bar{Y}}^2} \tag{10}$$

$$p_{\bar{U}} = \sqrt{p_{\bar{X}}^2 + p_{\bar{Y}}^2} \tag{11}$$

and similarly for the other precision indexes.

The probable error of a sum is less than the sum of the probable errors of the components. Rather, it is the square root of the sum of the squared probable errors of the components.

It is evident that where $\bar{U} = \bar{X} - \bar{Y}$, the equation corresponding to Eq. 8 will be

$$\Sigma u^2 = \Sigma x^2 - 2\Sigma xy + \Sigma y^2 \tag{8a}$$

and that the final expressions for $\sigma_{\bar{U}}$ and $p_{\bar{U}}$ will be identical with Eqs. 10 and 11.

3. Cases Involving a Product or a Quotient. Let

$$\bar{U} = \bar{X}\bar{Y} \tag{12}$$

Then, with the same assumptions as were made in the preceding section, we obtain

$$U_1 = X_1 Y_1, \text{ etc.} \tag{13}$$

$$\bar{U} + u_1 = (\bar{X} + x_1)(\bar{Y} + y_1) = \bar{X}\bar{Y} + x_1\bar{Y} + y_1\bar{X} + x_1y_1, \text{ etc.} \tag{14}$$

and, since the product x_1y_1 is of the second order in comparison with the other terms

$$u_1 = x_1\bar{Y} + y_1\bar{X}, \text{ etc.} \tag{15}$$

and

$$\Sigma u^2 = \bar{Y}^2\Sigma x^2 + 2\bar{X}\bar{Y}\Sigma xy + \bar{X}^2\Sigma y^2 \tag{16}$$

As before,

$$\Sigma xy = 0 \tag{17}$$

so that

$$\sigma_{\bar{U}}^2 = \frac{\Sigma u^2}{n^2} = \frac{\bar{Y}^2\Sigma x^2}{n^2} + \frac{\bar{X}^2\Sigma y^2}{n^2} \tag{18}$$

$$= \bar{Y}^2\sigma_{\bar{X}}^2 + \bar{X}^2\sigma_{\bar{Y}}^2$$

and finally

$$\frac{\sigma_{\bar{U}}^2}{\bar{U}^2} = \frac{\sigma_{\bar{X}}^2}{\bar{X}^2} + \frac{\sigma_{\bar{Y}}^2}{\bar{Y}^2} \tag{19}$$

and

$$\frac{p_U^2}{U^2} = \frac{p_X^2}{X^2} + \frac{p_Y^2}{Y^2} \tag{20}$$

Following a procedure very similar to the above, it is not difficult to show that for the case of a quotient, where

$$U = \frac{\overline{X}}{\overline{Y}} \tag{12a}$$

the expressions obtained for σ_U and p_U are exactly those of Eqs. 19 and 20. The proof of this fact is the subject of one of the problems at the end of the chapter.

4. Cases Involving Multiplying Constants and Constant Powers. Let

$$U = A\overline{X}^\alpha \tag{21}$$

On the basis of the assumptions made in the previous two sections, we obtain in order

$$U_1 = AX_1^\alpha, \text{ etc.} \tag{22}$$

$$\overline{U} + u_1 = A(\overline{X} + x_1)^\alpha, \text{ etc.} \tag{23}$$

$$u_1 = A\alpha x_1 \overline{X}^{\alpha-1}, \text{ etc.} \tag{24}$$

and

$$\Sigma u^2 = A^2\alpha^2\overline{X}^{2\alpha-2}\Sigma x^2 = \frac{\alpha^2\overline{U}^2}{\overline{X}^2}\Sigma x^2 \tag{25}$$

whence

$$\frac{\sigma_U}{U} = \alpha\frac{\sigma_X}{X} \tag{26}$$

and

$$\frac{p_U}{U} = \alpha\frac{p_X}{X} \tag{27}$$

Note that the α in Eqs. 26 and 27 is the square root of α^2, and hence may always be taken as positive, regardless of the sign of α in Eq. 21.

5. The General Case. Let

$$\overline{U} = f(\overline{X}, \overline{Y}) \tag{28}$$

Applying Taylor's expansion and making the assumptions of the previous sections, we obtain, evaluating the partial derivatives at $U = \overline{U}$

$$\overline{U} + u_1 = f(\overline{X} + x_1, \overline{Y} + y_1)$$

$$= f(\overline{X}, \overline{Y}) + \left(\frac{\partial U}{\partial X}\right) x_1 + \left(\frac{\partial U}{\partial Y}\right) y_1 + \cdots \qquad [29]$$

$$u_1 = \left(\frac{\partial U}{\partial X}\right) x_1 + \left(\frac{\partial U}{\partial X}\right) y_1 + \cdots \qquad [30]$$

$$\Sigma u^2 = \left(\frac{\partial U}{\partial X}\right)^2 \Sigma x^2 + 2\left(\frac{\partial U}{\partial X}\right)\left(\frac{\partial U}{\partial Y}\right) \Sigma xy + \left(\frac{\partial U}{\partial Y}\right)^2 \Sigma y^2 \cdots \qquad [31]$$

$$\Sigma xy = 0 \qquad [17]$$

so that

$$\sigma_{\overline{U}}^2 = \left(\frac{\partial U}{\partial X}\right)^2 \sigma_{\overline{X}}^2 + \left(\frac{\partial U}{\partial Y}\right)^2 \sigma_{\overline{Y}}^2 \qquad [32]$$

and

$$p_{\overline{U}}^2 = \left(\frac{\partial U}{\partial X}\right)^2 p_{\overline{X}}^2 + \left(\frac{\partial U}{\partial Y}\right)^2 p_{\overline{Y}}^2 \qquad [33]$$

Obviously, Eqs. 32 and 33 apply to the special cases discussed above.

6. Solutions of Illustrative Problems. (a) With what precision may the sine of an angle in the neighborhood of 75° be determined when the probable error of the angle measurement is 0.02°?

Solution:

$$\overline{U} = \sin \overline{X} \qquad [34]$$

$$p_{\overline{U}} = \left(\frac{\partial U}{\partial X}\right) p_{\overline{X}} \qquad [35]$$

$$p_{\overline{U}} = (\cos 75°) \times 0.02° \times \frac{1 \text{ radian}}{57.3°} = 0.26 \frac{0.02}{57} = 0.00009 \quad [36]^{[1]}$$

(b) What is the computed first radiation constant and its probable error, using the relation

$$\sigma = \frac{2\pi^5 k^4}{15 h^3 c^2} \qquad [2]$$

and the following values for k, h, and c?

$$k = 1.3803 \times 10^{-16} \ (1 \pm 0.00023) \ \text{erg/(molecule } K°)$$

$$h = 6.6283 \times 10^{-27} \ (1 \pm 0.00013) \ \text{erg sec}$$

$$c = 2.99776 \times 10^{10} \ (1 \pm 0.000013) \ \text{cm/sec}$$

---

[1] That the radian is a natural unit for the sine of an angle and for its probable error as well as for the angle itself is generally ignored. That it may be so considered seems supported by the well-known expansion

$$\sin \theta = \theta - \theta^3/3! + \theta^5/5! - \cdots$$

Solution:

Applying Eq. 33, one obtains

$$p_\sigma{}^2 = \left(\frac{\partial \sigma}{\partial k}\right)^2 p_k{}^2 + \left(\frac{\partial \sigma}{\partial h}\right)^2 p_h{}^2 + \left(\frac{\partial \sigma}{\partial c}\right)^2 p_c{}^2$$

$$= \left(\frac{4\sigma}{k}\right)^2 p_k{}^2 + \left(\frac{3\sigma}{h}\right)^2 p_h{}^2 + \left(\frac{2\sigma}{c}\right)^2 p_c{}^2 \tag{37}$$

$$\frac{p_\sigma{}^2}{\sigma^2} = 16\frac{p_k{}^2}{k^2} + 9\frac{p_h{}^2}{h^2} + 4\frac{p_c{}^2}{c^2}$$

$$= 16(0.00023)^2 + 9(0.00013)^2 + 4(0.000013)^2 \tag{38}$$

$$p_\sigma = 0.0010\sigma \tag{39}$$

and the constant, after its value has been separately determined, may be reported as

$$\sigma = 5.660 \times 10^{-5}\ (1 \pm 0.0010)\ \text{erg}/(\text{cm}^2\ \text{sec}\ K^{\circ 4}) \tag{40}$$

7. Cases Where the Precision Indexes of the Component Quantities Are Not Independent. Any propagation equation will yield incorrect results unless the directly observed precision indexes are truly independent. Special care should be taken when using one of the special-case equations. Thus, if

$$\overline{U} = 2\overline{X} \tag{41}$$

we may find $p_{\overline{U}}$ correctly by Eq. 27 on the basis that $\overline{U} = A\overline{X}^\alpha$ with $A = 2$ and $\alpha = 1$. Then

$$p_{\overline{U}} = \frac{\overline{U}}{\overline{X}}\,p_{\overline{X}} = 2p_{\overline{X}} \tag{42}$$

If, however, we use Eq. 11 assuming $\overline{U} = \overline{X} + \overline{Y}$ and that $X_1 = Y_1$, $X_2 = Y_2$, etc., we obtain

$$p_{\overline{U}} = \sqrt{p_{\overline{X}}{}^2 + p_{\overline{X}}{}^2} = \sqrt{2}p_{\overline{X}} \tag{43}$$

which is too small by the factor $\sqrt{2}$. This error arises in accepting the assumption, made during the derivation of Eq. 11, that the precision indexes of $\overline{X}$ and $\overline{Y}$ are independent and that therefore Σxy is negligibly small or zero. However, the assumption of independency is not justified here and Σxy cannot be set equal to zero.

Similarly, to find $p_{\overline{U}}$ when $\overline{U} = \overline{X}^2$, we use Eq. 27 on the basis $\overline{U} = A\overline{X}^\alpha$ with $A = 1$ and $\alpha = 2$, and not Eq. 20 on the assumption that $\overline{U} = \overline{X}\overline{Y}$ where $\overline{X} = \overline{Y}$. Simple cases such as these can usually be handled without difficulty if the general propagation law, Eq. 32 or

Eq. 33, is applied, but they do indicate how difficulties arise when the component precision indexes for $\overline{X}$, $\overline{Y}$, etc., are not independent.

A somewhat more complex case is illustrated in Eq. 3. If one views the quantity n as the simple ratio of two measured quantities and attempts to apply Eq. 20, he will neglect the fact that the numerator and denominator are not independent. The correct procedure for this case is the subject of one of the problems at the end of the chapter.

A still more complex case cited by Birge [1] is that of finding the precision index of the Sackur-Tetrode constant, S_0, as defined by

$$S_0 = R_0 \ln \frac{(2\pi k)^{3/2} e_0^{5/2}}{h^3 N_0^{5/2}} \qquad [44]$$

of which R_0, k, e_0, h, and N_0 represent, in order, the ideal gas constant, the Boltzmann atomic constant, the base of natural logarithms, the Planck constant, and the Avogadro number. Actually, not one of the terms on the right-hand side of the equation is independent of the others. Thus,

(1) $$R_0 = \frac{v_n A_n}{T_0 J_{15}} \qquad [45]$$

where v_n, A_n, T_0, and J_{15}, representing respectively the molal volume of an ideal gas under standard conditions, the standard atmosphere, the ice-point, and the mechanical equivalent of heat, are independently measured,

(2) $$N_0 = \frac{Fc}{e} \qquad [46]$$

where F, c, and e, representing, in order, the faraday, the ratio of the escoulomb to the abcoulomb, and the electronic charge, are independently measured,

(3) $$k = \frac{R_0}{N_0} = \frac{v_n A_n e}{T_0 J_{15} Fc} \qquad [47]$$

and

(4) $$h = e\,\frac{h}{e} \qquad [48]$$

The last equation is necessarily thus written because not h but h/e can be directly measured.

The calculation of the precision index of S_0 is even more complicated than Eq. 44 would lead one to believe. In the process, one normally substitutes for R_0, k, h, and N_0 the values given by Eqs. 45 to 48 and

[1] Birge, R. T., *Am. Phys. Teacher*, **7**, 356 (1939).

follows up with the standard procedure discussed earlier. The equation obtained by the substitution is

$$S_0 = \frac{v_n A_n}{T_0 J_{15}} \ln \frac{(2\pi)^{3/2} e_0^{5/2} \left(\dfrac{v_n A_n}{T_0 J_{15}}\right)^{3/2}}{e}{(Fc)^4 \left(\dfrac{h}{e}\right)^3} \qquad [49]$$

8. Use of the Law of Propagation of Precision Indexes in Planning a Precision Experiment. When it is desired to obtain U with a certain precision, p_U, we may use Eq. 33 to calculate the maximum permissible values of $p_{\bar{X}}$ and $p_{\bar{Y}}$. Thus, one method of measuring the surface tension of water, T, makes use of the equation

$$T = \frac{rhdg}{2} \qquad [50]$$

where h is the height of rise of water in a capillary tube of internal radius r, d is the density of water, and g is the acceleration of gravity. Assume that a precision of T is desired such that $p_T/T = 0.001$. We then wish to find the maximum allowable precision indexes for r, h, d, and g, first to see whether or not they are attainable, and second, in order that excessive time, money, and labor are not spent in measuring one or more of these quantities to a higher precision than is necessary. By Eq. 33

$$\left(\frac{p_T}{T}\right)^2 = \left(\frac{p_r}{r}\right)^2 + \left(\frac{p_h}{h}\right)^2 + \left(\frac{p_d}{d}\right)^2 + \left(\frac{p_g}{g}\right)^2 \qquad [51]$$

To obtain a preliminary estimate, we assume that r, h, d, and g may be obtained with equal fractional precision. The maximum permissible fractional probable error is then given by

$$\frac{p_X}{X} = \sqrt{\frac{1}{4}\left(\frac{p_T}{T}\right)^2} = 0.0005 \qquad [52]$$

where X may represent r, h, d, or g. Thus for the approximate consistent set of values for r, h, d, and g of 0.3 mm, 5 cm, 1 g/cm^3, and 980 cm/sec^2, the corresponding probable errors should not exceed 0.0001 mm, 0.02 mm, 0.0005 g/cm^3, and 0.5 cm/sec^2. Ordinarily it would be extremely difficult to obtain r and h with this precision. However, d and g may both be easily obtained to precisions greater than those specified. Hence, d and g may be assumed to be without error in this calculation of permissible probable errors for the component quantities. Eq. 51 now reduces to

$$\left(\frac{p_T}{T}\right)^2 = \left(\frac{p_r}{r}\right)^2 + \left(\frac{p_h}{h}\right)^2 = (0.001)^2 \qquad [53]$$

Assuming that r and h may be measured with equal precision, we now have

$$\frac{p_r}{r} = \frac{p_h}{h} = 0.0007 \tag{54}$$

It follows that the precision for T that is sought requires probable errors for r and h which shall be of the order of 0.0002 and 0.035 mm or less.

It seems highly improbable that such precisions may be obtainable for r and h. A conclusion to be drawn is that the method is unsatisfactory for obtaining the surface tension of water with the desired precision. If we still wish to measure the surface tension with a relative probable error of only 0.001, some other method such as the pressure-drop method should be considered and analyzed similarly.

9. Summary. When a quantity, $\overline{U}$, cannot be measured directly but must be calculated from the mean values of two or more independently measured quantities, $\overline{X}$ and $\overline{Y}$ say, the precision indexes of $\overline{U}$ may be calculated from those of $\overline{X}$ and $\overline{Y}$ with the aid of the law of propagation of precision indexes. In general, if

$$\overline{U} = f(\overline{X}, \overline{Y}) \tag{28}$$

the probable error of $\overline{U}$, $p_{\overline{U}}$, may be obtained by the equation

$$p_{\overline{U}}{}^2 = \left(\frac{\partial U}{\partial X}\right)^2 p_{\overline{X}}{}^2 + \left(\frac{\partial U}{\partial Y}\right)^2 p_{\overline{Y}}{}^2 \tag{32}$$

and the standard deviation, $\sigma_{\overline{U}}$, by the equation

$$\sigma_{\overline{U}}{}^2 = \left(\frac{\partial U}{\partial X}\right)^2 \sigma_{\overline{X}}{}^2 + \left(\frac{\partial U}{\partial Y}\right)^2 \sigma_{\overline{Y}}{}^2 \tag{33}$$

For special cases of Eq. 28, the corresponding expressions for $p_{\overline{U}}$ are given in Table I.

TABLE I

CORRESPONDING SPECIAL FORMS OF EQS. 28 AND 32

$\overline{U}$	$p_{\overline{U}}$
$\overline{X} \pm \overline{Y}$	$\sqrt{p_{\overline{X}}{}^2 + p_{\overline{Y}}{}^2}$
$\overline{X}\,\overline{Y}$ or $\dfrac{\overline{X}}{\overline{Y}}$	$\overline{U}\sqrt{\left(\dfrac{p_{\overline{X}}}{\overline{X}}\right)^2 + \left(\dfrac{p_{\overline{Y}}}{\overline{Y}}\right)^2}$
$A\overline{X}^\alpha$	$\alpha \dfrac{\overline{U}}{\overline{X}} p_{\overline{X}}$

It is important to check the independence of the precision indexes of the component quantities $\overline{X}$ and $\overline{Y}$, for if they are dependent in part on the same measurements, Eqs. 32 and 33 are not valid. The law of propagation is also valuable in planning precision experiments. If U is desired with a certain $p_{\overline{U}}$, we may, assuming $\overline{X}$ and $\overline{Y}$ to be of equal relative precisions, calculate, from Eq. 32, maximum allowable values for $p_{\overline{X}}$ and $p_{\overline{Y}}$. Then, knowing the approximate values of $p_{\overline{X}}$ and $p_{\overline{Y}}$, we can tell which quantities may be measured roughly, which more carefully than usual, and generally, whether the experiment is a good one or a poor one for obtaining U with the desired precision.

PROBLEMS

1. A length of approximately 10 cm is measured several times with the aid of a calibrated scale. It is concluded that the probable error of the mean of the readings taken at one end of the length is 0.03 mm; of those at the other end, 0.05 mm. What is the probable error of the mean of the length determinations?

2. Show that Eqs. 19 and 20 serve as propagation equations for the case where $\overline{U} = \overline{X}/\overline{Y}$. Do not use Eqs. 32 and 33.

3. The probable error of a single reading with a given voltmeter is 0.20 volt; the corresponding quantity for a given ammeter, 0.015 amp. What are the percentage probable errors of single determinations of wattages of lamps at their rated wattages, obtained from readings on these instruments for the case of (a) a 500-watt, 115-volt lamp; (b) a 60-watt 115-volt lamp; (c) a 60-watt, 32-volt lamp; and (d) a 60-watt, 8-volt lamp?

4. Assuming the curves of Fig. 2 of Chapter IV to have geometric slopes of approximately one and one-half respectively at points p and q, determine the relative precisions with which the actual slopes at these points may be determined. Assume that lines ab and de are approximately equal in length and that the actual probable errors for all length measurements are equal.

5. The relation between resistivity and temperature for polished tungsten follows closely the law

$$\frac{\rho}{\rho_0} = \left(\frac{T}{T_0}\right)^{1.200}$$

Granted that ρ_0, the value at the gold-point, 1336° K is precise, that elsewhere ρ may be so carefully measured that the relative probable error of a single determination is 0.005%, and that the exponent of T/T_0 has a probable error of 0.005, within what probable error can a person locate the temperature of a polished tungsten filament by means of a single resistivity measurement in the neighborhood of (a) 1200° K, (b) 1800° K, and (c) 2500° K?

6. With what precision may the density of a 10 gm steel bearing-ball of approximate density 7.85 gm/cm³ be obtained, if the probable error of the determination of its average radius is 0.015 mm, and of its mass, 0.05 mg?

7. The length of a lamp filament of assumed circular cross-section is measured with a rule permitting estimations of length to 0.1 mm. As an average of 10 measurements, 273.45 mm with an average deviation from the mean of 0.24 mm is obtained. Its diameter, measured in various azimuths at various cross-sections with an instrument permitting estimations to 0.001 mm similarly yielded, as a consequence of 50 measurements, 0.2550 mm with an average deviation from the mean of 0.0015 mm. From a single weighing, its mass is determined as 268.45 mg with an estimated uncertainty of 0.05 mg. Assume the scales for the length and diameter measurements exact. If the probable-error method is used in reporting precision, what values may reasonably be reported for the length of the wire, its cross-section, its radiating surface, and its density?

8. In a measurement of the index of refraction of a 60° glass prism for the D_1 line ($\lambda = 5895.93$ A), the data in the table below were obtained. Assuming the scale exact, what is the computed index of refraction? Its probable error? (Note that, as shown in Eq. 3, the prism angle appears in both the numerator and the denominator.)

MEASUREMENT OF PRISM ANGLE

No. of Readings	Side of Prism to Which Telescope is Normal	Mean Scale Reading	Probable Error of Individual Reading
10	Incident	80° 45′ 30″	20″
10	Emergent	200° 23′ 45″	25″

MEASUREMENT OF DEVIATION ANGLE AT MINIMUM DEVIATION

No. of Readings	Telescope Position Measured	Mean Scale Reading	Probable Error of Individual Reading
10	For undeviated ray	80° 45′ 30″	20″
30	For deviated ray	27° 15′ 20″	40″

9. For the degree of dissociation, x, of HI at 629° K, Bodenstein [1] obtained 0.1914, 0.1953, 0.1968, 0.1956, 0.1937, 0.1938, 0.1949, 0.1948, 0.1954, and 0.1947. The relation between x and the equilibrium constant K, for such a reaction as

$$H_2 + I_2 \rightleftharpoons 2HI$$

is

$$K = \left(\frac{x}{2(1 - x)} \right)^2$$

Determine the equilibrium constant for the dissociation of HI at 629° K and its probable error.

[1] Bodenstein, Max, Z. physik. Chem., **22**, 1 (1897).

CHAPTER X

THE ADJUSTMENT OF CONDITIONED MEASUREMENTS

1. Introduction. Independent measurements are often made on quantities that are known or assumed to be related according to one or more specific laws. Such measurements are said to be conditioned. Their means are not necessarily the most probable values of the quantities measured. They must be adjusted to conform to the law or laws relating the quantities. Thus, for the three angles of a triangle we may obtain as mean values, 30° 2′, 60° 2′, and 90° 1′. We could not certify such values, however, since the sum of the three angles must equal 180° exactly. In general, if k quantities are related by n equations, adjustments are necessary when more than $k - n$ quantities are independently measured.

In this chapter we consider the problem of adjustment first for a simple case, and then for the general case, in which the relation between the variables is linear. Later we consider cases involving products, powers, and more complicated relations. The treatment of adjustments here given assumes that the measurements obey the normal distribution law. It further assumes that the most probable values for the k unknown adjusted means are those which yield a maximum probability of occurrence for the weighted measured means. In accord with the principle of least squares (Chap. VI, p. 163), this condition is equivalent to applying the condition of a minimum to the weighted sum of the squares of the deviations of the measured means from their adjusted values.

2. Equally Weighted Observations of Linearly Related Quantities. Consider first the quadrilateral survey problem of determining the most probable values for the elevations of three points B, C, and D above a base A. Using the same letters B, C, and D to represent the elevations also, let us assume the following independent observations, all of equal weight:

Quantity	Measurement (feet)
B	10.0
C	18.0
D	4.0
$C-B$	9.0
$C-D$	12.0
$B-D$	5.0

Taking account of the uncertainties of measurements, we may express these observations in equation form by

$$B \qquad\qquad - 10.0 \text{ ft} = \Delta_1 \qquad\qquad [1]$$

$$C \qquad\qquad - 18.0 \text{ ft} = \Delta_2 \qquad\qquad [2]$$

$$D - \quad 4.0 \text{ ft} = \Delta_3 \qquad\qquad [3]$$

$$-B + C \qquad - \quad 9.0 \text{ ft} = \Delta_4 \qquad\qquad [4]$$

$$C - D - 12.0 \text{ ft} = \Delta_5 \qquad\qquad [5]$$

$$B \qquad - D - \quad 5.0 \text{ ft} = \Delta_6 \qquad\qquad [6]$$

of which the Δ's represent the unknown adjustments that are necessary. These six observation equations, involving only three unknowns, show clearly the need of adjustment. From them, following the least-squares principle and making the sum of the squares of the Δ's a minimum, we shall form three so-called *normal* equations involving only B, C, and D as unknowns. Their solution will yield the most probable values for the elevations sought.

Before proceeding farther with the special problem, consider the general solution. Let there be n linear observation equations, of equal weight, involving k (where $k < n$) independently measurable quantities, $Q_1, Q_2, \cdots Q_k$. Thus, in the adjusted form, they are

$$a_1 Q_1 + b_1 Q_2 + \cdots k_1 Q_k - X_1 = \Delta_1$$
$$a_2 Q_1 + b_2 Q_2 + \cdots k_2 Q_k - X_2 = \Delta_2 \qquad\qquad [7]$$
$$\cdot$$
$$\cdot$$
$$\cdot$$
$$a_n Q_1 + b_n Q_2 + \cdots k_n Q_k - X_n = \Delta_n$$

Here X_1 represents the observed value of $(a_1 Q_1 + b_1 Q_2 + \cdots k_1 Q_k)$, etc., and the Δ's represent the small unknown adjustments necessary for consistency. Comparing Eqs. 7 one by one with Eqs. 1 to 6, we see that Q_1, Q_2, Q_3 represent the quantities B, C, D; that the coefficients a_1, b_1, c_1 take the values 1, 0, 0; that a_2, b_2, c_2 take the values 0, 1, 0, etc.

It is necessary that all the Δ's of Eq. 7 be of the same physical nature, since their squares are to be added.

Maximum probability of occurrence of the observed set of X's requires, as stated, that $\Sigma \Delta^2$ shall be a minimum. Since the Q's are the independent variables, it further follows that

$$\frac{\partial(\Sigma \Delta^2)}{\partial Q_1} = \frac{\partial(\Sigma \Delta^2)}{\partial Q_2} = \cdots = \frac{\partial(\Sigma \Delta^2)}{\partial Q_k} = 0 \qquad\qquad [8]$$

Considering now only

$$\frac{\partial(\Sigma\Delta^2)}{\partial Q_1} = 0 \qquad [9]$$

rewrite the observation equations as

$$a_1 Q_1 + A_1 = \Delta_1$$
$$a_2 Q_1 + A_2 = \Delta_2 \qquad [10]$$
$$\cdot$$
$$\cdot$$
$$\cdot$$
$$a_n Q_1 + A_n = \Delta_n$$

where A_1 replaces $(b_1 Q_2 + \cdots k_1 Q_k - X_1)$ etc. It follows that, as an abbreviation,

$$\frac{\partial(\Sigma\Delta^2)}{\partial Q_1} = \frac{\partial}{\partial Q_1}(Q_1{}^2\Sigma a^2 + 2Q_1\Sigma aA + \Sigma A^2)$$

$$= 2[(\Sigma a^2)Q_1 + \Sigma aA] = 0 \qquad [11]$$

The summations here as well as those in the following equations are strictly of the type $\Sigma a_i a_i$ and $\Sigma a_i A_i$. By an exactly similar procedure, we obtain

$$(\Sigma b^2)Q_2 + \Sigma bB = 0$$
$$(\Sigma c^2)Q_3 + \Sigma cC = 0$$
$$\cdot \qquad\qquad [12]$$
$$\cdot$$
$$\cdot$$
$$(\Sigma k^2)Q_k + \Sigma kK = 0$$

These equations are the normal equations for the unknown adjusted Q-values and are exactly equal to them in number. Replacing the abbreviations $A, B, \cdots K,$ by their equals leads to the following forms, more suitable for computational purposes:

$$(\Sigma a^2)Q_1 + (\Sigma ab)Q_2 + (\Sigma ac)Q_3 + \cdots (\Sigma ak)Q_k - \Sigma aX = 0$$
$$(\Sigma ab)Q_1 + (\Sigma b^2)Q_2 + (\Sigma bc)Q_3 + \cdots (\Sigma bk)Q_k - \Sigma bX = 0$$
$$(\Sigma ac)Q_1 + (\Sigma bc)Q_2 + (\Sigma c^2)Q_3 + \cdots (\Sigma ck)Q_k - \Sigma cX = 0$$
$$\cdot \qquad\qquad [13]$$
$$\cdot$$
$$\cdot$$
$$(\Sigma ak)Q_1 + (\Sigma bk)Q_2 + (\Sigma ck)Q_3 + \cdots (\Sigma k^2)Q_k - \Sigma kX = 0$$

The values for Q_1, Q_2, Q_k obtained by solving Eqs. 13 simultaneously will be the most probable values for those quantities. Inspection shows that Eqs. 13 may be obtained from Eqs. 7 rather simply.   To obtain the first normal equation, one merely multiplies each of Eqs. 7 by the coefficient of its Q_1 and takes the sum.   Similar procedures yield the other normal equations.   Note that the summations involving the Δ's, in view of Eqs. 10 and 11, equate to zero.   For the worker who has occasion to solve numerous sets of normal equations, the mastery of some systematic method of solution, such as that of Gauss or of Doolittle, is recommended.   For others, the method of determinants, given in Appendix 1, should prove most convenient.

Returning to the problem of the quadrilateral survey, we find, as a result of the specified treatment, that our special-case normal equations become

$$3B - C - D - 6.0 \text{ ft} = 0$$

$$-B + 3C - D - 39.0 \text{ ft} = 0 \tag{14}$$

$$-B - C + 3D + 13.0 \text{ ft} = 0$$

Note, in this connection, that the X_1 of Eq. 1 is $+10$ ft, not -10 ft. There result, for B, C, and D in order, $9\frac{1}{2}$ ft, $17\frac{3}{4}$ ft, and $4\frac{3}{4}$ ft; and for the Δ's, likewise in order, $-\frac{1}{2}$ ft, $-\frac{1}{4}$ ft, $\frac{3}{4}$ ft, $-\frac{3}{4}$ ft, 1 ft, and $-\frac{1}{4}$ ft.   He who doubts that the above set of Δ's possesses the least value for $\Sigma\Delta^2$ is invited to test it against any other set, however obtained.

Consider as a second case that of the angles of a plane triangle.   Let the angles be α, β, and γ, and their measured values, A, B, and C, all equally precise.   What are their most probable values?   There are but two independently valued angles; the third angle, γ say, is to be considered as $180° - \alpha - \beta$.   Our observation equations are, accordingly

$$\alpha \qquad - A \qquad\qquad = \Delta_1$$

$$\beta - B \qquad\qquad = \Delta_2 \tag{15}$$

$$-\alpha - \beta + (180° - C) = \Delta_3$$

The normal equations become

$$2\alpha + \beta + (C - A - 180°) = 0$$
$$\alpha + 2\beta + (C - B - 180°) = 0 \tag{16}$$

whence

$$\beta = \frac{180° - C - A + 2B}{3}$$

$$\alpha = \frac{180° - C - B + 2A}{3} \tag{17}$$

3. Unequally Weighted Observations of Linearly Related Quantities.
Referring to the previously considered problem of determining the most
probable elevations at the corners of a quadrilateral, let probable errors
be given for the measured quantities. With B, C, and D representing,
as before, elevations above A, assume as the available data

Quantity	Measurement (feet)	Probable Error (feet)	Weight
B	10.0	0.2	25.0
C	18.0	0.5	4.0
D	4.0	0.6	2.8
C–B	9.0	0.4	6.2
C–D	12.0	0.8	1.6
B–D	5.0	1.0	1.0

As shown elsewhere, weights are chosen proportional to the inverse
squares of the probable errors. The procedure is the same as before,
except that now we consider in effect the first observation equation
repeated 25.0 times, the second, 4.0 times, etc. The normal equations
for the general case with linear relationships become

$$(\Sigma wa^2)Q_1 + (\Sigma wab)Q_2 + \cdots - (\Sigma waX) = 0$$

$$(\Sigma wab)Q_1 + (\Sigma wb^2)Q_2 + \cdots - (\Sigma wbX) = 0$$

$$\vdots$$

[18]

$$(\Sigma wak)Q_1 + (\Sigma wbk)Q_2 + \cdots - (\Sigma wkX) = 0$$

In computing the coefficients Σwa^2, Σwab, etc., of Eqs. 18, a tabulation
such as that employed in Table I will be found very helpful in the elimination of computational errors.

For our special case of elevations at the corners of the quadrilateral,
the normal equations involving weights become

$$32.2B - 6.2C - 1.0D - 199.2 \text{ ft} = 0$$

$$-6.2B + 11.8C - 1.6D - 147.0 \text{ ft} = 0 \qquad [19]$$

$$-1.0B - 1.6C + 5.4D + 13.0 \text{ ft} = 0$$

Solution of Eqs. 19 yields 9.86 ft, 18.30 ft, and 4.84 ft for B, C, and D.
These values differ appreciably from those obtained on the basis of equal
weights.

TABLE I

ILLUSTRATING A CONVENIENT CHECKING ARRANGEMENT FOR USE IN FINDING THE
COEFFICIENTS OF THE NORMAL EQUATIONS (THREE IN NUMBER AS ILLUSTRATED)
FOR WEIGHTED CONDITIONED MEASUREMENTS

wa	waa	wab	wac	waX	Sums
25.0	25.0	0	0	250.0	275.0
0	0	0	0	0	0
0	0	0	0	0	0
−6.2	6.2	−6.2	0	−55.8	−55.8
0	0	0	0	0	0
1.0	1.0	0	−1.0	5.0	5.0
					224.2
Totals	32.2	−6.2	−1.0	199.2	224.2

wb		wbb	wbc	wbX	Sums
0		0	0	0	0
4.0		4.0	0	72.0	76.0
0		0	0	0	0
6.2		6.2	0	55.8	62.0
1.6		1.6	−1.6	19.2	19.2
0		0	0	0	0
					157.2
Totals		11.8	−1.6	147.0	157.2

wc			wcc	wcX	Sums
0			0	0	0
0			0	0	0
2.8			2.8	11.2	14.0
0			0	0	0
−1.6			1.6	−19.2	−17.6
−1.0			1.0	−5.0	−4.0
					−7.6
Totals			5.4	−13.0	−7.6

4. Observations of Nonlinearly Related Quantities. In a large percentage of cases, conditioned quantities are related by nonlinear equations. Four examples may be cited. (1) The first concerns c_2, the second radiation constant; h_1, Planck's constant; c, the velocity of light; and k, Boltzmann's atomic constant; which are related by the equation

$$c_2 = \frac{hc}{k} \qquad [20]$$

Although all four quantities may be independently measured, the values of only three may be independently specified for a consistent set of the constants. (2) The second concerns the four independently measurable quantities: μ, the porous plug effect; γ, the ratio of the two specific heats; $(dT/dv)_p$; and $(dp/dT)_v$, where T, p, and v have their accustomed significances; so related by the equation

$$\mu = \frac{\gamma - 1}{\gamma} \frac{T - v(dT/dv)_p}{T(dp/dT)_v} \qquad [21]$$

that only three of the quantities may be independently specified. Although T and v are also independently measurable, they may be obtained so accurately, relative to the other four constants, that they do not enter into any question of adjustments but serve to represent states to which adjustments between those four may be ascribed. (3) The third concerns the independently measurable quantities: h, Planck's constant; e, the electronic charge; R_H, Rydberg's constant for the $_1H^1$ atom; c, the velocity of light; and m_0, the rest-mass of the electron; which are related by

$$\frac{h}{e} = \left(\frac{2\pi^2 e^2 Z^2}{R_H c \left(\dfrac{e}{m_0} \right)} \right)^{1/3} \qquad [22]$$

As will be noted in one of the problems, the adjustments that seem to be required in this particular case are so great as to cause concern regarding methods of measurement and theoretical relations. (4) The fourth involves the specific heat quantities: c_p; c_v; γ; and $T(dp/dT)_v(dv/dT)_p$, a quantity equal to the universal gas constant R for the case of an ideal gas; which are related by the two equations

$$c_p - c_v = T \left(\frac{dp}{dT} \right)_v \left(\frac{dv}{dT} \right)_p \qquad [23]$$

and

$$\gamma = \frac{c_p}{c_v} \qquad [24]$$

The method of adjustment for nonlinear cases is well illustrated by a treatment of case (1) above. Here we conveniently write as our observation equations

$$\frac{h}{X_1} = 1 + \Delta_1$$

$$\frac{c}{X_2} = 1 + \Delta_2$$

$$\frac{k}{X_3} = 1 + \Delta_3 \qquad [25]$$

$$\frac{c_2}{X_4} = \frac{hc}{kX_4} = 1 + \Delta_4$$

where the X's and the Δ's have the significance given earlier in this chapter. Assuming the Δ's to be small in comparison with unity, we write Eqs. 25 in logarithmic form, thus:

$$\ln \frac{h}{X_1} = \ln h - \ln X_1 = \Delta_1$$

$$\ln \frac{c}{X_2} = \ln c - \ln X_2 = \Delta_2$$

$$\ln \frac{k}{X_3} = \ln k - \ln X_3 = \Delta_3 \qquad [26]$$

$$\ln h + \ln c - \ln k - \ln X_4 = \Delta_4$$

It should be noted that the Δ's, as well as all the other members of Eqs. 26, are numerics.[1] That these Δ's shall all be of the same physical nature is important, since otherwise, the summation $\Sigma \Delta^2$ can not be applied in an adjustment.

Consider next the weights assigned to Eqs. 26. Generally, certain probable errors will be given for the X's; if not, weights are assigned arbitrarily. With probable errors given, the corresponding probable

---

[1] In order that "$\ln h - \ln X_1$" shall be a numeric and that both h and X_1 shall be quantities possessing physical dimensions it is evident that the logarithms of h and X_1 shall contain, in addition to the logarithms of their respective numerics, logarithms of the units in which the quantities are expressed. These additional terms cancel when the difference of the logarithms of the quantities is taken. In all natural equations involving logarithms of physical quantities, something like the foregoing will always enter to make the checking of units possible.

errors for the ln X's follow at once. The principles of propagation of precision indexes indicate that

$$p_{(\ln X_1)} = \frac{p_{X_1}}{X_1}$$

.
.
.

[27]

$$p_{(\ln X_4)} = \frac{p_{X_4}}{X_4}$$

The inverses of the squares of these probable errors are the weights sought. With weights once assigned to Eqs. 26, we follow the procedure leading to Eqs. 19, and obtain

$$(w_1 + w_4) \ln h \qquad + (w_4) \ln c \qquad - (w_4) \ln k$$
$$- (w_1 \ln X_1 + w_4 \ln X_4) = 0$$

$$(w_4) \ln h + (w_2 + w_4) \ln c \qquad - (w_4) \ln k$$
$$- (w_2 \ln X_2 + w_4 \ln X_4) = 0 \quad [28]$$

$$- (w_4) \ln h \qquad - (w_4) \ln c + (w_3 + w_4) \ln k$$
$$- (w_3 \ln X_3 - w_4 \ln X_4) = 0$$

Using "observed" values for h, c, k, and c_2,[1] namely

Quantity	Value
h	6.6283×10^{-27} (1 ± 0.00013) erg sec
c	2.99776×10^{10} (1 ± 0.000013) cm/sec
k	1.3803×10^{-16} (1 ± 0.00023) erg/K°
c_2	1.432 (1 ± 0.002) cm K°

we obtain for their respective weights,

$$w_1 : w_2 : w_3 : w_4 = \left(\frac{1}{0.00013}\right)^2 : \left(\frac{1}{0.000013}\right)^2 : \left(\frac{1}{0.00023}\right)^2 : \left(\frac{1}{0.002}\right)^2$$
$$= 240 : 24000 : 80 : 1$$

[29]

A great variation in the weights is to be noted. Substitution in Eqs. 28 leads to

$$241 \ln h + \ln c - \ln k - (240 \ln X_1 + \ln X_4) = 0$$

$$\ln h + 24001 \ln c - \ln k - (24000 \ln X_2 + \ln X_4) = 0 \qquad [30]$$

[1] Physics Staff of the University of Pittsburgh, *Outline of Atomic Physics*, New York, John Wiley & Sons, 1937, 2nd Ed., p. 391.

$$- \ln h - \ln c + 81 \ln k - (80 \ln X_3 - \ln X_4) = 0$$

from which we obtain

$$h = 6.6283 \times 10^{-27} \text{ erg sec}$$

$$c = 2.99776 \times 10^{10} \text{ cm/sec}$$

$$k = 1.3804 \times 10^{-16} \text{ erg/K}°$$

$$c_2 = 1.4394 \text{ cm K}°$$

[30a]

Because of the very low weighting of X_4, the "observed value" for c_2, the values of h, c, and k are not appreciably changed in the adjustment. This might have been concluded at the beginning and we might as well have computed c_2 in accord with Eq. 20 and taken that as the adjusted value. The value to be thus computed is 1.4396 cm K°, only greater by 2 in the fourth decimal place. As will be seen from the discussion of the *short method* of the following section, the actual labor of carrying out the final computations may be reduced considerably.

One point of general importance in addition to that of the method of adjustment follows from the foregoing discussion. It is that, if one or more of the X's is so highly weighted as to "swamp" the weights of the others, those highly weighted values may well be accepted as fixed and not susceptible of adjustment.

Sometimes it is not apparent at once how to adjust the given data so that the Δ's directly involved in any adjustment will always be of the same nature. Consider the second example cited above. Let the quantities directly measured and for which we have probable errors be μ, γ, $(dT/dv)_p$, and $(dp/dT)_v$. The simple procedure here is to introduce functions of the latter three quantities, H for $\dfrac{\gamma - 1}{\gamma}$, J for $T - v(dT/dv)_p$, and K for $T(dp/dT)_v$. The principles of propagation of precision indexes permit the determinations of probable errors for H, J, and K. Eq. 21 may now be rewritten as

$$\mu = \frac{HJ}{K} \tag{31}$$

and, as in Eq. 20, adjustments are now possible for the quantities entering Eq. 31. Given the adjusted values for H, J, and K, the procedure for finding the adjusted values of γ, $(dT/dv)_p$, and $(dp/dT)_v$ is obvious.

Let us also consider the fourth example cited above for which we have to adjust four independently measured values connected theoretically according to two relations. Here we write as our observation equations

$$c_p - M_1 = \Delta_1 \qquad [32]$$

$$c_v - M_2 = \Delta_2 \qquad [33]$$

$$\gamma = \frac{c_p}{c_v} - M_3 = \Delta_3 \qquad [34]$$

$$T\left(\frac{dp}{dT}\right)_v \left(\frac{dv}{dT}\right)_p - M_4 = c_p - c_v - M_4 = \Delta_4 \qquad [35]$$

Evidently Δ_3 differs in physical nature from the other Δ's and some change must be made. The simplest thing is to revise Eq. 34, writing it as

$$c_p - M_3 c_v = \Delta_3 c_v = \Delta'_3 \qquad [36]$$

Since both sides of Eq. 34 have been multiplied by the same quantity c_v in obtaining Eq. 36, it is obvious that Δ'_3 compared with the left side of Eq. 36 is as much an infinitesimal as is Δ_3 compared with γ. Further, since the multiplier c_v, like the c_v of Eqs. 33 and 35, is an assumed adjusted value and not an experimental value, the weight that will be assigned to Eq. 36 will be $(1/c_v p_{M_3})^2$. We may now proceed to the adjustment of c_p and c_v as desired, using Eqs. 32, 33, 35, and 36.

5. Short Method for a Common Type of Adjustment. Where all of the quantities to be adjusted or functions of them taken singly can be related linearly in a single equation and where each measured value represents a value obtained for one of the quantities to be adjusted, a certain simplification of procedure is possible. As such a case consider the adjustments for the quantities in the equation

$$\sigma = \frac{2\pi^5}{15} \frac{k^4}{h^3 c^2} \qquad [37]$$

of which σ represents the fourth power radiation constant (often referred to as the Stefan-Boltzmann constant), k the Boltzmann atomic constant, h Planck's constant, and c the velocity of light. For these equations we have the values [1] given in the upper half of Table II. If one substitutes the given values for k, h, and c of Eq. 37, he will

---

[1] Physics Staff of the University of Pittsburgh, *Atomic Physics*, New York, John Wiley & Sons, 1937, 2nd Ed., pp. 389–391.

obtain 5.660×10^{-5} erg/(cm²sec K°⁴) for σ, a value which does not check with the stated observed value and shows the need of adjustment.

TABLE II

CERTAIN QUANTITIES AND FUNCTIONS AND THEIR VALUES FOR USE IN ILLUSTRATING A SHORT METHOD FOR A COMMON TYPE OF ADJUSTMENT

Quantity or Function	Value	Logarithm of Numeric
c	2.99776×10^{10} (1 ± 0.000013) cm/sec	10.47680
h	6.6283×10^{-27} (1 ± 0.00013) erg/sec	$\overline{27}.82140$
k	1.3803×10^{-16} (1 ± 0.00023) erg/(molecule K°)	$\overline{16}.13997$
σ	5.735×10^{-5} (1 ± 0.0020) erg/(cm² sec K°⁴)	$\overline{5}.75853$
$2\pi^5/15$	40.803	1.61069
A		$\overline{20}.65709$
X_1		$\overline{5}.75853$
X_2		$\overline{79}.46420$
X_3		63.44012
D		-0.00576

Of the values reported, it is seen that the fractional probable error for c is so small compared with that for σ that c, because of its "swamping effect," may be treated as exact in the adjustment process. Rearrangement of Eq. 37 yields

$$\log \sigma + \log h^3 + \log \frac{1}{k^4} = \log \frac{2\pi^5}{15} - \log c^2 \qquad [38]$$

which takes account of the stated "swamping" precision of c and may be identified term by term with

$$Q_1 + Q_2 + Q_3 = A \qquad [39]$$

of which the separate Q's are to be viewed as the quantities needing adjustment.

A stated condition for the type of adjustment being considered assumes for the observation equations, Eqs. 7

$$Q_1 - X_1 = \Delta_1$$

$$Q_2 - X_2 = \Delta_2 \qquad [40]$$

$$Q_3 - X_3 = \Delta_3$$

With weights w_1, w_2, w_3, these lead in the regular manner to normal equations which when solved yield

$$Q_1 = X_1 + \frac{B}{w_1} D$$

$$Q_2 = X_2 + \frac{B}{w_2} D \qquad [41]$$

$$Q_3 = X_3 + \frac{B}{w_3} D$$

of which

$$B = \frac{w_1 w_2 w_3}{w_1 w_2 + w_2 w_3 + w_3 w_1} \qquad [42]$$

and

$$D = A - (X_1 + X_2 + X_3) \qquad [43]$$

D represents the discrepancy for which adjustments must be made. The fractions B/w_1, B/w_2, and B/w_3 must and do add up to unity. The manner of obtaining from Q_1, Q_2, etc., the desired adjusted values for the original quantities in any individual case will be obvious.

In accord with the above, the abbreviated method of adjustment for quantities whose functional relation is expressible by a linear equation consists of (1) selecting the necessary functions Q_1, Q_2, etc., for each quantity and the form of the linear relation, (2) determining the weights w_1, w_2, and w_3 to be ascribed to the values X_1, X_2, etc., determined experimentally or otherwise for the linearly related functions or quantities, (3) determining the discrepancy, D, to be adjusted among the linearly related functions, (4) splitting up the discrepancy into component parts which are proportional to the reciprocals of the computed weights, (5) applying these component parts to the appropriate X_1, X_2, etc., values, and (6) computing the adjusted values for the quantities whose functions were related linearly.

Applying the outlined procedure to the adjustment of σ, h, and k, need for which was indicated above, we note that step (1) has already been carried through above and that the functions which have been selected as Q_1, Q_2, and Q_3 of Eq. 39 are in order log σ, log h^3, and log $(1/k^4)$ and that log $(2\pi^5/15c^2)$ has been represented by A. Applying step (2) we obtain for weights w_1, w_2, w_3 of X_1, X_2, X_3 the relation

$$\frac{1}{w_1} : \frac{1}{w_2} : \frac{1}{w_3} = (0.0020)^2 : (3 \times 0.00013)^2 : (4 \times 0.00023)^2$$

$$\doteq \frac{25}{31} : \frac{1}{31} : \frac{5}{31} \qquad [44]$$

Since the last three members of this equation sum up to unity, it follows that, in order, they represent the values of B/w_1, B/w_2, and B/w_3 as they appear in Eqs. 41. For step (3) the necessary data are listed in the lower half of Table II, and the value to be computed for the discrepancy D in accord with Eq. 43 is seen to be -0.00576. Following step (5), the partition of D into components in proportion to B/w_1, B/w_2, and B/w_3 yields in order -0.00464, -0.00019, and -0.00093. These applied to X_1, X_2, and X_3 in accord with Eqs. 41 yield

$$Q_1 = \overline{5}.75389$$
$$Q_2 = \overline{79}.46401 \qquad [45]$$
$$Q_3 = 63.43919$$

Step (6) leads to

$$\sigma = 5.674 \times 10^{-5} \text{ erg}/(\text{cm}^2\text{sec K}^{\circ 4})$$
$$h = 6.6277 \times 10^{-27} \text{ erg sec} \qquad [46]$$
$$k = 1.3810 \times 10^{-6} \text{ erg}/(\text{molecule K}^\circ)$$

While probable errors for each of these three values may be determined by the method that follows, it has not been so done here. Note, however, that the adjustment for σ is about $5\frac{1}{2}$ times greater than the indicated probable error of the observed value and that the adjustment for k is twice the probable error. The situation leaves doubt as to whether or not the adjustment is advisable.

6. Probable Errors of Adjusted Observations. The solution of Eqs. 18 leads to the following expression for Q_1:

$$Q_1 = \frac{\begin{vmatrix} \Sigma waX & \Sigma wab & \cdots & \Sigma wak \\ \Sigma wbX & \Sigma wb^2 & \cdots & \Sigma wbk \\ & & \cdot \\ & & \cdot \\ & & \cdot \\ \Sigma wkX & \Sigma wbk & \cdots & \Sigma wk^2 \end{vmatrix}}{\begin{vmatrix} \Sigma wa^2 & \Sigma wab & \cdots & \Sigma wak \\ \Sigma wab & \Sigma wb^2 & \cdots & \Sigma wbk \\ & & \cdot \\ & & \cdot \\ & & \cdot \\ \Sigma wak & \Sigma wbk & \cdots & \Sigma wk^2 \end{vmatrix}} = \alpha_1 X_1 + \alpha_2 X_2 + \cdots \alpha_n X_n \qquad [47]$$

where α_1, α_2, $\cdots \alpha_n$ are complicated but easily derivable in terms of the coefficients of X_1, X_2, $\cdots X_n$ appearing in the summations ΣwaX, ΣwbX, and their minors, etc.   It follows that

$$p_{Q_1} = \sqrt{\alpha_1{}^2 p_{X_1}{}^2 + \alpha_2{}^2 p_{X_2}{}^2 + \cdots \alpha_n{}^2 p_{X_n}{}^2} \qquad [48]$$

and likewise for the probable errors of the other Q's.

For the simple case, already treated, of the elevations of three corners of a quadrilateral above the fourth, where the observations are all of equal weight, we have

$$3B - C - D - (X_1 - X_4 + X_6) = 0$$
$$-B + 3C - D - (X_2 - X_4 + X_5) = 0 \qquad [49]$$
$$-B - C + 3D - (X_3 - X_5 - X_6) = 0$$

There follow

$$B = \tfrac{1}{2}X_1 + \tfrac{1}{4}X_2 + \tfrac{1}{4}X_3 - \tfrac{1}{4}X_4 + \tfrac{1}{4}X_6$$
$$C = \tfrac{1}{4}X_1 + \tfrac{1}{2}X_2 + \tfrac{1}{4}X_3 + \tfrac{1}{4}X_4 + \tfrac{1}{4}X_5 \qquad [50]$$
$$D = \tfrac{1}{4}X_1 + \tfrac{1}{4}X_2 + \tfrac{1}{2}X_3 - \tfrac{1}{4}X_5 - \tfrac{1}{4}X_6$$

where X_1, X_2, etc., stand for the readings 10.0 ft, 18.0 ft, etc.   It follows, in accord with the principles of propagation of precision indexes for sums, that

$$p_B = \sqrt{\frac{p_{X_1}{}^2}{4} + \frac{p_{X_2}{}^2}{16} + \frac{p_{X_3}{}^2}{16} + \frac{p_{X_4}{}^2}{16} + \frac{p_{X_6}{}^2}{16}} \qquad [51]$$

Further, since the probable errors of all the X's are the same, we also have

$$p_B = p_C = p_D = \frac{p_{X_1}}{\sqrt{2}} = \frac{p_{X_2}}{\sqrt{2}} = \cdots \qquad [52]$$

Assuming 0.6 ft as the probable error for each of the six measurements, the probable error for the adjusted values for B, C, and D is found to be 0.4 ft, a value less than the assumed 0.6 ft.

7. The Present (1940) Status Relative to the Evaluation of the Constants of Atomic Physics.   The constants particularly under consideration here are the electronic charge, e, the rest mass of the electron, m_0, and Planck's constant, h.   Many of the measurements of atomic physics involve functions of these three quantities.   For example, Rydberg's constant for an infinite mass, R_∞ is defined by

$$R_\infty = \frac{2\pi^2 e^4 m_0}{ch^3} \qquad [53]$$

of which c represents the velocity of light.   While Rydberg's constant is among the quantities most precisely determined, the precision for c

TABLE III

SUMMARY SHOWING EXPERIMENTAL RESULTS OBTAINED FROM ELEVEN DIFFERENT TYPES OF ATOMIC MEASUREMENTS LEADING TO VALUES FOR THE ELECTRONIC CHARGE

There is also shown (fifth column) the dependence of these experimental values on the values of the first ten auxiliary constants listed in Table IV. A' represents the remainder of A after factoring out the constants indicated. The next to the last column gives the formulas for e_n (e_n is the value of e which represents the given experiment on the Birge-Bond diagram). The last column gives the values of e_n computed in accord with these formulas and an assumed h' of 6.6100×10^{27} erg sec. The meanings attached to the symbols of the fifth column are given in Table IV.

POINT	DESCRIPTION	COMBINATION OF CONSTANTS MEASURED	EXPERIMENTAL VALUE, A	DEPENDENCE OF A ON CERTAIN CONSTANTS. FORMULA FOR A	FORMULA FOR e_n	e_n FOR BIRGE-BOND DIAGRAM IN 10^{-10} ESU
1	Ruled grating	e	$(4.8025 \pm 0.0004) \times 10^{-10}$ esu	$(F\,qck_\lambda^3)A'$	e	4.8025 ± 0.0004
2	Oil drop	e	$(4.8036 \pm 0.0048) \times 10^{-10}$ esu	$(c/r)A'$	e	4.8036 ± 0.0048
3	Limit of continuous x-rays	h/e	$(1.3763 \pm 0.0004) \times 10^{-17}$ esu	$(k_\lambda r/c^2)A'$	$(1/A)h'$	4.8026 ± 0.0014
4	Ionization and excitation	h/e	$(1.3745 \pm 0.0013) \times 10^{-17}$ esu	$(r/c^2)A'$	$(1/A)h'$	4.8090 ± 0.0045
5	Radiation constant c_2	h/e	$(1.3730 \pm 0.0029) \times 10^{-17}$ esu	$(R_0/c^2 Fa)A'$	$(1/A)h'$	4.8145 ± 0.0101
6	Stefan-Boltzmann constant	$e/h^{3/4}$	$(2.0778 \pm 0.0020) \times 10^{10}$ esu	$(Fqc^{3/2}/R_0)A'$	$(A)h'^{3/4}$	4.8168 ± 0.0046
7	Electron diffraction	$(h/e)(e/m_0)^{1/2}$	$(1.00084 \pm 0.00058) \times 10^{-8}$ esu	$[(r/c)^{1/2}k_\lambda]A'$	$(cR_\infty A^2/2\pi^2)^{1/3}h'^{1/3}$	4.7964 ± 0.0019
8	Electron diffraction	h/m_0	(7.274 ± 0.016) erg sec/gm	$(k_\lambda)A'$	$(cR_\infty A^2/2\pi^2)^{1/4}h'^{1/2}$	4.7972 ± 0.0026
9	Compton effect	h/m_0	(7.264 ± 0.012) erg sec/gm	$(k_\lambda c)A'$	$(cR_\infty A^2/2\pi^2)^{1/4}h'^{1/2}$	4.7956 ± 0.0020
10	Specific charge	e/m_0	$(1.7591 \pm 0.0002) \times 10^7$ emu $[(5.2734 \pm 0.0006) \times 10^{17}$ esu$]$	Depends on method	$(c^2 R_\infty A/2\pi^2)^{1/5}h'^{3/5}$	4.7963 ± 0.0002
11	X-ray photoelectrons	$(e/m_0)(e/h)$	$(3.8220 \pm 0.0029) \times 10^{34}$ esu	$(c^3 p^2/k_\lambda r^2)A'$	$(cR_\infty A/2\pi^2)^{1/6}h'^{2/3}$	4.7953 ± 0.0006
12	Rydberg number	$e^4 m_0/h^3$	$(1.666564 \pm 0.000083) \times 10^{14}$	$(1/c)A'$		

is still higher.   Usually both but sometimes only the latter is treated as exact when adjustments involving them are undertaken.

Adjusting observed data in the field of atomic physics to obtain consistent values has attracted the attention of many physicists.   Among them we cite Birge,[1] Bond,[2] Dunnington,[3] DuMond,[4] and Darwin,[5] since

TABLE IV

AUXILIARY CONSTANTS USED BY DUNNINGTON IN HIS STUDY OF ATOMIC CONSTANTS

[See Table III]

SYMBOL	DESCRIPTION	VALUE USED
F	Faraday in international coulombs/gm. equiv. wt.	96494.0 ± 1.5
c	Velocity of light in cm/sec	$(2.99776 \pm 0.00015) \times 10^{10}$
p	Conversion factor from N.B.S. int. to absolute ohms	1.000485 ± 0.000007
q	Conversion factor from N.B.S. int. to absolute amperes	0.999970 ± 0.000020
r/p	Conversion factor from N.B.S. int. to absolute amperes	0.999926 ± 0.000020
r	Conversion factor from N.B.S. int. to absolute volts	1.0000411 ± 0.000022
R_{H^1}	Rydberg constant for H^1 in cm^{-1}	109677.76 ± 0.05
R_0	Gas constant in ergs/(mole K°)	$(8.3136 \pm 0.0010) \times 10^7$
k_A	Ratio of mass spectrograph to chemical atomic wt.	1.000275 ± 0.000020
k_λ	Ratio of ruled grating to Siegbahn wavelengths (Bearden)	1.00203 ± 0.00002
R_∞	Rydberg constant for infinite mass in cm^{-1}	109737.42 ± 0.06
h'	Arbitrarily adopted value of Planck's constant in erg sec	6.6100×10^{-27}

their contributions are basic to the present discussion.   References to other work will be found in the paper by Dunnington.   Altogether Dunnington lists results from eleven types of measurements (Table III) involving e, h, and m_0 and functions of them as subject to adjustment.

[1] Birge, R. T., *Rev. Modern Phys.*, **1**, 1 (1929); **13**, 233 (1941).
[2] Bond, W. N., *Phil. Mag.*, **10** (1930); **12** (1931).
[3] Dunnington, F. G., *Rev. Modern Phys.*, **11**, 65–83 (1939).
[4] DuMond, J. W. M., *Phys. Rev.*, **56**, 153 (1939).
[5] Darwin, C. G., *Proc. Phys. Soc.*, **52**, 202–09 (1940).

Darwin includes the determination of R_∞ as a twelfth. In Table III it is shown also just how these measurements involve the e, h, and m_0 and also certain other experimental constants whose values (Table IV) are ordinarily accepted as exact to a higher order of certainty. The experimental values with their probable errors as recorded might be used, as some have been, to obtain adjusted least-squares values in accord with the method described above. Before so doing it seemed

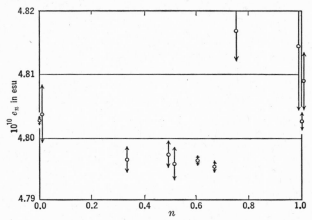

FIG. 1. A Birge-Bond diagram for testing the consistency of experimental data concerned with the atomic constants e, h, and m_0. The meanings of e_n and n are stated in the legend of Table III, where the data for this graph are to be found.

wise to Dunnington, as it had to others before him, to test for consistency. Assuming the highly precise value for R_∞ as fixed, it is evidently possible to eliminate e or h or m_0 from the expression given in the third column of the table and to modify the experimental values accordingly. If, for instance, the expression obtained by electron diffraction, namely

$$\frac{h}{e}\left(\frac{e}{m_0}\right)^{1/2} = (1.00084 \pm 0.00058) \times 10^{-8} \text{ esu} \qquad [54]$$

is so treated and m_0, with the aid of Eq. 53, is expressed in terms of e, h, and accepted values for R_∞ and c (Table IV), one obtains

$$\frac{e}{h^{1/3}} = (0.25558 \pm 0.00006) \text{ esu} \qquad [55]$$

If further, one substitutes an approximate rounded value, say 6.6100×10^{-27} erg sec, for h, he obtains an approximate value, e_n, for e. Making this substitution, Eq. 55 yields

$$e_n = (4.7964 \pm 0.0019) \times 10^{-10} \text{ esu} \qquad [56]$$

as shown for the seventh item in the last column of Table III. This procedure of first eliminating m_0 and then substituting a rounded value for h' has been followed by Dunnington. Further, he has presented the series of e_n values obtained in a Birge-Bond diagram (Fig. 1), in which e_n is plotted as a function of n, the power of h corresponding to a power of unity for e in the various expressions similar to Eq. 55.

The half-lengths of the lines of spread associated with any one point on the Birge-Bond diagram represents the uncertainties of the computed e_n's. Should the values have been satisfactorily consistent all points would have fallen on a single average horizontal line or so near that their lines of spread would have crossed or nearly crossed it. This is very far from being the case. There are three groups of values each of which separately seems to have external consistency. Whether or not the whole group may be said to have external consistency as that is defined in Chapter VIII is left for a problem to be found at the end of this chapter. To some, adjustments for a case such as this is without much meaning. Dunnington and others on this basis have sought for possible errors of theory or for faulty experimental procedure.

With A_1, A_2, A_3, etc., as the experimental values of Table III, Eq. 54 may be rewritten as

$$\ln \frac{h}{e} + \tfrac{1}{2} \ln \frac{e}{m_0} = \ln A_7 \qquad [57]$$

If, further, approximate rounded values h', e', and m'_0 are introduced, we may rewrite Eq. 57 as

$$\ln \left[\frac{h'}{e'} \left(1 + \frac{\Delta(h/e)}{h'/e'} \right) \right] + \tfrac{1}{2} \ln \left[\frac{e'}{m'_0} \left(1 + \frac{\Delta(e/m_0)}{e'/m'_0} \right) \right] = \ln A_7 \quad [58]$$

and, since the Δ terms will be very small quantities, as

$$\frac{\Delta(h/e)}{h'/e'} + \tfrac{1}{2} \frac{\Delta(e/m_0)}{e'/m'_0} = \ln A_7 - \ln \frac{h'}{(e'm'_0)^{1/2}} \qquad [59]$$

Darwin showed that if the Δ terms were assumed to represent coordinates and we write

$$\frac{\Delta(h/e)}{h'/e'} = x \qquad [60]$$

$$\frac{\Delta(e/m_0)}{e'/m'_0} = y \qquad [61]$$

$$\frac{\Delta e}{e'} = z \qquad [62]$$

our Eq. 57 reduces to

$$x + \tfrac{1}{2} y = B_7 \pm \Delta B_7 \qquad [63]$$

of which B_7 representing the right-hand member of Eq. 59 and ΔB_7, its computed uncertainty are both small and dimensionless. The other ten equations similar to Eq. 63 have similar small values for their B's. All are simple and none involves more than two of the unknowns. The actual magnitude of the ΔB's will depend on accepted values for P_B, e.g., 0.95. A certain convenience of treatment follows, due to the possibility of thinking of the x, y, z quantities as space coordinates and of the ΔB's as defining slab-shaped regions in this space to which the equations predict probable limitations of actual values for x, y, and z. For further details the reader is referred to the original article. After a discussion of the discrepancies, Darwin singled out items 1, 10, and 12 of Table III as most likely correct and from these three alone concluded that the most probable values for the quantities desired are

$$e = 4.8025 \times 10^{-10} \text{ esu} \tag{64}$$

$$\frac{e}{m_0} = 1.7591 \times 10^7 \text{ emu} \tag{65}$$

$$h = 6.6243 \times 10^{-27} \text{ erg sec} \tag{66}$$

A satisfactory adjustment of the discrepancies has not been found.

8. Summary. If k quantities are known or assumed to be related by n equations, and if more than $k - n$ of the quantities are measured independently of one another, the means of the independent sets of measurements are no longer the most probable values of the quantities measured but must be adjusted to give values consistent with respect to the n conditioning equations. The adjustment procedure when the quantities are linearly related and the measurements are of equal weight consists of the following steps:

(1) Write in their adjusted forms n observation equations similar to the following two

$$a_1 Q_1 + b_1 Q_2 + \cdots k_1 Q_k - X_1 = \Delta_1$$
$$a_2 Q_1 + b_2 Q_2 + \cdots k_2 Q_k - X_2 = \Delta_2 \tag{7}$$

of which the Q's are the related quantities; the X's the independently observed values for functions of these quantities related as shown by the various constant coefficients a, b, c, $\cdots k$; and the Δ's the necessary adjustments.

(2) Multiply each of the n observation equations by the coefficient of Q_1 in that equation and add the n resulting equations to obtain the first normal equation

$$(\Sigma a^2)Q_1 + (\Sigma ab)Q_2 + \cdots (\Sigma ak)Q_k - \Sigma aX = 0 \tag{13a}$$

The summations involving the Δ's are zero.

(3) Repeat step (2) $k - 1$ times, substituting in turn, however, the coefficients of the other Q's to obtain altogether k normal equations.

(4) Solve the k normal equations simultaneously to obtain the adjusted values of $Q_1, Q_2, \cdots Q_k$.

(5) Obtain the probable errors of the adjusted quantities by applying Eqs. 51 and 52.

When the independently observed values $X_1, X_2, \cdots$ have the weights $w_1, w_2, \cdots$, the procedure is identical with that above, except that the first observation equation is multiplied by w_1, the second by w_2, etc. The normal equations then have the form

$$(\Sigma wa^2)Q_1 + (\Sigma wab)Q_2 + \cdots (\Sigma wak)Q_k - \Sigma waX = 0$$

$$\vdots \quad [18]$$

$$(\Sigma wak)Q_1 + (\Sigma wbk)Q_2 + \cdots (\Sigma wk^2)Q_k - \Sigma wkX = 0$$

Adjustment procedure when the quantities are nonlinearly related depends on the type of relationship. No general rules can be set up. It is necessary, in any case, to write the observation equations in such a form that the differences between the observed and adjusted values are in the same units for all the quantities to be adjusted, since the squares of these differences are to be added and the sum made a minimum.

Where all of the quantities to be adjusted or functions of them taken singly can be related linearly in a single equation and where each measured value represents a value obtained for one of the quantities to be adjusted, a much shortened procedure is possible. With the quantities or functions arranged as a sum in the equation of condition that must be satisfied, one substitutes measured values and computes a discrepancy which is to be eliminated. The adjustment is completed by dividing up this discrepancy among the various quantities or functions in inverse proportion to their weights.

To obtain the probable errors and other precision indexes of the adjusted quantities (1) the solutions for the adjusted quantities, as obtained from the normal equations, are arranged for each as a sum of terms each consisting of an exact coefficient and a measured quantity with a given precision index, and (2) the principle for obtaining the precision index of a sum is then applied.

PROBLEMS

1. Find the most probable elevations of B, C, D, and E above A (the lowest) when the following observations are made. Assume all determinations to have probable errors of 2.0 ft. What is the probable error of the final determinations?

$$B = 102 \text{ ft} \qquad\qquad C - B = 400 \text{ ft}$$
$$C = 500 \text{ ft} \qquad\qquad C - D = 349 \text{ ft}$$
$$D = 150 \text{ ft} \qquad\qquad D - E = \;\; 72 \text{ ft}$$
$$E = \;\; 80 \text{ ft} \qquad\qquad B - E = \;\; 20 \text{ ft}$$

2. Let the observed values for the angles of a plane triangle be $60° 10' \pm 1'$, $60° 2' \pm 2'$ and $60° 0' \pm 5'$. What are the most probable values of the angles?

3. Measurements of the y-components of the separations of the star images of stars α, β, γ, δ, and ϵ (indicated in the order of increasing y) are as given below. Determine the most probable values of the y-components for these star images measured with respect to the image of star α.

Separation	Distance (mm)	Separation	Distance (mm)
β–α	0.063 ± 0.005	γ–β	0.150 ± 0.003
γ–α	0.219 ± 0.004	δ–β	0.193 ± 0.005
δ–α	0.250 ± 0.007	δ–γ	0.041 ± 0.006

4. Given the following assumed measured values for CO_2 at 50 A and $100°$ C:

$$c_p = (0.275 \pm 0.005) \text{ cal}/(\text{gm C°})$$

$$c_v = (0.191 \pm 0.002) \text{ cal}/(\text{gm C°})$$

$$\gamma = 1.417 \pm 0.005$$

$$T \left(\frac{dp}{dT}\right)_v \left(\frac{dv}{dT}\right)_p = (0.0815 \pm 0.0040) \text{ cal}/(\text{gm C°})$$

determine the adjusted values for c_p, c_v, and γ.

5. From direct thermal measurements, with ΔG representing the change in Gibbs' function (the chemists' free energy) for the reaction specified, the following have been obtained:

(a) $\quad C_2H_6 \rightleftharpoons 2C + 3H_2 \qquad\qquad \Delta G = (+8{,}260 \pm 200) \text{ cal}$

(b) $2H_2 + 2C \rightleftharpoons C_2H_4 \qquad\qquad \Delta G = (+15{,}820 \pm 300) \text{ cal}$

From equilibrium constant determinations, the following has been reported:

(c) $\quad C_2H_6 \rightleftharpoons C_2H_4 + H_2 \qquad\qquad \Delta G = (+23{,}330 \pm 10) \text{ cal}$

Though some uncertainty has been expressed as to the justification for adjustment here, we are justified in using the data conditionally. What, in view of relation c, are the most probable values of ΔG for the reactions a and b?

6. Do the data of Table III satisfy either the Rossini and Deming or the Birge test for external consistency as set forth in Chapter VIII? Making use of the χ^2-procedure, determine the probability of occurrence of the e_n values of that table on the assumption of an expected normal frequency distribution.

7. Using the method employed by Darwin to obtain the needed simplified observation equations, determine the adjusted values for e, e/m_0, and h which follow from standard procedure. What are their probable errors?

CHAPTER XI

LEAST-SQUARES EQUATIONS REPRESENTING OBSERVED DATA

1. Introduction. Of the many products of least squares, that which is most valued is the method which it provides for the determination of the best equation of a specified type to represent observed data. Although strictly covered above under the most general case of the Adjustment of Observations, the method, because of its importance, is reconsidered here in a fashion more directly applicable to the determination of least-squares equations.

Often the constant appearing in a desired equation is important for the operation of an instrument or the application of a principle. In other instances it stands for a constant of nature and represents the goal of an experiment. Particularly in this latter case there seems justification for the accuracy which the least-squares method yields. Examples of such constants are the photoelectric constants h/e and ω/e of the Einstein equation

$$V_0 = \frac{h}{e}\nu - \frac{\omega}{e} \qquad [1]$$

the first radiation constant (often called the Stefan-Boltzmann constant), σ, appearing in the fourth-power radiation equation

$$\ln \mathcal{R} = \ln \sigma + 4(\ln T) \qquad [2]$$

and the gravitational acceleration of a freely falling body, g, as it appears in the well-known equation

$$s = s_0 + v_0 t + \frac{gt^2}{2} \qquad [3]$$

When one relies chiefly upon the eye in fitting a curve to plotted data, a tendency, difficult to overcome, is that of giving undue weights to the end points of the plot even though it is understood that the intermediate points are equally reliable and should be given equal weight. This tendency is particularly undesirable in the numerous cases where the extreme points are such because of added difficulties experienced in making observations in their regions and the regions beyond. By the

238

method of least squares, however, one may give either equal or unequal weights, as desired, to the various points of the plot.

Granted the type of equation to be used and the weighting of the data, there is no prospect for the obtaining of a more satisfactory equation than that which the least-squares method yields. There is, however, one drawback to its general use, and that is the great amount of labor which it ofttimes but not always entails. For this reason it may often be supplanted, with some slight sacrifice of confidence in the result, by one of the substitute methods of Chapter III combined with the method of successive approximations.

The method of least squares does not indicate the best form of equation, whether linear, or quadratic, or of other type, for the representation of given data. At most, it yields the most probable values for the constants entering an equation of an assumed form, whatever that form may be. In line with this, one sees possibilities of many least-squares equations for the same given set of data, each being a best representation for its own type of equation. Of these, the actual form selected, as noted in Chapter III, will generally depend upon theoretical considerations or the will or the intuition of the worker.

In this chapter we discuss particularly the theory and the process for cases where $y = f(x)$ takes the form of a straight line or a parabola, simple cases to which many others may be reduced. Shortened methods for special conditions, probable errors of constants determined by least-squares methods, and a criterion for closeness of fit of a least-squares equation are also considered. Special attention is directed, in case computing machines are not available, to the time saved when starting with an assumed approximate equation.

2. The Straight Line with Liability of Error Limited to the Dependent Variable. The constant which describes the variation of the resistivity of a metallic element with temperature at high temperatures is an important characteristic of the metal which helps to distinguish it from other metals. It is represented by $\dfrac{T}{\rho}\dfrac{d\rho}{dT}$ and is obtained from a plot of $\log \rho = f(\log T)$. Data of this kind for molybdenum,[1] as taken from Fig. 1 of the paper referred to, are given in Table I and Fig. 1.

Here we seek the least-squares equation for a straight line to represent the data just referred to. Conveniently representing $\log T$ by x and $\log \rho$ by y, the form taken by the equation is

$$y = a + bx$$

of which b is the constant in which we are the more interested.

[1] Worthing, A. G., *Phys. Rev.*, **28**, 190 (1926).

In accord with the least-squares principle, or, what is the same, the maximum probability principle, the line desired is a line characterized by a minimum for the sum of the squares of the deviations of the plotted points from it.   A difficulty appears at once.   Shall distances be taken at right angles to the line?   If so, the equation obtained will apply only to the particular arbitrary coordinate scales selected for the figure. With any other selection, different values will be obtained for a and b. How, in the general case with y and x differing in nature, we may select coordinate scales justifying the application of the least-squares principle to perpendicular distances between the plotted points and the least-squares line will be discussed later.

Here, following the usual and least arduous procedure, we shall assume the deviations, the sum of whose squares is to be a minimum, to be those that are strictly parallel to the y-axis.   This is equivalent to assuming that the x-measurements are exact and that the values of the dependent y-variable only are liable to errors.   Now the procedure is direct and simple.

Where y represents values defined by the least-squares equation

$$y = a + bx \tag{4}$$

and y_0, the observed values, we seek, as in connection with the adjustment of conditioned observations (see p. 217), to minimize, with respect to both a and b, $\Sigma(y_0 - y)^2$ or what is the same, $\Sigma(y_0 - a - bx)^2$. Where n represents the number of observed points, all assumed determined with the same precision, there follow

$$\frac{\partial}{\partial a}[\Sigma(y_0 - a - bx)^2] = 0 \tag{5}$$

$$\frac{\partial}{\partial b}[\Sigma(y_0 - a - bx)^2] = 0 \tag{6}$$

from which we obtain

$$na + b\Sigma x = \Sigma y_0 \tag{7}$$

$$a\Sigma x + b\Sigma x^2 = \Sigma xy_0 \tag{8}$$

It is well to emphasize here that in Eqs. 7 and 8, the unknowns are a and b, and that the summations involving x and y_0 are known quantities.   From these equations, we obtain

$$a = \frac{\Sigma x^2 \Sigma y_0 - \Sigma x \Sigma xy_0}{n\Sigma x^2 - (\Sigma x)^2} \tag{9}$$

$$b = \frac{n\Sigma xy_0 - \Sigma x \Sigma y_0}{n\Sigma x^2 - (\Sigma x)^2} \tag{10}$$

We may next proceed to tabulate the given values of x and y_0, to obtain the summations entering Eqs. 9 and 10 to solve for a and b, and finally to substitute in Eq. 1 to obtain the relation sought.

Excepting, however, certain instances where computing machines are available, much time may often be saved by first introducing a convenient linear relation

$$y' = a' + b'x \qquad [11]$$

which represents approximately the relation sought. One then treats by the least-squares method the differences Δy_0 between the observed y_0's and the y''s given by this assumed relation, to obtain a relation

$$\Delta y = \Delta a + \Delta bx \qquad [12]$$

The final desired relation follows at once from Eqs. 11 and 12.

$$y = y' + \Delta y = (a' + \Delta a) + (b' + \Delta b)x = a + bx \qquad [13]$$

We shall follow this plan. With the convenience of dealing with small numbers in mind, it is often found desirable, as noted also in Chapter III, to replace y or x or both by simple functions of those variables. This procedure will also be made use of in what follows.

Inspection of the x and y_0 columns of Table I shows that the numbers represented by x^2 and xy_0 will be unwieldy. One obvious advantage is obtained, as shown in the table, by making the substitution

$$x' = x - 3.2000 \qquad [14]$$

and treating the x' of this equation as the x of Eqs. 11 to 13.

TABLE I

DATA SHOWING THE RESISTIVITY, ρ, OF MOLYBDENUM AS A FUNCTION OF TEMPERATURE, T, AS USED IN ILLUSTRATING THE PROCEDURE INVOLVED IN FINDING THE LEAST-SQUARES EQUATION OF A STRAIGHT LINE

T (°K)	ρ ($\mu\Omega$ cm)	x (log T)	y_0 (log ρ)	x' $(x-3.2000)$	Δy_0 (y_0-y')	$10^6 x'^2$	$10^6 x'\Delta y_0$	$y_0 - y$
2289	61.97	3.3596	$\bar{5}.7922$	$+0.1596$	-0.0013	25472	-207.5	-0.0001
2132	57.32	3.3288	$\bar{5}.7584$	$+0.1288$	$+0.0003$	16589	$+ 38.6$	$+0.0014$
1988	52.70	3.2986	$\bar{5}.7218$	$+0.0986$	-0.0016	9720	-158.0	-0.0006
1830	47.92	3.2625	$\bar{5}.6805$	$+0.0625$	-0.0014	3906	$- 87.5$	-0.0005
1489	37.72	3.1729	$\bar{5}.5765$	-0.0271	-0.0023	734	$+ 62.3$	-0.0017
1286	32.09	3.1092	$\bar{5}.5064$	-0.0908	$+0.0008$	8245	$- 72.6$	$+0.0012$
1178	28.94	3.0711	$\bar{5}.4616$	-0.1289	-0.0002	16615	$+ 25.8$	$+0.0001$
				$+0.2027$	-0.0057	81281	-398.9	-0.0002

For the convenient approximate solution, we may assume (Fig. 1)

$$y' = \overline{5}.6100 + 1.150x' \tag{15}$$

For the Δy_0 there follows, as also shown in the table

$$\Delta y_0 = y_0 - y' = y_0 - (\overline{5}.6100 + 1.150x') \tag{16}$$

The quantities now subject to least-squares treatment are the relatively very small numerics x' and Δy_0.

In accord with the requirements of Eqs. 9 and 10, we next form the squares x'^2 and the products $x'\Delta y_0$, determine the sums $\Sigma x'$, $\Sigma \Delta y_0$, $\Sigma x'^2$, and $\Sigma x'\Delta y_0$, and substitute the values obtained in the equations to obtain Δa and Δb.   So doing leads to

$$\Delta a = \frac{(81281 \times 10^{-6})(-0.0057) - (0.2027)(-398.9 \times 10^{-6})}{7(81281 \times 10^{-6}) - (0.2027)^2}$$
$$= -0.0007 \quad [17]$$

$$\Delta b = \frac{7(-398.9 \times 10^{-6}) - (0.2027)(-0.0057)}{7(81281 \times 10^{-6}) - (0.2027)^2} = -0.0031 \tag{18}$$

There follow

$$\Delta y' = -0.0007 - 0.0031x' \tag{19}$$

$$y = y' + \Delta y' = \overline{5}.6093 + 1.1469x'$$

$$= \overline{5}.6093 + 1.1469(x - 3.2000) \tag{20}$$

Eq. 20 is the least-squares equation which best represents the data of Table I and Fig. 1, and 1.1469 is the least-squares value found for the important constant $\dfrac{T}{\rho}\dfrac{d\rho}{dT}$.   How well the equation fits the data is shown in the final column of the table under $y_0 - y$.   That the two end differences should be the smallest is a matter of chance.   The close agreement leaves little doubt as to the correctness of the assumption that $\dfrac{T}{\rho}\dfrac{d\rho}{dT}$ is a characteristic constant.   Just how much of the 1.1469 is significant cannot be stated without the treatment of more experimental data.   Without doubt the 9 is without real significance.

With weights assigned, w_1 for point 1, w_2 for point 2, etc., the procedure is very similar to that described.   Corresponding to x_1, we then

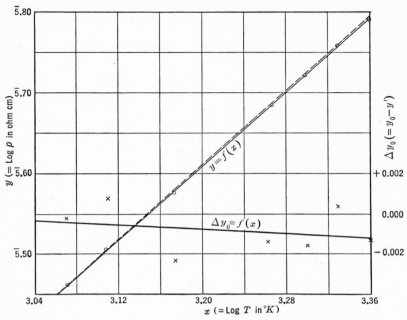

Fɪɢ. 1. Graph of log resistivity of molybdenum as a function of log temperature. The dashed line represents the assumed convenient approximate relation. The ×× points represent the differences between observed values and those predicted by that assumed approximate relation. The line $\Delta y_0 = f(x)$ represents the least-squares relation for those differences. The full line $y = f(x)$ represents the least-squares relation for the original data.

have, effectively, w_1 observations averaging to y_1, etc. Simple reasoning shows that for weighted observations

$$a = \frac{\Sigma wx^2 \Sigma wy_0 - \Sigma wx \Sigma wxy_0}{D} \qquad [21]$$

and

$$b = \frac{\Sigma w \Sigma wxy_0 - \Sigma wx \Sigma wy_0}{D} \qquad [22]$$

where

$$D = \Sigma w \Sigma wx^2 - (\Sigma wx)^2 \qquad [23]$$

3. Procedures Leading to Shortened Computations. Often, but not always, the labor involved in least-squares computations may be reduced appreciably or greatly by following certain procedures. At least four possibilities may be named. Two of them have already been illustrated in the preceding section. The first consists of introducing new variables to take the place of those given in the original data.   Referring to the preceding section, note that the independent variable T was replaced by $\log T - 3.200$ and that ρ was replaced by $\log \rho$.   The gain has been twofold, that of obtaining a linear form for the function and that of obtaining numbers with reduced magnitudes with which to deal. As will be noted in a later section, such a change for the dependent variable involves a change of weight.   This change, really rather unimportant for the case illustrated, was ignored in the application referred to.

The second procedure, also illustrated above, consists of assuming a convenient approximate relation between the two variables, taking the differences between the observed and the resulting corresponding computed values of the dependent variable, and applying the normal least-squares procedures to such differential values.   See in this connection Eqs. 15 and 16 above and the column of Table I headed Δy_0.   The gain has been a very considerable reduction in magnitude of the numerics involved.

The third procedure consists in making slight adjustments to yield values for the dependent variable corresponding to more convenient rounded values for the independent variable.   In making such adjustments, the definite trend of the relation should be observed.   How this may be done and the gain obtained thereby is well illustrated in Table II. A rough plot of the data indicates a straight-line relationship with an expected rate of variation of α_v with pressure of about 1.34×10^{-8} $\text{K}^{\circ -1}/\text{mm-Hg}$.   Applying this common rate to all values of α_v, the indicated adjusted values follow directly.   When, further, the first two named procedures are applied in addition, the problem of finding the desired α_v will be found to be quite brief and simple.   The carrying through of such a computation is left for a problem to be found at the end of the chapter.   To what extent adjustments of this type may be safely made may well be left to one's common sense.   Any error introduced on this account into the result for the case considered is obviously inappreciable.

The fourth procedure consists in taking or selecting data in advance for least-squares treatment in such manner that successive values for the independent variable shall differ by the same constant amount, say 10 cm, 5 min, 40 ft/sec, etc.   This procedure is only applicable where the dependent variable may be equated to a polynomial such as

$$y = a + bx + cx^2 + dx^3$$

involving the independent variable only to the third power (at present) or less.   When such is the case, it is possible, with change of variable,

TABLE II

PORTION OF DATA REPORTED BY BEATTIE,[1] OF MASSACHUSETTS INSTITUTE OF
TECHNOLOGY IN A DETERMINATION OF THE CONSTANT VOLUME COEFFICIENT α_v
OF NITROGEN AT $0°$ C AND ZERO PRESSURE AND CERTAIN ADJUSTMENTS OF THAT
DATA TO YIELD MORE CONVENIENT VALUES FOR LEAST-SQUARES TREATMENT

Unadjusted		Adjusted	
p mm–Hg	$10^7 \alpha_v$ K$^{°-1}$	p mm–Hg	$10^7 \alpha_v$ K$^{°-1}$
998.28	36740.48	1000.00	36740.71
749.66	36707.01	750.00	36707.06
599.59	36686.30	600.00	36686.36
449.42	36666.57	450.00	36666.65
333.11	36651.84	330.00	36651.40

[1] Beattie, James A., Report on the Thermodynamic Temperature of the Ice Point, from a symposium
on *Temperature, Its Measurement and Control in Science and Industry*, New York, The Reinhold Publishing Corporation, 1941, p. 85.

to make use of the procedure developed by Baily and the tables computed by Cox and Matuschak whose uses are described below.

**4. Nonlinear Forms of Equations That May Be Readily Reduced to
Linear Forms for Least-Squares Treatment.** Of these we cite Cauchy's
two-term equation for the index of refraction of a substance

$$n = a + \frac{b}{\lambda^2} \qquad [24]$$

the common decay law

$$I = I_0 e^{-\alpha x} \qquad [25]$$

the normal frequency distribution of errors

$$y = y_0 e^{-h^2 x^2} \qquad [26]$$

the law for the variation of field strength in the neighborhood of an
infinitely long, uniformly charged circular wire of unknown diameter

$$E(r + a) = b \qquad [27]$$

and the potential energy for a system of two bodies experiencing mutually attracting and repelling forces

$$V = ar^{-m} - br^n \qquad [28]$$

The first of these is actually linear in n and $1/\lambda^2$ though not in n and λ. The others may be changed to the following forms for convenience:

$$\ln I = \ln I_0 - \alpha x \qquad [29]$$

$$\ln y = \ln y_0 - h^2 x^2 \qquad [30]$$

$$\frac{b}{E} = r + a \qquad [31]$$

$$V r^m = a - b r^{m+n} \qquad [32]$$

in which forms the equations are linear in terms of the functions multiplying the constants sought and may be treated accordingly.

5. The Straight Line through the Origin, $y = bx$, with y Only Liable to Error. Sometimes y is known to be proportional to x. Then the best value for the single constant b in the relation

$$y = bx \qquad [33]$$

is to be determined. This is the case for the radiancy of a black body where

$$\mathcal{R} = \sigma T^4 \qquad [34]$$

which takes the form of Eq. 33 when T^4 is represented by x. Here we imagine T^4 plotted as abscissas and $\mathcal{R}$ as ordinates. The procedure outlined above, on the assumption that a is zero, and that y, or $\mathcal{R}$, only is liable to error, leads to a simple expression for b.

Substitution of $a = 0$ into Eqs. 7 and 8 leads to two expressions for b, namely

$$\left[b = \frac{\Sigma y_0}{\Sigma x} \right]_{\text{(Eq. 7)}} \qquad [35]$$

and

$$\left[b = \frac{\Sigma x y_0}{\Sigma x^2} \right]_{\text{(Eq. 8)}} \qquad [35a]$$

The former depends on the partial derivative of a summation with respect to a and gives the best value for b subject to the condition that the best value for a is incidentally zero. The latter, however, depends on a derivative with respect to b of the summation $\Sigma(y_0 - bx)^2$ based on the condition that a is zero. It gives a best value for b for the condition that the graphed straight line must pass through the x, y origin. Corresponding to the original specified condition, Eq. 35a is the one to be used.

For unequally weighted pairs of values, we have

$$b = \frac{\Sigma w x y_0}{\Sigma w x^2} \qquad [36]$$

For the constant σ, we have accordingly, for the case of equal weights given to observation equations of the type of Eq. 34

$$\sigma = \frac{\Sigma \mathcal{R} T^4}{\Sigma (T^4)^2} \tag{37}$$

Eq. 35a forms the basis for much work in Correlation. (See Chap. XII.)

6. Change of Weights Implied by a Change of Variables. Instead of following the procedure outlined in the preceding section for obtaining a most probable value of the first radiation constant σ, at least two other reasonable methods may be followed to yield least-squares values. The three methods will normally yield different best values unless account is taken of the variation in method.

First, let Eq. 34 be rearranged to read

$$\ln \mathcal{R} = \ln \sigma + 4 \ln T \tag{38}$$

We may imagine $\ln \mathcal{R}$ as the dependent variable plotted as a function of $\ln T$, the independent variable whose values, as those for T^4 in the preceding section, we shall treat as free from error.

Accordingly we seek the least-squares line whose slope is 4, and in particular its intercept on the $\ln \mathcal{R}$ axis. Equating b of Eq. 10 to 4, solving for Σxy_0, and substituting in Eq. 9 yields

$$a = \frac{\Sigma y_0 - 4 \Sigma x}{n} \tag{39}$$

whence

$$\sigma = \ln^{-1} \left[\frac{\Sigma \ln \mathcal{R} - 4 \Sigma \ln T}{n} \right] \tag{40}$$

a value which is also obtained by merely averaging the values of $\ln \sigma$ as given by Eq. 38 and then taking the antilog.

Second, we may rearrange Eq. 34 to read

$$\frac{\mathcal{R}}{T^4} = \sigma + 0 \frac{a}{T^4} = \sigma \tag{41}$$

Similarly, we may imagine $\mathcal{R}/T^4$ the dependent variable plotted as a function of the independent variable $1/T^4$ which is assumed free from error. Now we seek the intercept for the least-squares line with a zero slope. Equating the b of Eq. 7 to zero leads at once to

$$a = \frac{1}{n} \Sigma y_0 \tag{42}$$

or

$$\sigma = \frac{1}{n} \Sigma \frac{\mathcal{R}}{T^4} \tag{43}$$

This value is a straight average of the dependent variable. The solution obtained by equating the b of Eq. 8 to zero is to be disregarded for a reason similar to that given in connection with Eq. 35.

That the procedures based on Eqs. 34, 38, and 41 will lead to different values for σ is evident. The explanation is that they tacitly ascribe different weights to the observed pairs of $\mathcal{R}, T$ values. Assuming values for T precise, consider what changes in weights have been tacitly given to the measurements of $\mathcal{R}$ in shifting from the procedure based on Eq. 34 to that based on Eq. 38. The answer is indicated by Eq. 33 of Chapter IX which expressed the law of propagation of probable errors and other precision indexes for the general case. Simplified for the present case of only one independent variable, it states that

$$p_{\ln \mathcal{R}} = \frac{d(\ln \mathcal{R})}{d\mathcal{R}} \, p_{\mathcal{R}} = \frac{1}{\mathcal{R}} \, p_{\mathcal{R}} \qquad [44]$$

Since, as shown in Chapter VIII, weights vary inversely as probable errors squared, we have

$$\frac{(w_{\ln \mathcal{R}})_1}{(w_{\ln \mathcal{R}})_2} = \frac{\left(\dfrac{1}{\mathcal{R}} \, p_{\mathcal{R}}\right)_2^2}{\left(\dfrac{1}{\mathcal{R}} \, p_{\mathcal{R}}\right)_1^2} = \frac{\mathcal{R}_1{}^2 \, p_{\mathcal{R}_2}{}^2}{\mathcal{R}_2{}^2 \, p_{\mathcal{R}_1}{}^2} \qquad [45]$$

Assuming that all $p_{\mathcal{R}}$'s are equal, this means that the corresponding values of $\ln \mathcal{R}$ should be weighted as the squares of their own $\mathcal{R}$'s. If this is done, one should obtain identical results for σ, whether starting with Eq. 34 or Eq. 38. Starting with the latter, one should naturally use the necessary modification of Eq. 40 to take account of the variable weighting. Of course, the weights tacitly given to the $\mathcal{R}$'s (not $\ln \mathcal{R}$'s) varied as $1/\mathcal{R}^2$, when the shift was made above to Eq. 40 and its $\ln \mathcal{R}$'s were treated as equally weighted.

Similarly consider the weights tacitly given to the measurements of $\mathcal{R}$ when the procedure initially based on Eq. 34 was changed to that based on Eq. 41. Here we obtain

$$p_{(\mathcal{R}/T^4)} = \frac{d(\mathcal{R}/T^4)}{d\mathcal{R}} \, p_{\mathcal{R}} = \frac{1}{T^4} \, p_{\mathcal{R}} \qquad [46]$$

and

$$\frac{[w_{(\mathcal{R}/T^4)}]_1}{[w_{(\mathcal{R}/T^4)}]_2} = \frac{\left(\dfrac{1}{T^4} \, p_{\mathcal{R}}\right)_2^2}{\left(\dfrac{1}{T^4} \, p_{\mathcal{R}}\right)_1^2} = \frac{T_1{}^8 \, p_{\mathcal{R}_2}{}^2}{T_2{}^8 \, p_{\mathcal{R}_1}{}^2} \qquad [47]$$

Assuming as before that all $p_\mathcal{R}$'s are equal, means that corresponding values for $\mathcal{R}/T^4$ should be weighted according to their own T^8. The weights tacitly given to values of $\mathcal{R}$ (not $\mathcal{R}/T^4$) when the shift was made above to Eq. 41 were as $1/T^8$. That weighting $\mathcal{R}/T^4$ as just indicated actually gives the same value for σ as does Eq. 37 is easily verified. With such weights given, as may be verified with the aid of Eqs. 21 and 22, we have, corresponding to Eqs. 42 and 43

$$a = \frac{\Sigma w \mathcal{R}/T^4}{\Sigma w} \qquad [48]$$

and

$$\sigma = \frac{\Sigma T^8 \mathcal{R}/T^4}{\Sigma T^8} = \frac{\Sigma \mathcal{R} T^4}{\Sigma (T^4)^2} \qquad [49]$$

the latter of which is identical with Eq. 37. Unfortunately, equivalence for the end results is not so simply shown when the first and second procedures are similarly tested. The conclusion follows that with proper account taken of changes in weight for the independent variable, it matters not in which of many interchangeable forms the data are given least-squares treatment.

The foregoing does not indicate in any way that, in an actual determination of σ, equal weights should be given to the $\mathcal{R}$'s rather than the ln $\mathcal{R}$'s or the $\mathcal{R}/T^4$'s.

7. Probable Errors for the Least-Squares Constants of a Linear Equation. The procedure here is similar to that given in Chapter X in the discussion of the probable errors of adjusted measurements. We wish to determine the reliability of the a and b of Eq. 4 as given by Eqs. 9 and 10 or Eqs. 21 and 22. For the present purpose Eqs. 21 and 22 may be rewritten as

$$a = \frac{\Sigma wx^2}{\Sigma w \Sigma wx^2 - (\Sigma wx)^2} \Sigma wy_0 - \frac{\Sigma wx}{\Sigma w \Sigma wx^2 - (\Sigma wx)^2} \Sigma wxy_0 \qquad [50]$$

$$= A \Sigma wy_0 - A' \Sigma wxy_0 = \Sigma [(A - A'x)wy_0]$$

$$b = \frac{\Sigma w}{\Sigma w \Sigma wx^2 - (\Sigma wx)^2} \Sigma wxy_0 - \frac{\Sigma wx}{\Sigma w \Sigma wx^2 - (\Sigma wx)^2} \Sigma wy_0 \qquad [51]$$

$$= B' \Sigma wxy_0 - B \Sigma wy_0 = \Sigma [(B'x - B)wy_0]$$

To these may be applied the law of propagation of probable errors as expressed for the general case in Eq. 32 of Chapter IX, namely

$$p_U{}^2 = \left(\frac{\partial U}{\partial X}\right)^2 p_X{}^2 + \left(\frac{\partial U}{\partial Y}\right)^2 p_Y{}^2 + \cdots \qquad [52]$$

Here, owing to weights being assigned to the various pairs of measured data, the p_{y_0} is that of the measurement having unit weight. It follows that

$$p_a = p_{y_0} \Sigma w (A - A'x) \qquad [53]$$

and

$$p_b = p_{y_0} \Sigma w (B'x - B) \qquad [54]$$

of which by definition

$$p_{y_0} = 0.675 \sqrt{\frac{\Sigma[w(y_0 - a - bx)^2]}{n-2}} \doteq 0.675 \sqrt{\frac{\Sigma[w(y_0 - a - bx)^2]}{n}} \qquad [55]\,^1$$

For the case of equal weights for the y's, the w's disappear from all of the expressions involved.

8. The Parabola, $y = a + bx + cx^2$ with y Only Liable to Error.
The procedure here is quite like that for the straight line. The assumed equation is

$$y = a + bx + cx^2 \qquad [55a]$$

There follow

$$\frac{\partial}{\partial a} [\Sigma(y_0 - a - bx - cx^2)^2] = 0$$

$$\frac{\partial}{\partial b} [\Sigma(y_0 - a - bx - cx^2)^2] = 0 \qquad [56]$$

$$\frac{\partial}{\partial c} [\Sigma(y_0 - a - bx - cx^2)^2] = 0$$

$$an + b\Sigma x + c\Sigma x^2 = \Sigma y_0$$

$$a\Sigma x + b\Sigma x^2 + c\Sigma x^3 = \Sigma xy_0 \qquad [57]$$

$$a\Sigma x^2 + b\Sigma x^3 + c\Sigma x^4 = \Sigma x^2 y_0$$

$$a = \frac{\left\{\begin{matrix}[\Sigma x^2 \Sigma x^4 - (\Sigma x^3)^2]\Sigma y_0 - [\Sigma x \Sigma x^4 - \Sigma x^2 \Sigma x^3]\Sigma xy_0 \\ + [\Sigma x \Sigma x^3 - (\Sigma x^2)^2]\Sigma x^2 y_0\end{matrix}\right\}}{\left\{\begin{matrix}[\Sigma x^2 \Sigma x^4 - (\Sigma x^3)^2]n - [\Sigma x \Sigma x^4 - \Sigma x^2 \Sigma x^3]\Sigma x \\ + [\Sigma x \Sigma x^3 - (\Sigma x^2)^2]\Sigma x^2\end{matrix}\right\}}$$

$$b = \frac{\left\{\begin{matrix}[\Sigma x^2 \Sigma x^3 - \Sigma x \Sigma x^4]\Sigma y_0 - [(\Sigma x^2)^2 - n\Sigma x^4]\Sigma xy_0 \\ + [\Sigma x \Sigma x^2 - n\Sigma x^3]\Sigma x^2 y_0\end{matrix}\right\}}{\left\{\begin{matrix}[\Sigma x^2 \Sigma x^4 - (\Sigma x^3)^2]n - [\Sigma x \Sigma x^4 - \Sigma x^2 \Sigma x^3]\Sigma x \\ + [\Sigma x \Sigma x^3 - (\Sigma x^2)^2]\Sigma x^2\end{matrix}\right\}} \qquad [58]$$

---

[1] See footnote on page 167. For the more precise form, the factor $n - 2$ replaces the more common $n - 1$. The reason is due to the fact that two arbitrary parameter, a and b, are involved. (See Birge, *Phys. Rev.*, **40**, 207 (1932)).

$$c = \frac{\left\{\begin{array}{l}[\Sigma x \Sigma x^3 - (\Sigma x^2)^2]\Sigma y_0 - [n\Sigma x^3 - \Sigma x \Sigma x^2]\Sigma x y_0 \\ \quad + [n\Sigma x^2 - (\Sigma x)^2]\Sigma x^2 y_0\end{array}\right\}}{\left\{\begin{array}{l}[\Sigma x^2 \Sigma x^4 - (\Sigma x^3)^2]n - [\Sigma x \Sigma x^4 - \Sigma x^2 \Sigma x^3]\Sigma x \\ \quad + [\Sigma x \Sigma x^3 - (\Sigma x^2)^2]\Sigma x^2\end{array}\right\}}$$

The denominators for the last three equations are identical.

Excepting certain types of cases as will appear in a later section, the least-squares method for equations other than the straight line are genally quite laborious. Here, however, much more than in the straight-line case, much time is saved if a convenient approximate solution is assumed and the least-squares principle is applied to the differences between the observed values and those predicted by that assumed relation.

9. Application of the Least-Squares Parabolic Equation to the Smoothing of Tabulated Data. In Chapter I it was indicated that a certain smoothing relation (Eq. 1) was based on the least-squares principle. It is now possible to show how the equation, namely

$$y = \frac{1}{35}\left[17y_0 + 12(y_{+1} + y_{-1}) - 3(y_{+2} + y_{-2})\right] \qquad [60]$$

may be derived. Here y_0 is the tabulated unsmoothed value corresponding to x_0. Similarly y_{+2}, y_{+1}, y_{-1}, and y_{-2} are the tabulated unsmoothed values corresponding to $x_0 + 2\Delta x$, $x_0 + \Delta x$, $x_0 - \Delta x$, and $x_0 - 2\Delta x$, and y is the smoothed value which is to replace y_0. Only five points on an assumed plot representing the data are used.

For the process of smoothing at any particular x, say x_0, much time is saved by a change of coordinates. Let x be replaced by x' [$= (x - x_0)/\Delta x$]. In the new coordinate system, the points to be treated are $(2, y_{+2})$, $(1, y_{+1})$, $(0, y_0)$, $(-1, y_{-1})$, and $(-2, y_{-2})$. The least-squares relation sought is

$$y = a + bx' + cx'^2 \qquad [61]$$

Since we are concerned only with the smoothed value for y at x_0, we need only to evaluate a of Eq. 58, which is the smoothed value sought. Evaluation, seeming long at first sight, is actually made short by the change from x to x' and y to y'. It will be found that $\Sigma x' = \Sigma x'^3 = 0$, that $\Sigma x'^2 = 10$, and that $\Sigma x'^4 = 34$. There follows

$$a = \frac{(340\Sigma y - 0\Sigma x'y - 100\Sigma x'^2 y)}{(340 \times 5 - 0 \times 0 - 100 \times 10)} \qquad [62]$$

$$= \frac{1}{35}\left[17y_0 + 12(y_{+1} + y_{-1}) - 3(y_{+2} + y_{-2})\right] \qquad [63]$$

which is the relation sought.

10. The Polynomial with x-Values Equally Spaced and Exact. A most comprehensive study of this particular field has been presented by Birge,[1] Condon,[2] and Birge and Shea.[3] A generalized, compact formula developed by them is presented in the paper last referred to. It will be discussed later. First, however, we shall discuss certain results and procedures which by virtue of the computations reported by Baily [4] and by Cox and Matuschak [5] are more readily applied.

The treatment of polynomials here given refers only to equations of the form

$$y = a + bx + cx^2 + dx^3 + \cdots \tag{64}$$

Further the assumption is made and if necessary the data are so manipulated (1) that the observed values of y are equally weighted, (2) that the successive values of x differ by a constant, (3) that the values of x are exact, and (4) that the values of x are arranged symmetrically with respect to a central zero value. Illustrative of the simplifying effects of these conditions, it has already been shown in the preceding section that, under the stated conditions, the rather formidable general expressions for the constants a, b, and c (Eqs. 58) of the least-squares equation for the parabola

$$y = a + bx + cx^2 \tag{55a}$$

reduces to rather simple expressions.

Treatments in accord with the above-stated conditions usually require a change of independent variable from x to X. Thus, where $\bar{x}$ represents one-half the sum of the initial and final values of x, Δx is the common x-interval, and the number of pairs of values is odd, X is defined by

$$X_o = \frac{x - \bar{x}}{\Delta x} \tag{65}$$

In case n is even, X is similarly defined by

$$X_e = \frac{x - \bar{x}}{\Delta x/2} \tag{66}$$

Thus defined, both X_o and X_e are whole numbers with both negative and positive values. For the odd series the values are

$$\cdots -3, -2, -1, 0, +1, +2, +3, + \cdots$$

for the even series

$$\cdots -5, -3, -1, +1, +3, +5, + \cdots$$

[1] Birge, *Phys. Rev.*, **13**, 360 (1919).
[2] Condon, U. E., *Univ. Calif. Pub. in Math.*, **2**, 55–56 (1927).
[3] Birge, R. T., and Shea, J. D.; Ibid., pp. 67–116.
[4] Baily, J. L., *Ann. Math. Statistics*, **2**, 355 (1931).
[5] Cox, G. C., and Matuschak, Margaret, *J. Phys. Chem.*, **45**, 362 (1941).

A simplification of Eq. 58 follows because now all summations of odd powers of X are equal to zero. As a result the a, b, and c of Eq. 58, now the a', b', and c', of an equation in X similar to Eq. 55a, reduce to

$$a' = \frac{\Sigma X^4}{n\Sigma X^4 - (\Sigma X^2)^2} \Sigma y - \frac{\Sigma X^2}{n\Sigma X^4 - (\Sigma X^2)^2} \Sigma X^2 y$$
$$= k_3 \Sigma y - k_4 \Sigma X^2 y \quad [67]$$

$$b' = \frac{n\Sigma X^4 - (\Sigma X^2)^2}{n\Sigma X^2 \Sigma X^4 - (\Sigma X^2)^3} \Sigma X y = k_2 \Sigma X y \quad [68]$$

$$c' = \frac{n}{n\Sigma X^4 - (\Sigma X^2)^2} \Sigma X^2 y - \frac{\Sigma X^2}{n\Sigma X^4 - (\Sigma X^2)^2} \Sigma y$$
$$= k_5 \Sigma X^2 y - k_4 \Sigma y \quad [69]$$

The k's are seen to be functions of X only and as such have been tabulated by Baily not only for the polynomial ending with X^2 but also for polynomials ending in X and X^3. The various k's entering and their designations by subscripts are shown in Table VI of Appendix 2, and values for these k's, as computed by Cox and Matuschak, for $2 < n < 51$ are presented in Tables VII and VIII. Though given to eight significant figures in these two tables, usually a much smaller number will suffice. Where the tables are applicable, computations are very greatly reduced by their use.

Illustrating the applicability of the method, let us consider certain data concerning a laboratory experiment relating to gravitational acceleration published by Pugh.[1] Though originally presented for least-squares treatment by a different procedure, they suffice well for our purposes. Using a falling-body apparatus with spark recording of positions at the ends of successive 1/30 sec intervals, the data given in the first two columns of Table III were obtained. The equation relating distance and time is

$$s = s_0 + v_0 t + \tfrac{1}{2} g t^2 \quad [3]$$

in which s and t replace the y and x of the preceding discussion. In accord with Eq. 66, the origin for the time axis is shifted to midway between the ends of the 7th and the 8th time intervals, and the interval of time that corresponds to a change of 1 in X is 1/60 sec. In the new coordinate system, in which t is replaced by $t + X\Delta t/2$, Eq. 3 becomes

$$s = (s_0 + v_0 \bar{t} + \tfrac{1}{2} g \bar{t}^2) + (\tfrac{1}{2} v_0 \Delta t + \tfrac{1}{2} g \bar{t} \Delta t) X + [\tfrac{1}{8} g (\Delta t)^2] X^2 \quad [70]$$

The successive terms in parentheses in order correspond to the a', b', and c' of Eqs. 67 to 69 and Table VI of Appendix 2. Since the acceleration g

[1] Pugh, E. M., *Am. Phys. Teacher*, **4**, 70 (1936).

TABLE III

Illustration of the Application of Baily's and Cox and Matuschak's Method to Falling-Body Data Presented by Pugh [1] for Use in Determining the Gravitational Acceleration g

t in units of $1/30$ sec	s in cm	X	X^2s in cm	
1	11.86	−13	2,004.34	$c' = k_5\Sigma X^2s - k_4\Sigma s$
2	15.67	−11	1,896.07	$k_5 = 21,462,912 \times 10^{-12}$
3	20.60	− 9	1,668.60	$k_4 = 13,950,893 \times 10^{-10}$
4	26.69	− 7	1,307.81	$k_5\Sigma X^2s = 1.40585$ cm
5	33.71	− 5	842.75	$k_4\Sigma s = 1.26993$ cm
6	41.93	− 3	377.37	$c' = 0.13592$ cm
7	51.13	− 1	51.13	$\Delta t = \frac{1}{30}$ sec
8	61.49	+ 1	61.49	
9	72.90	3	656.10	$g = \dfrac{8c'}{(\Delta t)^2} = 978.6\ \dfrac{\text{cm}}{\text{sec}^2}$
10	85.44	5	2,136.00	
11	99.08	7	4,854.92	
12	113.77	9	9,215.37	
13	129.54	11	15,674.34	
14	146.48	13	24,755.12	
Totals	910.29		65,501.41	

[1] *Am. Phys. Teacher*, **4**, 70 (1936).

only is desired, it suffices to solve for c', using the tables, and then for g, whose value is given by

$$g = \frac{8c'}{(\Delta t)^2} \qquad [71]$$

Some of the details are shown at the right in Table III. As is evident, the procedure is not unduly prolonged.

In many instances data that may well be given least-squares treatment similar to that above are subject to the theoretical condition that the constant a of Eq. 64 is zero. One may be tempted to meet this difficulty in the application of the Cox and Matuschak tables by dividing both sides of Eq. 64 by x, treating y/x as z in the equation

$$z = b + cx + dx^2 + \cdots \qquad [72]$$

and then finally returning to the original form of Eq. 64. In so doing, however, the original y-values will no longer have their original equal weights, but instead will be tacitly given weights proportional to their corresponding x^2's. Tables similar to those by Cox and Matuschak computed for the case of $a = 0$ would be much appreciated.

Consider next the more general formula of Birge and Shea, already referred to. Their form for the polynomial equation of the jth degree is

$$y = a_{0j} + a_{1j}x + a_{2j}x^2 + \cdots \tag{73}$$

Curiously, all coefficients, $a_{0j}\cdots a_{jj}$, can be worked out as definitely related to final coefficients of the form a_{jj} of which the j is not always the j of the polynomial sought. For the coefficient a_{jj} they found

$$a_{jj} = \frac{(2u - j)!(2j + 1)!}{(2u + j + 1)!(j!)^2} \sum_{r=0 \text{ or } \frac{1}{2}}^{r=u} \begin{bmatrix} y_r + (-1)^j y_{-r} \\ \text{or} \\ y_0 \end{bmatrix}$$

$$\sum_{s=0}^{s=j} \frac{(-1)^s(u - r)!(2u - s)!(j + s)!}{(u - r - s)!(2u - j)!(j - s)!(s!)^2} \tag{74}$$

where n represents the number of observations, u equals $\frac{1}{2}(n - 1)$, and r and s are parameters with successive values differing by unity. For n odd, the lowest value of r is 0; for n even, $\frac{1}{2}$. In case j is even and r is 0, but for no other case, the central member of the above expression for a_{jj} is y_0 rather than the expected $2y_0$.

For the condition $j = 2$, the coefficient a_{22} may be obtained from a direct application of the above equation, and the remaining coefficients, a_{02} and a_{12}, may be determined from the following

$$a_{02} = a_{00} - \frac{n^2 - 1}{12} a_{22} \tag{75}$$

and

$$a_{12} = a_{11} \tag{75a}$$

For other values of j the reader is referred to the original paper.

11. Least-Squares Procedure for Relations Other than Those Expressible in Power Series. Generally, a procedure involving an assumed approximate relation as illustrated above for a simple straight line will simplify and considerably shorten the computations connected with many least-squares determinations. In fact, in some instances, procedure is extremely difficult or even stopped where such advantage of an assumed approximate relation is not taken. This is the case where the equation does not form or cannot be converted into a power series with the constants sought or some functions of them as the coefficients of the power terms. Illustrating such a relation, we have

$$y = a \sin(\omega t + b) \tag{76}$$

with a and b to be determined. This relation will be treated in some detail in the following section. Another relation is

$$y = a + \frac{b}{x^c} \qquad [77]$$

with a, b, and c to be determined.

Let $y = f(x)$ be a desired relation of known form involving undetermined parameters a, b, c, etc. Let $y' = f(x)$ represent the approximate equation. We may write, in accord with Taylor's expansion

$$\Delta y = y - y' = \left(\frac{\partial y'}{\partial a}\right) \Delta a + \left(\frac{\partial y'}{\partial b}\right) \Delta b + \left(\frac{\partial y'}{\partial c}\right) \Delta c + \cdots \qquad [78]$$

In evaluating the partials, as suggested by the primes, the assumed values of a, b, $c, \cdots$, as expressed in $y' = f(x)$ are used. To illustrate, where $y = f(x)$ takes the forms of Eqs. 76 and 77, we are able, using the approximation principle, tc reduce the problems to finding the constants Δa, Δb, and Δc for the following:

$$\Delta y = \sin (\omega t + b') \times \Delta a + a' \cos (\omega t + b') \times \Delta b \qquad [79]$$

$$\Delta y = \Delta a + \frac{1}{x^{c'}} \Delta b - \frac{b' \ln x}{x^{c'}} \Delta c \qquad [80]$$

The quantities a', b', and c' are constants, obtainable by one of the methods of Chapter III. The equations are linear in Δa, Δb, and Δc and are subject to standard least-squares treatment. Since the partial derivatives involve a', b', or c', it is of importance that the assumed relation shall approximate the final relation rather closely. If the first approximation is not sufficiently close, a second may be required.

The equations yielding Δa and Δb of Eq. 79 are obtained in a manner similar to that yielding Eqs. 9 and 10, from which a and b were obtained in the straight-line case. The equations obtained are also similar. Where three corrections, as Δa, Δb, and Δc, are involved, the procedure is like that described above for the parabola, and the equations have a certain similarity.

Once Δa, Δb, $\Delta c, \cdots$ have been determined, the corrected values for a, b, $c, \cdots$ are obtained readily, since they are merely $a' + \Delta a$, $b' + \Delta b$, $c' + \Delta c, \cdots$

12. The Sine Curve with Angle Measurements Free from Error. The procedure which we shall follow here will differ slightly from that suggested in the preceding section. It will be simplified to the extent that we shall assume an approximate value for the b but not for the a of Eq. 76.

TABLE IV

SHOWING A CONVENIENT FORM FOR MAKING COMPUTATIONS, AND SAMPLE COMPUTATIONS LEADING TO A LEAST-SQUARES EQUATION OF THE FORM $y = a \sin(\omega t - \epsilon)$ IN ACCORD WITH EQS. 81 TO 86

(Certain of D. C. Miller's ether drift data [1] interpreted as showing azimuthal angular motion with respect to the ecliptic are here used. As ϵ', $0.15 \times 360°$ has been chosen.

t sidereal day	θ deg	y_0 deg	$\cos\theta$	$\sin\theta$	y_0^2 deg^2	$y_0\cos\theta$ deg	$y_0\sin\theta$ deg	$\cos\theta\sin\theta$	$\cos^2\theta$
0.00	−54	−25	0.588	−0.809	625	−14.70	20.22	−0.4757	0.3457
0.05	−36	−26	0.809	−0.588	676	−21.03	15.29	−0.4757	0.6545
0.10	−18	− 4	0.951	−0.309	16	− 3.80	1.24	−0.2939	0.9044
0.15	0	7	1.000	0.000	49	7.00	0.00	0.0000	1.0000
0.20	18	6	0.951	0.309	36	5.71	1.85	0.2939	0.9044
0.25	36	13	0.809	0.588	169	10.51	7.64	0.4757	0.6545
0.30	54	30	0.588	0.809	900	17.64	24.27	0.4757	0.3457
0.35	72	26	0.309	0.951	676	8.03	24.73	0.2939	0.0955
0.40	90	32	0.000	1.000	1,024	0.00	32.00	0.0000	0.0000
0.45	108	40	−0.309	0.951	1,600	−12.36	38.04	−0.2939	0.0955
0.50	126	32	−0.588	0.809	1,024	−18.82	25.89	−0.4757	0.3457
0.55	144	21	−0.809	0.588	441	−16.99	12.35	−0.4757	0.6545
0.60	162	11	−0.951	0.309	121	−10.46	3.40	−0.2939	0.9044
0.65	180	− 5	−1.000	0.000	25	5.00	0.00	0.0000	1.0000
0.70	−162	−16	−0.951	−0.309	256	15.22	4.94	0.2939	0.9044
0.75	−144	3	−0.809	−0.588	9	− 2.43	−1.76	0.4757	0.6545
0.80	−126	−21	−0.588	−0.809	441	12.35	16.99	0.4757	0.3457
0.85	−108	−22	−0.309	−0.951	484	6.80	20.92	0.2939	0.0955
0.90	− 90	−29	0.000	−1.000	841	0.00	29.00	0.0000	0.0000
0.95	−72	−32	0.309	−0.951	1,024	− 9.89	30.43	−0.2939	0.0955
					10,437	−22.22	307.44	0.0000	12.0004

$$a = \frac{1}{A} = \frac{10437 \times 12.0004 - (-22.22)^2}{307.44 \times 12.0004 - 0.0(-22.22)} \text{ deg} = 34.09°$$

$$\delta = \frac{10437 \times 0.0 - (-22.22)(307.44)}{10437 \times 12.0004 - (-22.22)^2} \text{ rad} = 0.0543 \text{ rad} = 3° \, 7'$$

$$\epsilon = \epsilon' + \delta = 54° + 3° \, 7' = 57° \, 7'$$

$$y = 34° \, 5.4' \sin\left(\frac{360°}{\text{sid. day}} t - 57° \, 7'\right)$$

[1] *Rev. Modern Phys.*, **5**, 203 (1939).

Assume the desired form of equation to be

$$y = a \sin (\omega t - \epsilon) \tag{81}$$

where a and ϵ are to be determined. From a plot of the data, estimate in advance, as is usually possible, an approximate value for ϵ, say ϵ'. Let δ represent $(\epsilon - \epsilon')$; θ, the angle $(\omega t - \epsilon')$; and A, the term $1/a$. Expansion of $\sin (\theta + \delta)$ in terms of sines and cosines leads at once to

$$Ay - \sin \theta + \delta \cos \theta = 0 \tag{82}$$

In determining the least-squares equation, A and δ, in terms of which the equation is linear, are to be evaluated. Regular procedure yields

$$\Sigma(Ay_0 - \sin \theta + \delta \cos \theta)^2 = \phi = \text{a minimum} \tag{83}$$

of which y_0 represents measured values corresponding to appropriate values of θ. Equating $\partial\phi/\partial A$ and $\partial\phi/\partial\delta$ separately to zero and solving for A and δ as before, leads to

$$A\Sigma y_0{}^2 - \Sigma y_0 \sin \theta + \delta\Sigma y_0 \cos \theta = 0 \tag{84}$$

$$A\Sigma y_0 \cos \theta - \Sigma \cos \theta \sin \theta + \delta\Sigma \cos^2 \theta = 0 \tag{84a}$$

$$A = \frac{\Sigma y_0 \sin \theta \, \Sigma \cos^2 \theta - \Sigma \cos \theta \sin \theta \, \Sigma y_0 \cos \theta}{\Sigma y_0{}^2 \cos^2 \theta - (\Sigma y_0 \cos \theta)^2} \tag{85}$$

$$\delta = \frac{\Sigma y_0{}^2 \Sigma \cos \theta \sin \theta - \Sigma y_0 \cos \theta \, \Sigma y_0 \sin \theta}{\Sigma y_0{}^2 \Sigma \cos^2 \theta - (\Sigma y_0 \cos \theta)^2} \tag{86}$$

Insertion of values for A and δ in Eq. 82 gives the relation sought. In case the first estimated ϵ' yields too large a δ, repetition of the process with a different ϵ' will be necessary. Table IV, which deals with a simple case, shows a convenient form for carrying out the computations. Probable errors for a and ϵ may be obtained by following a procedure much like that for the probable errors for the constants a and b of a straight-line equation.

13. The Least-Squares Equation of the Type $y = a + bx$ when Liability of Error Occurs with Both x and y. Although mathematically we may consider x an independent variable with values arbitrarily chosen and as such not liable to error, in reality in physical problems, such is not always the situation. Frequently neither x nor y can be said to be more independent as a variable than the other. Both are measured and the values obtained for both are subject to errors of measurement. Consider the case of the measurement of the temperature and the radiancy of a black body for some particular condition of operation. Such is the justification for that which follows.

Since x and y will generally differ in physical nature, it is necessary to treat certain simple functions of these variables rather than x and y themselves. These functions must be either dimensionless or expressible in the same physical units. Otherwise there seems to be no logical way of properly weighting them. Starting with

$$y = a + bx \qquad [87]$$

as the relation sought, we first express x and y, in effect, in terms of their probable errors as units, writing

$$p_y \frac{y}{p_y} = a + bp_x \frac{x}{p_x} \qquad [88]$$

Then dividing through by a, we have

$$\beta Y' = 1 + \alpha X' \qquad [89]$$

where α, β, X', and Y' stand in succession for bp_x/a, p_y/a, x/p_x, and y/p_y. All quantities are now dimensionless and the probable errors of both X' and Y' are unity.

Imagine a plot showing $Y' = f(X')$ with the same scale (this is important) for both X' and Y'. The problem is now resolved to that of finding the straight line to which U, the sum of the squares of the perpendicular distances from the points to the line, is a minimum. Standard procedure, using observed values for X' and Y', yields

$$U = \sum \frac{(1 + \alpha X' - \beta Y')^2}{\alpha^2 + \beta^2} \qquad [90]$$

Application of the least-squares principle, namely, that the partial derivatives $\partial U/\partial \alpha$ and $\partial U/\partial \beta$ shall be separately equal to zero, yields equations which are to be solved for α and β. If then α, β, X', and Y' are replaced by their equals in terms of a, b, x, and y, one obtains expressions which may be solved to yield the desired values for a and b. Differentiations of Eq. 90 with respect to α and to β separately yield on slight rearrangement,

$$\sum \left[(1 + \alpha X' - \beta Y') \left(\frac{X'}{\alpha} - \frac{1}{\beta^2} + \frac{Y'}{\beta} \right) \right] = 0 \qquad [91]$$

and

$$\sum \left[(1 + \alpha X' - \beta Y') \left(\frac{X'}{\alpha} + \frac{1}{\alpha^2} + \frac{Y'}{\beta} \right) \right] = 0 \qquad [92]$$

Combining Eqs. 91 and 92, keeping in mind that the summation process prevents equating the indicated factors separately to zero, we obtain

$$\Sigma(1 + \alpha X' - \beta Y') = n + \alpha \Sigma X' - \beta \Sigma Y' = 0 \qquad [93]$$

Replacing α, β, X' and Y' by their equivalents and solving for a, one obtains

$$a = \frac{1}{n}\,(\Sigma y - b\Sigma x) \qquad [94]$$

Similar treatment of Eq. 91, together with the elimination of a by means of Eq. 94, leads to a second-degree equation in b, namely

$$b^2 + b\,\frac{(p_y/p_x)^2[(\Sigma x)^2 - n\Sigma x^2] - [(\Sigma y)^2 - n\Sigma y^2]}{\Sigma x \Sigma y - n\Sigma xy} - \left(\frac{p_y}{p_x}\right)^2 = 0 \qquad [95]$$

Eqs. 94 and 95 may be solved to yield the desired a and b. For values of p_x small in comparison to p_y, the value of b reduces to that given by Eq. 10, which was derived for the case where y only is liable to error. Similarly the value for a reduces to that given by Eq. 9.

Though occasions justifying the application of Eqs. 94 and 95 occur rather often, their use seems to be very infrequent.

14. Criterion for Closeness of Fit. When one determines by the least-squares method an empirical equation of the form, say

$$y = a + bx + cx^2 \qquad [55a]$$

to represent observed data, certain questions sometimes rise. For instance, is the cx^2 term necessary? Or, should another term dx^3 be added? It is obvious that, if y is a single-valued function of x, and there are n pairs of values given, an equation similar to Eq. 55a containing n terms on the right-hand side with n arbitrary constants could be derived which would fit the data exactly. Nevertheless, the data may not justify the use of more than two or three terms of the power series. For the decision, a criterion is needed. That which is used, except for certain simple cases, is based on Gauss' mean-square deviation.

A simple case, such as has just been referred to, arises sometimes when the data, $y = f(x)$, are in tabular form with values of y tabulated to correspond to equal intervals of x. As indicated in Table II of Chapter III, the successive differences may then indicate the form of equation which will represent the data suitably. In particular, if the successive differences of the nth order of y for a constant Δx are constant or vary therefrom but slightly and then only in a haphazard manner, the $f(x)$ takes the form of a polynomial in x with n as the highest exponent. Accordingly, where the original data are such as to yield tabulations of the type referred to, successive differences may indicate just how many terms of a polynomial are justified. Where such is the case, this procedure of obtaining successive differences is the simplest for determining how many terms shall be included in the $f(x)$ polynomial. On the other hand, such successive differences may leave some uncertainty as to where approximate constancy actually occurs, and there may then be need of a more positive test as to the number of terms for the best polynomial. Of course, this simple test is not applicable at all where the y-values do not correspond to x-values at regularly spaced intervals, or where the equation actually representing the data does not belong to the group of equations which can be tested in this manner.

The Gauss criterion states that the closest fit is possessed by the equation that yields a minimum for the quotient obtained when the sum of the squares of the deviations (or residuals) of the observed from the computed values for y is divided by the number of observed pairs of (x,y) values less the number of arbitrary constants involved. In equation form, with n as the number of observed pairs and m the number of arbitrary constants or free parameters, the criterion is

$$\Omega = \frac{\Sigma(y_0 - y)^2}{n - m} = \text{a minimum} \qquad [96]$$

Application to determine the most suitable equation is not the real purpose of this criterion. Rather it is of value in determining which of two representations is the more suitable—to answer, for instance, in some particular case questions like those asked at the beginning of this section. At best the process is likely to be rather long and tedious.

An interesting application of the foregoing criterion has been made by Wensel and Tuckerman,[1] of the National Bureau of Standards at Washington, D. C. A published paper on the thermoelectric power of rhodium as a function of temperature for the range 850° C to 1350° C seemed to show a discontinuity occurring at about 1100° C. As a consequence, the original authors in presenting equations to represent their data gave two least-squares relations of the form of Eq. 55a, one for the range 850° C to 1100° C, the other for the range 1100° C to 1350° C. After reviewing the work, Wensel and Tuckerman decided to apply the Gauss criterion. They compared the Ω-value according to Eq. 96 for two least-squares parabolic relations each involving three free parameters and each covering one-half the full range with the Ω-value for a single parabolic relation covering the whole range. It was resolved to the comparison of a fit involving six free parameters with one involv-

[1] Wensel, H. T., and Tuckerman, L. B., *Rev. Sci. Instruments*, **9**, 237 (1938).

ing only three. (See Fig. 16 of Chap. II, in which the authors present the two points of view graphically.)

The results obtained by Wensel and Tuckerman are shown in Fig. 2 and Table V. It is seen that the single parabola covering the whole range yields the smaller value for the criterion expressed in Eq. 96 and therefore possesses the closer fit. Incidentally it was concluded that

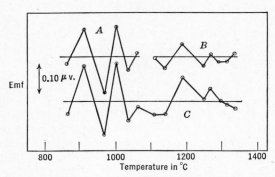

Fig. 2. Showing deviations $(y_0 - y)$ between observed and least-squares emf's for rhodium against platinum for cases (A), a parabolic relation for the range $850°$ C $< T < 1100°$ C, (B), a parabolic relation for the range $1100°$ C $< T < 1350°$ C, and (C), a parabolic relation for the range $850°$ C $< T < 1350°$ C. The results are summarized in Table V.

the supposition of a thermoelectric discontinuity is not justified. Incidentally also, in view of precision index considerations, it would seem that the values given in the table for Ω, $\dfrac{\Sigma(y_0 - y)^2}{n - m}$, are not significant to the extent shown.

TABLE V

Showing Certain Details for the Application of the Criterion
for Closeness of Fit, as Applied by Wensel and Tuckerman
[The data contained are those plotted in Fig. 2]

Case	n No. of observations	m No. of free parameters	$n - m$	$\Sigma(y_0 - y)^2$ in $(\mu v)^2$	$\dfrac{\Sigma(y_0 - y)^2}{n - m}$ in $(\mu v)^2$
Two parabolas	14	6	8	0.0434	0.00542
One parabola	14	3	11	0.0527	0.00479

15. Summary. Of the many products of least squares, among the most valued is the method it provides for determining the arbitrary constants for a best equation of a specified type to represent observed data.   The types here considered are limited (1) to those involving two variables only, one independent, the other dependent, and (2) to those possessing linearly related arbitrary constants or such structures that those constants or functions of them may be linearly related.

For the case where the specified linear relation is given by

$$y = a + bx \qquad [4]$$

it is common, but not necessary, to assume that the y-values only are subject to variation.   The condition that the sum of the squares of the deviations of the observed y_0's from the y's given for the same x's by the least-squares equation shall be a minimum, leads, when applied, to definite expressions for a and b.   For equally weighted values of y_0, n in number, they are

$$a = \frac{\Sigma x^2 \Sigma y_0 - \Sigma x \Sigma x y_0}{n \Sigma x^2 - (\Sigma x)^2} \qquad [9]$$

$$b = \frac{n \Sigma x y_0 - \Sigma x \Sigma y_0}{n \Sigma x^2 - (\Sigma x)^2} \qquad [10]$$

For y_0-values having varying weights w, the equations become instead

$$a = \frac{\Sigma w x^2 \Sigma w y_0 - \Sigma w x \Sigma w x y_0}{\Sigma w \Sigma w x^2 - (\Sigma w x)^2} \qquad [21]$$

$$b = \frac{\Sigma w \Sigma w x y_0 - \Sigma w x \Sigma w y_0}{\Sigma w \Sigma w x^2 - (\Sigma w x)^2} \qquad [22]$$

Many equations may be altered in form to make them effectively linear and thus subject to least-squares treatment.

Disregarding weights one may obtain more than one least-squares value for a given constant by using the same basic relation expressed differently.   For the first radiation constant, for instance, we have for the equally weighted forms

$$\sigma = \frac{\Sigma \mathcal{R} T^4}{\Sigma (T^4)^2} \qquad [37]$$

$$\sigma = \ln^{-1} \left[\frac{\Sigma \ln \mathcal{R} - 4 \Sigma \ln T}{n} \right] \qquad [40]$$

and

$$\sigma = \frac{1}{n} \Sigma \frac{\mathcal{R}}{T^4} \qquad [43]$$

It is shown that, when one shifts from one to another of such forms for computation purposes, changes of weight have been tacitly given to the different items of data and that, when allowances are made for these changes, the same results may be expected by the different procedures.

Probable errors, p_a and p_b, may be computed for the least-squares constants. The constants a and b of Eqs. 21 and 22 may be written as

$$a = \Sigma[(A - A'x)wy_0] \qquad [50]$$

and

$$b = \Sigma[(B'x - B)wy_0] \qquad [51]$$

of which A, A', B', and B are functions of the precise variable x only. Following the principles developed in connection with the propagation of precision indexes, one obtains

$$p_a = p_{y_0}\Sigma w(A - A'x) \qquad [53]$$

$$p_b = p_{y_0}\Sigma w(B'x - B) \qquad [54]$$

of which p_{y_0} is the probable error of the observation having unit weight and is defined by

$$p_{y_0} = 0.675 \sqrt{\frac{\Sigma[w(y_0 - a - bx)^2]}{n - 2}} \qquad [55]$$

The parabola

$$y = a + bx + cx^2 \qquad [55a]$$

treated in a manner similar to that for the straight line yields the cumbersome expressions of Eqs. 58 for the constants a, b, and c. However, when certain conditions are fulfilled these expressions are much simplified.

For the special conditions (1) that the given or observed values of y are equally weighted, (2) that the successive values of x differ by a constant, (3) that the values of x are exact, and (4) that the values of x are arranged symmetrically with respect to a central zero value, the least-squares equations for the evaluation of the arbitrary constants for polynomials, involving x-terms up to at least the third degree, are all greatly simplified. A change of variable from x to X to meet condition (4) is necessary, and to make the difference specified by condition (2) the numeric 1 is convenient. For the case that n the number of pairs of values is odd or even, X is defined by

$$\left(X_o = \frac{x - \bar{x}}{\Delta x}\right)_{n \text{ odd}} \qquad [65]$$

or by

$$\left(X_e = \frac{x - \bar{x}}{\Delta x/2}\right)_{n \text{ even}} \qquad [66]$$

With this change each coefficient of the least-squares polynomial becomes expressible as a single term or as the difference between two terms, each of which consists of the product of a function of x and a summation such as Σy_0, $\Sigma X y_0$, $\Sigma X^2 y_0$, or $\Sigma X^3 y_0$. The method of combining the functions of X due to Baily is shown in Table VI of Appendix 2. Values for these functions of X, as tabulated by Cox and Matuschak for values of n up to 50, will be found in Tables VII and VIII of Appendix 2. With the aid of these tables, many otherwise rather formidable least-squares evaluations become rather simple. A generalized expression for the coefficients of a polynomial of any degree as developed by Birge and Shea is given by Eq. 74.

In certain instances the equation connecting observed data cannot be transformed directly to yield a linear relation connecting the coefficients to be determined. In this case with $y = f(x)$ representing the desired relation, and a, b, and c the desired coefficients (1) an approximation $y' = f(x)$ is assumed and (2) the difference $(y - y')$ is then developed in accord with Taylor's series and treated in the form

$$\Delta y = y - y' = \left(\frac{\partial y'}{\partial a}\right) \Delta a + \left(\frac{\partial y'}{\partial b}\right) \Delta b + \cdots \qquad [78]$$

The correction to an assumed ordinary sine relation then becomes

$$\Delta y = \sin (\omega t + b') \times \Delta a - a' \cos (\omega t + b') \times \Delta b \qquad [79]$$

of which a' and b' are assumed approximate values for a and b.

The constants for a least-squares equation of the type

$$y = a + bx \qquad [4]$$

when both x and y are liable to error are given by a solution of the simultaneous equations

$$a = \frac{1}{n}(\Sigma y - b\Sigma x) \qquad [94]$$

and

$$b^2 + b\frac{(p_y/p_x)^2[(\Sigma x)^2 - n\Sigma x^2] - [(\Sigma y)^2 - n\Sigma y^2]}{\Sigma x \Sigma y - n\Sigma xy} - \left(\frac{p_y}{p_x}\right)^2 = 0 \qquad [95]$$

A criterion for closeness of fit for cases in which y only is liable to error is contained in Gauss' mean-square deviation. Where y_0 is the observed value, y the corresponding least-squares value, n the number of observed pairs of values, and m the number of arbitrary constants or free parameters for the equation, the criterion in equation form becomes

$$\Omega = \frac{\Sigma(y_0 - y)^2}{n - m} = \text{a minimum} \qquad [96]$$

Of all equations, that which yields the least value for Ω is assumed to best represent the given data.

PROBLEMS

1. Millikan (*Phys. Rev.*,**7**, 355, 1916, Figs. 5 and 6), in a determination of Planck's constant, h, by the photoelectric method using sodium, found that for certain wavelengths of radiation, λ, certain stopping potentials, V (actually, as measured, stopping potentials less contact emf between sodium and copper), were required to just prevent a photoelectric current in the cell used. From a straight-line plot of V as a function of frequency, c/λ, he obtained h/e, the theoretical slope of the line. This he combined with the electronic charge, e, which he had measured otherwise, to obtain h, the quantity desired. The data (these values are taken from the curves of Fig. 5, and may not check Millikan's values precisely) plotted are:

λ (A)	V (Volts)
2535	0.520
3126	−0.385
3650	−0.915
4047	−1.295
4339	−1.485
5461	−2.045

Using Millikan's data and the least-squares method, determine h/e. Then, using Millikan's 1916 value for e, namely 4.774×10^{-10} escoulombs, see how closely you agree with the value $h = 6.56 \times 10^{-27}$ erg sec which he obtained from this particular set.

2. One of the best methods of determining the ice point on the Kelvin temperature scale is that of determining for a gas, α, the limiting mean coefficient of pressure increase at constant volume on heating from $0°$ C to $100°$ C, as the pressure approaches zero, and computing its reciprocal. Data for such a computation obtained by Beattie are given in Table II. Using the data there presented as adjusted and giving equal weight to each determination of α_v and assuming the relation $\alpha_v = \alpha + F_v\, p$, where F_v is a constant, compute a least-squares value for α and for T_0. Also determine its probable error. The suggested treatment is somewhat different from that actually used by Beattie. Small corrections applied to α_v values to yield values expected for 1000.00 mm–Hg, 750.00 mm–Hg, etc., and change of the dependent variable to α_v less a convenient constant, will reduce the labor of computation very greatly without affecting the result appreciably.

3. If the broken line, given by $y = \alpha\theta$ for the range $0 < \theta < \pi/2$ and by $y = \alpha(\pi-\theta)$ for the range $\pi/2 < \theta < \pi$, is to be represented as well as possible by the single term $a_1 \sin \theta$, show that the best value for a_1 is that prescribed for the first term of the Fourier half-range sine series which represents the line. Given that instead it is to be represented by $a_3 \sin 3\theta$, show that the best value for a_3 is then the third term of the same series.

4. On the basis of least squares, derive the best equation of the type $y = \sum_{m=1}^{4} (a_m \sin m\theta + b_m \cos m\theta)$ to represent 20 given values for points throughout the range $0 < \theta < 2\pi$ having equal θ-separations. Assume the y-values to be such that the $b_0/2$ term is negligible. (Use if necessary the derivable relation

$$\sum_{r=1}^{p} \sin^2 \left(rm \frac{2\pi}{2p} \right) = \frac{p}{2} = \sum_{r=1}^{p} \cos^2 \left(rm \frac{2\pi}{2p} \right)$$

of which p, m, and r are integers.)

5. In studying the changes of enthalpy, H (often called heat content or total heat) of sodium sulfate solutions, Wallace and Robinson (*J. Am. Chem. Soc.*, **63**, 958 (1941)), obtained the following data for 20° C:

M_1	M_2	$H_{M_2} - H_{M_1}$
Moles of Sodium Sulfate per Kg Water		Cal per Mole of Sodium Sulfate
0.005366	0.002692	-28.6 ± 2.8
.002692	.001351	-23.6 ± 0.8
.001351	.0006778	-17.3 ± 1.2
.0006778	.0003401	-14.8 ± 2.1
.0003401	.0001705	-11.8 ± 3.5
.0001705	.0000856	$- 5.5 \pm 5.5$

Assume H expressible as a power series in $M^{\frac{1}{2}}$

$$H = H° + AM^{\frac{1}{2}} + BM + CM^{\frac{3}{2}} + \cdots \qquad [1]$$

and that

$$S = A + 2BM^{\frac{1}{2}} + 3CM + \cdots \qquad [2]$$

where

$$S = \left(\frac{\partial H}{\partial M^{\frac{1}{2}}} \right)_{P,T}$$

From Eq. 2 the average slopes over an interval $M_1^{\frac{1}{2}}$ to $M_2^{\frac{1}{2}}$ is found to be

$$\bar{S} = A + B(M_2^{\frac{1}{2}} + M_1^{\frac{1}{2}}) + C(M_2 + M_1^{\frac{1}{2}} M_2^{\frac{1}{2}} + M_1) + \cdots \qquad [3]$$

where

$$\bar{S} \equiv \frac{\Delta H}{\Delta M^{\frac{1}{2}}} = \frac{H_{M_2} - H_{M_1}}{M_2^{\frac{1}{2}} - M_1^{\frac{1}{2}}}$$

Using the above data for the heat of dilution of sodium sulfate and the condition Eq. 3 and assuming that three terms of Eq. 1 suffice to represent the dependence of H upon M, Wallace and Robinson obtained for A and B the values 2193 cal (mol Na$_2$SO$_4$)$^{-\frac{3}{2}}$(KgH$_2$O)$^{\frac{1}{2}}$ and -7418 cal (mol Na$_2$SO$_4$)$^{-2}$(KgH$_2$O). Check these values.

6. The 1939 determination of the specific heat of water in terms of the 15° C calorie at the Bureau of Standards by Osborne, Stimson and Ginnings [1] yielded the following:

T in °C	c_p in $\dfrac{\text{cal}}{\text{gm C}°}$	T in °C	c_p in $\dfrac{\text{cal}}{\text{gm C}°}$
0	1.00762	55	0.99919
5	1.00392	60	0.99967
10	1.00153	65	1.00024
15	1.00000	70	1.00091
20	0.99907	75	1.00167
25	0.99852	80	1.00253
30	0.99826	85	1.00351
35	0.99818	90	1.00461
40	0.99828	95	1.00586
45	0.99849	100	1.00721
50	0.99878		

Determine a least-squares equation to represent the above data of the type

$$c_p = a + b\tau + c\tau^2 + d\tau^3$$

where τ represents $T - 0°$ C. If a computing machine is not available, round off c_p values to the fourth decimal place or use only values corresponding to 0° C, 10° C, 20° C, etc.

7. The van't Hoff isochore $\left[\dfrac{d}{dT} \ln K_p\right]_p = \dfrac{\Delta H}{RT^2}$ or $\left[\dfrac{d\,(\ln K_p)}{d\,(1/T)}\right]_p = -\dfrac{\Delta H}{R}$ of which K_p is an equilibrium constant, ΔH the heat of reaction, R the ideal gas constant, and T the absolute temperature, is one of the most important equations of chemical thermodynamics. Slopes taken from a curve showing $\ln K_p = f(1/T)$ permit of a determination of heat of reaction as a function of temperature. For the reaction $N_2 \rightleftharpoons 2N_1$, Lewis and von Elbe [2] have tabulated published data which in part are as follows:

T in °K	300	400	600	800	1000	1200	1600	2000
$\log K_p$ in A	118.1	86.9	55.8	40.2	30.9	24.6	16.8	12.0

Derive (1) a least-squares equation showing $\ln K_p = f(1/T)$, and (2) an equation showing $\Delta H = f(T)$ for the dissociation of nitrogen.

8. Cragoe of the Bureau of Standards (*Am. Inst. Phys. Symposium on Temperature*, etc., Reinhold Publishing Corporation, New York, 1941, p. 104) in a discussion of the "slopes of PV isotherms" of real gases calls attention to their "importance in atomic-weight determinations, in gas analysis," etc. He cited certain data on nitrogen at 0° C which were obtained by Michels, Wouters, and de Boer at the van der Waals Laboratory in Amsterdam and presented various least-squares

[1] Osborne, N. S., Stimson, H. F., and Ginnings, D. C., *J. Research Nat. Bur. Standards*, **23**, 197 (1939).

[2] Lewis, B., and von Elbe, G., *Combustion, Flames and Explosions of Gases*, p. 382, Cambridge, at the University Press, 1938.

equations to represent them. The data and one of the equations for all pairs equally weighted follow:

$\dfrac{p}{p_0}$	$\dfrac{v_0}{v}$	$\dfrac{pv}{p_0v_0}$
19.0215	19.1606	0.99274
23.7629	23.9734	.99122
28.4968	28.7894	.98983
33.1101	33.4951	.98851
37.9526	38.4409	.98730
42.7435	43.3413	.98621
47.4376	48.1401	.98541
52.2160	53.0328	.98460

$$10^5 \ln \frac{pv}{p_0v_0} = (-45.3236 \pm 0.352)\left(\frac{v_0}{v} - 1\right) + 0.29885\left(\frac{v_0}{v} - 1\right)^2$$

This equation may be checked rather closely without undue labor by (1) plotting $\ln \dfrac{pv}{p_0v_0} = f\left(\dfrac{v_0}{v} - 1\right)$, (2) obtaining, with the aid of the physical slopes of the curve at appropriate points, values of $\ln \dfrac{pv}{p_0v_0}$ and then of $\ln \dfrac{pv}{p_0v_0} \Big/ \left(\dfrac{v_0}{v} - 1\right)$ for neighboring equally spaced values of $\left(\dfrac{v_0}{v} - 1\right)$ as 18.10, 22.95, 27.80, etc., and (3) applying to such pairs of values the method which makes use of the tables by Cox and Matuschak. What change of weights is involved? Check Cragoe's equation.

9. One method of determining the optical constants of a metal consists in determining the reflectivities of the polished metal for light polarized respectively in the plane of incidence, $R_{||}$, and perpendicular to that plane, $R_{\perp}$. One of the authors [1] has done this for tungsten and obtained the following tabulated values.

Angle of Incidence	$R_{||}$	$R_{\perp}$
76°	82.5%	12.30%
77	83.0	11.60
78	84.0	11.05
79	84.5	11.15
80	85.6	11.60
81	86.6	12.40
82	87.9	14.40

On the basis of Chauvenet's criterion two $R_{||}$ values have been discarded. The angle of principal incidence is the angle for which the ratio $R_{||}/R_{\perp}$ is a maximum. Using least-squares procedure and the above data, determine the angle of principal incidence, also the angle of principal azimuth ψ which is defined by

$$\tan^2 \psi = \frac{R_{\perp}}{R_{||}}$$

for the angle of principal incidence.

[1] Worthing, A. G., *J. Optical Soc. Am.*, **13**, 647 (1926).

CHAPTER XII

CORRELATION

1. Introduction. In the discussions of Chapter XI leading to least-squares expressions for $y = f(x)$, we tacitly assumed that, for each given value of x, there corresponded a single definite value of y. In the language of the section about to be developed, we assumed a correlation of unity. We now consider cases where y is, in addition, a function of other variables which may not be known. In particular we wish to determine within what range of certainty a mathematical relation, developed to express the interdependency of two variables, may be accepted for yielding definite values for one variable when values for the other are given.

Generally we speak of correlations between factors, or accomplishments, or attributes, or characteristics whose dependencies on one another are only partial. Most often, perhaps, we think not so much of the physical dependence of these attributes on each other as of their dependence on certain other attributes which may only be surmised. It thus has meaning to speak of correlations (a) between students' grades in mathematics and in physics (Table I and Fig. 1), (b) between the daily temperatures at noon at Pittsburgh and the corresponding temperatures for succeeding days at New York, (c) between the heights of fathers and the heights of their sons, (d) between the average rainfall in a region during some one month as June, say, and the average corresponding temperature, (e) between the stellar magnitudes of stars and their proper motions, etc.

It is evident from Fig. 1 that physics and pre-math test grades are somehow related, since on the average, students with high math grades made higher physics grades than the students with low math grades. However, the scattering of the points about the least-squares line which has been drawn is very great and cannot be ascribed to random errors. In cases like this the variables are said to be stochastically related or correlated, rather than causally or functionally related as in Chapter XI. Stochastic relationships may be nonlinear as well as linear and may exist among three or even more variables.

In this chapter we treat first the case of two variables assumed linearly related. The correlation coefficient, r, is derived and its signifi-

270

TABLE I

GRADES IN BEGINNING MATHEMATICS AND PHYSICS AT THE UNIVERSITY
OF PITTSBURGH OBTAINED BY A GROUP OF 69 STUDENTS

[The mathematics course preceded the physics course]

No.	Pre-Math Grades, X	Physics Grades, Y	No.	Pre-Math Grades, X	Physics Grades, Y
1	58	112	36	78	164
2	59	141	37	79	134
3	63	113	38	97	215
4	58	161	39	83	204
5	50	134	40	96	243
6	81	188	41	91	184
7	55	120	42	83	129
8	78	143	43	82	167
9	76	200	44	77	200
10	80	232	45	96	158
11	91	157	46	66	200
12	74	143	47	86	247
13	47	113	48	69	115
14	90	202	49	80	173
15	85	174	50	95	222
16	71	147	51	97	181
17	71	134	52	82	188
18	78	143	53	64	126
19	73	137	54	72	72
20	54	150	55	69	134
21	82	197	56	52	101
22	57	163	57	73	156
23	78	183	58	87	174
24	55	126	59	59	194
25	72	201	60	52	127
26	94	206	61	71	169
27	87	177	62	93	199
28	86	203	63	70	129
29	62	129	64	88	151
30	82	209	65	76	159
31	84	251	66	85	160
32	92	225	67	82	202
33	72	104	68	82	169
34	67	154	69	72	139
35	77	148			

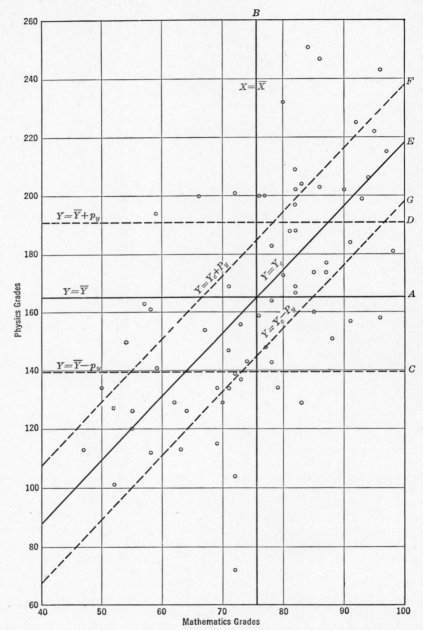

FIG. 1.   Diagram showing a correlation between the mathematics and the physics grades obtained by a group of students. See Table I.

cance, limitations, and uses discussed. For the case of two variables nonlinearly related, we define and discuss the correlation index, ρ. The coefficient of multiple correlation is then defined for the case where the dependent variable is correlated linearly with two or more independent variables. Finally, we define the coefficient of partial correlation to describe the correlation (linear) between two variables when a third is held constant.

2. The Correlation Coefficient, r. When variables X and Y are correlated rather than functionally related, we should no longer speak of a "best" Y-value to correspond to each X-value but only of a most probable Y-value about which observed values may be distributed according to some frequency distribution law. Obviously, the closer the observed values are to the most probable value, the more definite is the relationship between Y and X. This postulate is the basis for the various numerical measures of the degree of correlation.

On the least-squares assumption that the observed set of data is the most probable set, the most probable Y-value for a given X-value is that given by the least-squares equation. For the case of two variables linearly related with one only assumed liable to error in measurement, this equation was derived in Chapter XI (Eqs. 4, 9, and 10). With the origin moved to the point represented by the means of the X- and Y-values, i.e., with change of variables to $x = (X - \bar{X})$ and $y = (Y - \bar{Y})$, the equation reduces, in case the X-values are assumed exact, to

$$y_c = \left(\frac{\Sigma xy}{\Sigma x^2}\right) x = bx \qquad [1]$$

As a measure of the dispersion of the observed y-values about the least-squares line, a quantity S_y called the *standard error of estimate* is introduced. Defined by

$$S_y = \sqrt{\frac{\Sigma(y - y_c)^2}{n}} \qquad [2]$$

it is the square root of the mean of squared deviations, not from an average but from values predicted by the least-squares line.

The actual correlation coefficient, r, is defined by

$$r = \sqrt{1 - \left(\frac{S_y}{\sigma_y}\right)^2} \qquad [3]$$

It is a numeric independent of the units of the variables correlated.

As heretofore, the σ of Eq. 3 denotes a standard deviation from a mean. But there is this difference: the mean as used here is merely an average, while heretofore it has been additionally a best value for some measured quantity. The quantity, r^2, is often called the coefficient of determination, and the quantity $(S_y/\sigma_y)^2$, the coefficient of alienation.

3. Limiting Values for r. Using Eq. 3, we can readily evaluate the limiting values which r may assume. Since $(S_y/\sigma_y)^2$ cannot be negative, the maximum value of r is 1, corresponding to $S_y = 0$; i.e., to $\Sigma(y - y_c)^2 = 0$. Thus, the maximum value of r occurs when all the observed points lie on the least-squares line (Fig. 2A). The minimum value of r is zero, corresponding to $(S_y/\sigma_y)^2 = 1$, or $S_y = \sigma_y$. For S_y

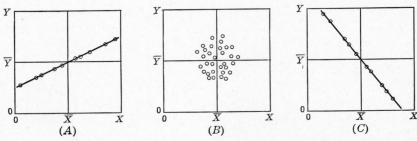

Fig. 2. Illustrating the distribution of observed points about the least-squares line for the extreme cases $(A)\ r = +1;\ (B)\ r = 0;\ (C)\ r = -1$.

to equal σ_y, it is necessary that $y_c = 0$ and that the least-squares line shall be parallel to the X-axis and intersect the Y-axis at $\overline{Y}$ (Fig. 2B). From Eq. 1 it is seen that $y_c = 0$ when $\Sigma xy = 0$, a relation which was recognized in the discussion of the propagation of precision indexes in Chapter IX as the condition for complete independence of variables x and y. Thus, the value $r = 0$ corresponds to complete lack of correlation. A negative correlation coefficient indicates that the assumed dependency is opposite to what has been supposed. It is, in effect, a positive coefficient for a reversed relation (Fig. 2C).

4. Correlation and Frequency Distribution. Though not evident from the foregoing, it is possible to show that the correlation coefficient r is definitely connected with the normal frequency distribution of measurements.[1] Similar to the distribution law for measurements of a single quantity (Chap. VI), namely

$$f(x)\ dx = \frac{h}{\sqrt{\pi}}\ e^{-h^2x^2}\ dx = \frac{1}{\sqrt{2\pi}\ \sigma_x}\ e^{-x^2/2\sigma_x^2}\ dx \qquad [4]$$

[1] Whittaker, E. T., and Robinson, G., *The Calculus of Observations*, London, Blackie & Son, Ltd., 1926.

it may be shown for the frequency distribution of pairs of measurements of separate quantities that

$$f(x,y) \; dx \; dy$$

$$= \frac{1}{2\pi\sigma_x\sigma_y\sqrt{1-r'^2}} \, e^{-(1/2)[(x^2/\sigma_x{}^2)-(2r'xy/\sigma_x\sigma_y)+(y^2/\sigma_y{}^2)]/(1-r'^2)} \; dx \; dy \quad [5]$$

In this latter expression, the r' represents an interdependence factor for the x and y variables. If x and y are independent of each other, i.e., if r' equals 0, the sign of the xy term will be as often positive as negative and will disappear from the expression for probability of occurrence in the $dx \; dy$ range. The expression then becomes

$$[f(x,y) \; dx \; dy]_{r'=0} = \frac{1}{2\pi \, \sigma_x \, \sigma_y} \, e^{-(1/2)[(x^2/\sigma_x{}^2)+(y^2/\sigma_y{}^2)]} \; dx \; dy \quad [6]$$

the well-recognized expression for the probability of simultaneous occurrence of a randomly chosen pair of x- and y-values when those values are unrelated, or, as we often say, of two unrelated phenomena. If, on the other hand, the relation between x and y is definite, i.e., if r equals unity, we have

$$[f(x,y) \; dx \; dy]_{r'=1} = 0 \quad [7]$$

This likewise is the expected value for the probability of a simultaneous occurrence of an x- and a y-value chosen at random when the relation between x and y is definite. The interdependence factor r' may be shown to be identical with the correlation coefficient r.

5. Pearson's Product Moment Formula. Eq. 3 is generally not the most convenient form for calculating the r for a particular set of data. To obtain such a form, we first replace y_c of Eq. 2 by its equivalent as given in Eq. 1, obtaining

$$S_y{}^2 = \frac{1}{n}\left[\Sigma y^2 - 2\frac{(\Sigma xy)^2}{\Sigma x^2} + \frac{(\Sigma xy)^2}{\Sigma x^2} \right] = \sigma_y{}^2 - \frac{(\Sigma xy)^2}{n\Sigma x^2} \quad [8]$$

Then, by the elimination of S_y from Eq. 3, we have

$$r = \sqrt{\frac{\sigma_y{}^2 - S_y{}^2}{\sigma_y{}^2}} = \sqrt{\frac{(\Sigma xy)^2}{\Sigma x^2 \Sigma y^2}} = \frac{\Sigma xy}{n\sigma_x\sigma_y} \quad [9]$$

Eq. 9 is known as Pearson's product moment formula. It is much more convenient than Eq. 3 for calculating r.

Going farther, we may use the short-method check equations for σ_x, σ_y, etc. (Chap. VII, Eq. 13), to express r in terms of the original variables X and Y. Then Eq. 9 becomes

$$r = \frac{\Sigma XY - n\overline{X}\overline{Y}}{\sqrt{(\Sigma X^2 - n\overline{X}^2)(\Sigma Y^2 - n\overline{Y}^2)}}$$

$$= \frac{n\Sigma XY - \Sigma X\Sigma Y}{\sqrt{[n\Sigma X^2 - (\Sigma X)^2][n\Sigma Y^2 - (\Sigma Y)^2]}} \quad [10]$$

Despite its formidable look, Eq. 10 is probably the most convenient form for calculating r. Especially is this true if a computing machine is available. Applying Eq. 10 to the 69 pairs of X- and Y-values of Table I, we obtain

$$\Sigma XY = 884{,}280 \quad [11]$$

$$\overline{X} = 75.7 \quad [12]$$

$$\overline{Y} = 165.3 \quad [13]$$

$$\Sigma X^2 = 406{,}727 \quad [14]$$

$$\Sigma Y^2 = 1{,}985{,}220 \quad [15]$$

$$r = 0.62 \quad [16]$$

Since in Eq. 9 and therefore also fundamentally in Eq. 10 only deviations from the means of the quantities being correlated enter to determine both the numerator and the denominator, the choice of zeros for the X and Y readings of Eq. 10 is arbitrary. To illustrate, in the correlating of the heights X of individuals with their weights Y, it suffices in applying Eq. 10 to use only heights in excess of some convenient value, such as 5 ft 8 in., and weights in excess of some convenient weight value, such as 160 lb. Further, since X and Y appear raised to the same powers in both the numerator and the denominator of Eq. 10, the units in which X and Y are expressed are also arbitrary. If for any reason computations are made more convenient thereby, in a problem like that just discussed, one might use the $\frac{1}{4}$ in. as the unit of height and 2 lb as the unit of weight. Just how advantageous these considerations are will appear in connection with the next section.

6. Correlation Coefficients for Grouped Data. When the number of pairs of items to be correlated is large, the calculation of r by the standard procedure may be time-consuming. In such cases it is desirable to shorten the process by grouping the item pairs as is done in a correlation table. Table II illustrates how this may be done for the mathematics-physics grades of Table I. Note that for the mathematics grades 6

TABLE II

An Illustration, Using the Data of Table I, of the Construction of a Correlation Table and the Computations Necessary for Obtaining r

Pre-Mathematics Grades (X)

Physics Grades (Y)

Interval	Mid-point	X'/Y'	f	fX'/fY'	fX'2/fY'2	45–55	55–65	65–75	75–85	85–95	95–105	Totals
						50	60	70	80	90	100	
						−2	−1	0	1	2	3	
		f				5	10	15	21	13	5	69
			fX'			−10	−10	0	21	26	15	42
				fX'2	fY'2	20	10	0	21	52	45	148
250–270	260	5	1	5	25				1 / 5			
230–250	240	4	2	8	32				1 / 4	1 / 8		
210–230	220	3	4	12	36					1 / 6	3 / 27	
190–210	200	2	13	26	52		1 / −2	2 / 0	6 / 12	4 / 16		
170–190	180	1	9	9	9				4 / 4	4 / 8	1 / 3	
150–170	160	0	14	0	0	1 / 0	2 / 0	3 / 0	4 / 0	3 / 0	1 / 0	
130–150	140	−1	12	−12	12	1 / 2	1 / 1	6 / 0	4 / −4			
110–130	120	−2	11	−22	44	2 / 8	6 / 12	2 / 0	1 / −2			
90–110	100	−3	2	−6	18	1 / 6		1 / 0				
70–90	80	−4	1	−4	16			1 / 0				
ΣfX'Y'						16	11	0	19	38	30	114
Totals			69	16	244							

$n = 69$
$\Sigma X' = 42$
$\Sigma Y' = 16$
$\Sigma(X')^2 = 148$
$\Sigma(Y')^2 = 244$
$\Sigma X'Y' = 114$

$$r = \frac{n\Sigma X'Y' - \Sigma X'\Sigma Y'}{\sqrt{[n\Sigma X'^2 - (\Sigma X')^2][n\Sigma Y'^2 - (\Sigma Y')^2]}}$$

$$= \frac{69 \times 114 - 42 \times 16}{\sqrt{[69 \times 148 - (42)^2][69 \times 244 - (16)^2]}}$$

$$= 0.61$$

ranges have been selected with midpoints at 50, 60, $\cdots$ 100, and that for the physics grades 10 ranges have been selected with midpoints at 80, 100, 120, $\cdots$ 260. In accord with the grouping principle, the pair of grades 57 for mathematics and 112 for physics is found in the cell, as it is called, which is at the intersection of the 55–65 column and the 110–130 row. All of the pairs of grades that fall within the limits prescribed for this cell are to be treated in the computation that follows as though the mathematics and physics grades were respectively 60 and 120. Table II shows that there are 6 pairs of grades to be so treated. For the ranges chosen in Table II, there is a difficulty arising when, for instance, the mathematics grade is just 65. Different procedures are then possible. The grade may be recorded with half weight in both the 55–65 and the 65–75 columns. Instead, it may be recorded with full weight in the 55–65 or lower column, with the understanding that, with the next similar occurrence, the grade will be recorded with full weight in the next higher column. Of course other rules may be set up in order that the effects of several such cases shall be negligible as to the combined results of the particular choices of assignment.

As for the standard procedure described above, Eq. 10 is basic for the computations contained in a correlation table. Note that, taking advantage of the feature pointed out above, regarding the arbitrariness of the zeros and the units of measurement, the rather large and cumbersome numbers used in expressing X and Y in Table II have been replaced by the convenient small numbers of X' and Y'. Values for X', Y', their frequencies f, fX', fY', fX'^2, and fY'^2 are shown in appropriately headed rows and columns. Values for $fX'Y'$, however, are to be found only in the lower right-hand corners of the cells.

As might be expected, the grouped-data method with its approximations yields for the data of Table I a result for r, namely 0.61, which is different from that obtained when the more precise method outlined above is used, namely 0.62. The difference, however, is quite insignificant, as will appear in the later discussion of the physical significance of the r that was found.

7. Physical Interpretation of a Correlation Coefficient. In general the value of the correlation coefficient provides the answer to the question: To what extent is Y dependent on X, judging from the particular tested sample from the infinite parent group of data? Two other questions are usually of equal importance: (1) How is the value obtained for r to be interpreted? (2) To what extent does the r obtained for the sample apply to the parent group? Thus, for the sample of data contained in Table I, the value 0.62 was obtained for r. The question of the reliability of this value must await the discussion of the following section. It is now desirable to consider the interpretation of 0.62 as a dependency indicator. There are two procedures.

The first interpretation procedure involves giving attention to the corresponding S_y/σ_y, the quantity whose square has been referred to above as the coefficient of alienation. As indicated above, it is the ratio (Fig. 1) of the standard y-deviation of the plotted points from the

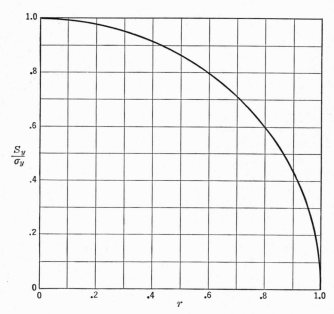

FIG. 3. Showing $S_y/\sigma_y = f(r)$ in accord with Eq. 17.

line representing the least-squares equation with y only liable to error, to the standard deviation of the same points from the y-mean. The higher the correlation, i.e., the greater the dependency of y on x, the smaller is S_y/σ_y. Rearrangement of Eq. 3 yields

$$r^2 + \left(\frac{S_y}{\sigma_y}\right)^2 = 1 \qquad [17]$$

whose locus on a plot, showing $S_y/\sigma_y = f(r)$, is a circle (Fig. 3).

The value of S_y/σ_y, corresponding to 0.62 for the value of r for the data of Table I, is 0.78. The value of σ_y for the same data, given by

$$\sigma_y = \sqrt{\frac{\Sigma Y^2}{n} - \bar{Y}^2} \qquad [18]$$

is 38.0. S_y is 29.6. Correspondingly, p_y $(= 0.675\sigma_y)$ and P_y $(= 0.675\,S_y)$ are 25.6 and 20.0.

Referring to Fig. 1, note that lines A and B are drawn parallel to the X- and Y-axes and indicate respectively the mean mathematics and the mean physics grades as shown by Eqs. 12 and 13. Lines C and D corresponding to

$$Y = \bar{Y} \pm p_y = 165.3 \pm 25.6 \qquad [19]$$

enclose between themselves one half of the plotted points. Line E is the locus of the least-squares equation computed according to Eq. 1. Its equation is

$$Y = Y_c = 165.3 + 1.843(X - 75.7) \qquad [20]$$

Lines F and G correspond to

$$Y = Y_c \pm P_y = 165.3 \pm 20.0 + 1.843(X - 75.7) \qquad [21]$$

Like lines C and D, lines F and G include between themselves one-half of the plotted points. The vertical separation of the latter two lines is less, however, than that of the first two, the ratio being that of S_y/σ_y or, what is the same, of P_y/p_y.

We may now interpret the significance of an r of 0.62 or of an S_y/σ_y of 0.78 as applied to the data of Table I. Given that a student has a grade of 90 in mathematics, what can we say of his probable performance in physics? Ignoring the correlation between mathematics and physics, our best estimate of his grade is 165.3 and the chance is 50% that the grade will lie between 139.7 and 190.9, i.e., in the range 165.3 ± 25.6. However, knowledge of the correlation between mathematics and physics grades, found from Table I, enables us to make a prediction in which we have considerably more confidence. From Fig. 1 we see that about 196 is the most probable physics grade for the student whose math grade is 90, and further, the chance is 50% that his grade will lie between 176 and 216, i.e., in the range 196 ± 20.0. The range for the predicted even chance, namely $2P_y$, computed on the correlation basis is only 0.78 of the corresponding range, namely $2p_y$, that results in case correlation is ignored.

In view of the foregoing one wonders why the ratio S_y/σ_y was not chosen in place of r to represent correlation. One evident answer is that with increased correlation there is a decreased value for S_y/σ_y.

In connection with the foregoing interpretation, no indication has been given of the reliability of the computed r, S_y/σ_y, p_y, and P_y. These features will be discussed in the next section.

A second interpretation of r treats it as a measure of common causes. If X is a linear function of $i + k$ independent variables which contribute equally to its values and Y is a similar linear function of $j + k$ independent variables, where k is the number of variables common to both X and Y, it may be shown that

$$r = \frac{k}{\sqrt{(i + k)(j + k)}} \qquad [22]$$

On this basis, it would seem that a correlation of 62% for mathematics-physics grades would indicate that about 62% of the characteristics or activities required for the two subjects are common characteristics. While this interpretation can doubtless be tested quantitatively in some instances, just how it can be so tested in the case just mentioned is not apparent.   Incidentally one would find it very difficult to so interpret a correlation coefficient of 0.95 relating the annual number of marriages in the Church of England and the standard mortality rate for the years 1866 to 1911.

It should be remembered that r is calculated on the assumptions that the values of Y and X are distributed normally and that, on the average, Y is directly (or inversely) proportional to X.   Any significance which r may have decreases as the distribution of Y or X departs from normality, and as the average relationship between Y and X becomes nonlinear.   With marked departures from normality or linearity, r loses all significance, and other measures of the degree of correlation should be used.

8. The Reliability of Computed Correlation Coefficients.   Question 2, asked at the beginning of the preceding section, is of interest here. If r were a variable whose variations for a number of samples from the same parent universe were to follow the normal distribution law, the answer to the question would be simple.   It would then be sufficient to calculate the precision indexes of r and interpret them in accord with the discussion of Chapters VI and VII.

For small and moderate values of r the equation

$$\sigma_r = \frac{1 - r^2}{\sqrt{n - 1}} \doteq \frac{1 - r^2}{\sqrt{n}} \qquad [23]$$

where n is the number of X, Y pairs in the sample, seems to hold rather well.   It fails, however, for small values of n and for values of r near the limits of its range of distribution, i.e., near 1 or -1.   In these regions the distribution of r is particularly skewed (Fig. 4).

To simplify computation for such skew distributions, Fisher [1] introduced the function

$$z = \tfrac{1}{2} \ln \frac{1 + r}{1 - r} = 1.15 \log \frac{1 + r}{1 - r} \qquad [24]$$

[1] Fisher, R. A., *Statistical Methods for Research Workers*, Chap. VI, 7th Ed. Oliver & Boyd, Edinburgh, 1938.

Its distribution is nearly normal regardless of the true value of r (see Table V, Appendix 2) and is subject to certain normal distribution procedures.

The standard deviation of z, σ_z, and its probable error, p_z, are found to be

$$\sigma_z = \frac{1}{\sqrt{n-3}} \qquad [25]$$

and

$$p_z = 0.675 \frac{1}{\sqrt{n-3}} \qquad [26]$$

where n is the number of pairs of values used in obtaining r or z. Using Eqs. 24 to 26, it is easy to calculate whether z, and hence also r, is

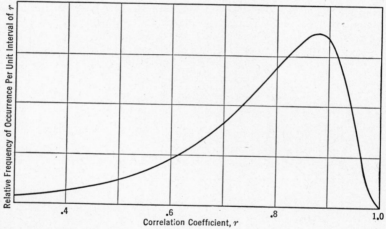

Fig. 4. Expected distribution for computed values of r, obtained from samples of 10 pairs of X,Y values chosen at random from an infinite parent universe whose r is 0.80.

significantly different from zero. Further, by the rule of propagation of precision indexes for related quantities, the standard deviation and the probable error of the difference of two values of z are

$$\sigma_{(z_2-z_1)} = \sqrt{\sigma_{z_2}{}^2 + \sigma_{z_1}{}^2 - 2r\sigma_{z_1}\sigma_{z_2}} \qquad [27]$$

and

$$p_{(z_2-z_1)} = \sqrt{p_{z_2}{}^2 + p_{z_1}{}^2 - 2rp_{z_2}p_{z_1}} \qquad [28]$$

It is accordingly relatively simple to calculate whether or not two values of z, and hence of r, are significantly different from each other. For translation to r, Table V of Appendix 2 is again helpful.

Illustrating the foregoing, consider the 69-pair sample of Table I, for which a correlation coefficient of 0.62 was obtained. Using Eqs. 24 to 26, we obtain in succession

$$z = 0.725 \qquad [29]$$

$$\sigma_z = 0.123 \qquad [30]$$

$$p_z = 0.083 \qquad [31]$$

With the aid of the table showing $r = f(z)$ referred to or by means of Eq. 24 directly, one finds that the limiting values of r corresponding to various assumed deviations in z involving σ_z and p_z are those shown in Table II. Inspection shows that the limits of uncertainty of r with

TABLE II

LIMITING VALUES OF THE CORRELATION COEFFICIENT r, COMPUTED AS 0.62, AND OF S_y/σ_y FOR THE DATA OF TABLE I TO CORRESPOND TO ASSUMED DEVIATIONS OF σ_z, $2\sigma_z$, $2.58\sigma_z$, AND p_z (EQS. 25 AND 26) IN z (COMPUTED AS 0.725, USING EQ. 24)

Deviation in z		Limits for z		Limits for r		Limits for S_y/σ_y	
		Upper	Lower	Upper	Lower	Upper	Lower
σ_z	0.123	0.85	0.60	0.69	0.54	0.72	0.84
$2\sigma_z$	0.246	0.97	0.48	0.75	0.45	0.66	0.90
$2.58\sigma_z$	0.316	1.04	0.41	0.78	0.39	0.62	0.92
p_z	0.083	0.81	0.64	0.67	0.56	0.74	0.82

change in assumed uncertainty in z vary more for the lower limit of r than for the higher limit in the case of a positive value for r. From the standpoint of probable errors, it is found equally probable that, for other samples similar to that of Table I, the new succeeding values of r will lie as frequently without as within the range $0.56 < r < 0.67$. For S_y/σ_y the range is $0.74 < S_y/\sigma_y < 0.82$. From the standpoint of the many who attach importance to the $2.58\sigma_z$ or 99% probability, it is very unlikely that any random sample from the parent universe of Table I will yield an r outside the range $0.39 < r < 0.78$ or an S_y/σ_y outside the range $0.62 < S_y/\sigma_y < 0.92$.

Still referring to the math-physics grades of Table I, we may next answer question 2 above, namely, "To what extent does the r obtained for the sample apply to the parent group?", by the following statements. If there were no correlation between math and physics grades, i.e., $r = 0$ for the parent group, the probability of obtaining the value 0.62 or higher for r, or what is the same, 0.725 or higher for z (Eq. 29), in a sample of 69 pairs of grades would be less than 0.0001. This is the probability of a deviation from the assumed zero value for z, whose value in terms of the observed σ_z is at least $0.725/0.123$, i.e., $5.9\sigma_z$. Hence, we may conclude that there is a decided correlation between the two grades. Further, on the basis of the 99% probability test for significance we may conclude that the value of r for the parent group from which the data of Table I are a sample lies between 0.39 and 0.78.

9. Regression Lines. The least-squares line, Eq. 1, expressing the average relationship between Y and X, or between y and x, on the assumption that Y or y only is liable to error, is called the regression line of y on x. This name originated with Galton, who first applied the theory of correlation to biological data. Considering how a population could remain in dynamic equilibrium if the offspring inherited the characteristics of the parents, Galton found, in a study of the heights of fathers and sons, that the sons deviated from the mean height less than the fathers; i.e., the sons regressed towards the mean. Thus, he called the line relating the heights of sons and fathers the line of regression.

Generally, two regression lines can be calculated for the case of two correlated variables; (1) the regression line of y on x—the least-squares line obtained on the assumption that x-values are exact, and (2) the regression line of x on y—the least-squares line obtained on the assumption that y-values are exact (Fig. 5). The equation of the regression line of y on x as given above is

$$y_c = \left[\frac{\Sigma xy}{\Sigma x^2} \right] x = bx \tag{1}$$

By analogy, the least-squares line obtained on the assumption that y-values are exact is

$$x_c = \left[\frac{\Sigma xy}{\Sigma y^2} \right] y \tag{32}$$

or, when expressed in the more common form

$$y'_c = \left[\frac{\Sigma y^2}{\Sigma xy} \right] x = b'x \tag{33}$$

From Eq. 9, it follows that

$$r = \sqrt{\frac{(\Sigma xy)^2}{\Sigma x^2 \Sigma y^2}} = \sqrt{\frac{y_c}{y'_c}} = \sqrt{\frac{b}{b'}} \tag{34}$$

Thus, the correlation coefficient between y and x is the square root of the ratio of the slopes of the two regression lines.

It is seen that r has the same value regardless of whether x or y is taken as the independent variable. None of the other coefficients to be discussed possesses this desirable property. Referring to Galton's

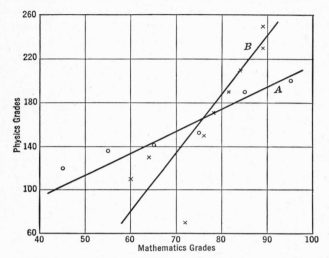

FIG. 5. A graphical method for computing correlation coefficients applied to the data of Table I and Fig. 1. The X-intervals are 10 units in length, with centers at mathematics grades 45, 55, 65, etc. The Y-intervals are 20 units long with centers at 70, 90, 110, etc. The lines of regression A, of Y on X, and B, of X on Y, were drawn with due regard to the central point $(\overline{X}, \overline{Y})$ and to the weights attached to each plotted point.

	Line A			Line B			
X	Y	wt	Y	X	wt		
95	200	$10\frac{1}{2}$	250	89.0	3	$\left(\dfrac{dy}{dx}\right)_A = b = 2.03$	
85	190	$18\frac{1}{2}$	230	89.0	3		
75	153	$20\frac{1}{2}$	210	84.0	$9\frac{1}{2}$		
65	141	$8\frac{1}{2}$	190	81.5	$9\frac{1}{2}$		
55	136	$9\frac{1}{2}$	170	78.0	$10\frac{1}{2}$	$\left(\dfrac{dy}{dx}\right)_B = b' = 5.3$	
45	120	$1\frac{1}{2}$	150	76.0	$13\frac{1}{2}$		
			130	64.0	$12\frac{1}{2}$		
			110	60.0	$6\frac{1}{2}$	$r = \sqrt{\dfrac{b}{b'}} = 0.62$	
			70	72.0	1		

conclusion that the heights of sons regressed toward the mean, one must conclude that, if the best relation between the heights of fathers and sons is linear, the heights of fathers likewise regress toward the mean.

10. A Graphical Method for Computing Correlation Coefficients. Eq. 34 is the basis for an approximate graphical method for evaluating r. This method consists in (1) plotting the data (Fig. 5); (2) dividing the X- and Y-axes into a convenient number of equal class intervals; (3) replacing the points in each X-interval by a weighted mean point (the ⊙'s of Fig. 5) and fitting the best straight line—the regression line of y on x—to these points; (4) replacing the points in each Y-interval by a weighted mean point (the ×'s of Fig. 5) and fitting the best straight line—the regression line of x on y—to these points; (5) computing the slopes of the two lines and substituting into Eq. 34 to obtain the desired r.

For many purposes the results obtained by this more rapid approximate method are sufficiently accurate. The data of Table I, when treated graphically as in Fig. 5, yielded 0.62 for r. This exact check with the value (Eq. 16) computed by the direct application of Eq. 10 is fortuitous. Computed values ranging from 0.59 to 0.65 would have been considered equally satisfactory as checks.

11. Nonlinear Correlation. When the relationship between two correlated variables is decidedly nonlinear (Fig. 6), the correlation coeffi-

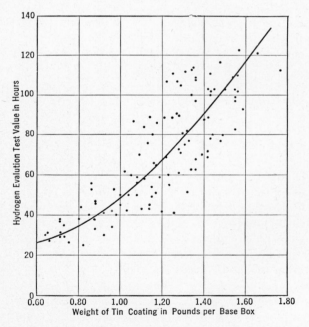

Fig. 6. An example of nonlinear correlation—hydrogen evolution test values plotted as a function of tin coating weights for hot dipped tin plate. Note that if the hydrogen evolution test value is taken as independent, the resultant regression curve would have a greater curvature than has the plotted curve. (*Courtesy of Mr. G. C. Jenison.*)

cient r loses its significance and indicates a lower degree of correlation than actually exists. In such cases the index of correlation, ρ, is considered by some to be more reliable. It is defined by the equation

$$\rho = \sqrt{1 - \frac{S_y^2}{\sigma_y^2}} \qquad [35]$$

The quantities represented by S_y and σ_y are analogous to those of Eq. 3 defining r; the only difference is that now S_y^2 is the mean of the squares of deviations of observed points from a least-squares curve (the regression curve) rather than from a least-squares line. The index of correlation differs from the correlation coefficient in two important respects. The first difference lies in the fact that for a given set of x and y values there is only a single value for r, but many values for ρ, a different value for each type of equation that may be used to represent the relation between y and x. Thus, a value of ρ has little or no meaning unless the form of the least-squares equation fitted to the data is also reported. The second difference between ρ and r arises from the fact that the value of r for a set of x- and y-values does not depend on which variable is assumed dependent and which independent, while the reverse is true for ρ. Consequently, it is customary to add a subscript to ρ, e.g., ρ_y, to indicate which variable is assumed dependent or subject to error.

Considering the uncertainties connected with the interpretation of any measure of correlation, it is doubtful that much is gained by calculating ρ instead of r unless the curvature of the regression curve is very marked.

12. Multiple Correlation. We may sometimes consider a variable X_1 to be dependent on two or more independent variables, X_2, $X_3 \cdots$, and desire to know the correlation between X_1 and X_2, $X_3 \cdots$ For this purpose, a coefficient of multiple correlation may be calculated. It is usually sufficient to consider X_1 a linear function of X_2, $X_3 \cdots$ Then the coefficient of multiple correlation between X_1, and X_2, $X_3 \cdots$, usually designated by the symbol $R_{1.23...}$, is the same as the simple coefficient of correlation between observed values of X_1 and corresponding values obtained from the least-squares equation

$$X_{1c} = a + bX_2 + cX_3 + \cdots \qquad [36]$$

for which the independent variables are X_2, X_3, etc. It is seen from Fig. 7 that for two independent variables, the coefficient of multiple correlation is analogous to r and to ρ except that the value of S_y^2 is now determined by the deviations of observed points from a least-squares plane rather than from a least-squares line or curve.

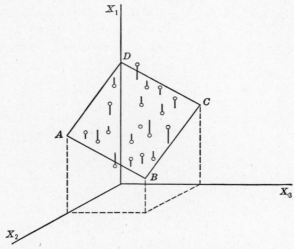

FIG. 7. Illustrating multiple correlation for the case where X_1 is viewed as dependent on X_2 and X_3. The short straight lines attached to the plotted observed points represent, on the assumption that X_1 only is liable to error, deviations of the observed X_1 from the plane of regression of X_1 on X_2X_3.

13. Partial Correlation.

The simple correlation coefficient between variables X_1 and X_2 indicates from one point of view, expressed above, the percentage of factors common in the determination of X_1 and X_2. If one such factor is the value of a third variable, X_3, it is sometimes desirable to determine the coefficient of partial correlation between X_1 and X_2; i.e., the coefficient of correlation between the values of X_1 and X_2 after the effects of X_3 on each has been deducted. Given a set of corresponding values of X_1, X_2, and X_3, the coefficient of partial correlation between X_1 and X_2 with the effect of X_3 removed—symbolized by $r_{12.3}$—is obtained by calculating first the least-squares line relating X_1 and X_3

$$X_{1c} = a_1 + b_{13}X_3 \qquad [37]$$

then the least-squares line relating X_2 and X_3

$$X_{2c} = a_2 + b_{23}X_3 \qquad [38]$$

and finally the simple correlation coefficient between the differences $(X_1 - X_{1c})$ and $(X_2 - X_{2c})$.

The effect of any number of other variables—X_3, X_4, X_5, etc.—may be simultaneously removed from the values of X_1 and X_2 in a similar manner and the partial correlation coefficient $r_{12.345...}$ obtained.

Calculations are usually simplified by use of the determinant R defined by

$$R = \begin{vmatrix} 1 & r_{12} & r_{13} & \cdots & r_{1k} \\ r_{21} & 1 & r_{23} & \cdots & r_{2k} \\ & & \cdot & & \\ & & \cdot & & \\ & & \cdot & & \\ r_{k1} & r_{k2} & r_{k3} & \cdots & 1 \end{vmatrix} \qquad [39]$$

where r_{12} $(= r_{21})$ is the simple correlation coefficient between X_1 and X_2, etc.   It may be shown that

$$r_{12.34\ldots k} = \frac{R_{12}}{\sqrt{R_{11}R_{22}}} \qquad [40]$$

where R_{12} represents the cofactor or the minor of r_{12} in the determinant R, etc.

14. Summary.   Where y is a function of x and of other unknown variables, it is sometimes desirable to express the dependency of y on x to the extent possible.   For this purpose the correlation coefficient, r, has been developed for cases where the relation is assumed linear and the index of correlation, ρ, for cases where the relation is nonlinear. The correlation coefficient is defined by

$$r = \sqrt{1 - \left(\frac{S_y}{\sigma_y}\right)^2} \qquad [3]$$

where σ_y is the standard deviation for the given distribution of values for the dependent variable and S_y, called the standard error of estimate, is a similar standard deviation for deviations from the least-squares line with the dependent variable y only liable to error, which best represents the plotted data.   With the origin of coordinates shifted to the means of the X's and the Y's, the least-squares equation for the best line is

$$y_c = \left(\frac{\Sigma xy}{\Sigma x^2}\right) x = bx \qquad [1]$$

and the expression for S_y is given by

$$S_y = \sqrt{\frac{\Sigma(y - y_c)^2}{n}} \qquad [2]$$

The limiting values for r are 0 and ± 1.   A negative correlation coefficient is in effect a positive coefficient for a supposed reversed relation.

Correlation coefficients may be shown to be connected with frequency distributions.

The most convenient formulas for computing r are

$$r = \frac{\Sigma xy}{n\sigma_x\sigma_y} \qquad [9]$$

and

$$r = \frac{n\Sigma XY - \Sigma X\Sigma Y}{\sqrt{[n\Sigma X^2 - (\Sigma X)^2][n\Sigma Y^2 - (\Sigma Y)^2]}} \qquad [10]$$

of which x and y differ from X and Y only in that the values for x and y are measured from the means of X and Y as origin while X and Y are measured from the physical origin associated with their actual measurements.

There are two ways of interpreting a correlation coefficient. The first consists in determining first the ratio S_y/σ_y and then noting that, by means of it, predicted values for Y to correspond to given values of X obtained with correlation procedure will deviate on the average from actual occurring values less than when correlation factors are ignored. The fractional amount less is precisely the ratio S_y/σ_y. The second method of interpreting r relates it to a function of the common factors, k, and noncommon factors, i and j, determining the magnitudes of the two variables being correlated. Thus

$$r = \frac{k}{\sqrt{(i + k)(j + k)}} \qquad [22]$$

Because the distribution of r-values is skewed, even when the distributions of the variables correlated are normal, procedures for determining precision indexes of an individual correlation coefficient are different from the normal procedure.

In the text the foregoing has been applied in some detail to the correlation of physics and mathematics grades obtained by a group of 69 students.

Two regression lines are distinguished. One is that of y on x. It is the least-squares line

$$y_c = \left[\frac{\Sigma xy}{\Sigma x^2}\right] x = bx \qquad [1]$$

The other is that of x on y. It is the least-squares line

$$y'_c = \left[\frac{\Sigma y^2}{\Sigma xy}\right] x = b'x \qquad [33]$$

Combined with Eq. 9, these equations lead to

$$r = \sqrt{\frac{(\Sigma xy)^2}{\Sigma x^2 \Sigma y^2}} = \sqrt{\frac{b}{b'}} \qquad [34]$$

Eq. 34 shows that, when linear correlation between two variables is sought, it is immaterial which variable is assumed to be the independent variable. Further, Eq. 34 serves as the basis for an abbreviated graphical method of determining correlation coefficients which is described fully in the text.

An index of correlation ρ defined by

$$\rho = \sqrt{1 - \frac{S_y{}^2}{\sigma_y{}^2}} \qquad [35]$$

has been developed for nonlinear cases. Here $S_y{}^2$ refers to deviations from a least-squares curve rather than from a straight line. In specifying values for ρ, the type of least-squares equation assumed and the variable assumed dependent must be stated.

Multiple correlation coefficients have been developed for cases where the dependent variable is viewed as a function of several independent variables.

Partial correlation coefficients have been developed for two variables for cases where the effects of other related variables have been eliminated.

PROBLEMS

1. The proper motion of a star is its apparent angular velocity about the sun as seen against the background of the celestial sphere. It is ordinarily expressed in seconds of arc per year. The parallax of a star is one-half the angle which the earth's orbit subtends at the star. It is ordinarily measured in seconds of arc. The greater a star's distance the less is its parallax. A certain correlation is to be expected between these two commonly measured quantities. For certain reasons it is much more convenient to find such a correlation for the logarithms of the proper motions and the parallaxes rather than for the quantities directly. Using the values for proper motion and parallax given by Russell, Dugan, and Stewart (*Astronomy*, Vol. 2, p. 637, Ginn & Company, 1927) for the 22 brightest stars, determine the correlation coefficient connecting the logarithms of those quantities. State in words the physical interpretation you are able to give to your computed value.

Star	Proper Motion (seconds/year)	Parallax (seconds)
α Canis Majoris (Sirius)	1.315	0.371
α Carinae	0.022	.005
α Centauri	3.682	.758
α Lyrae (Vega)	0.348	.124
α Aurigae (Capella)	0.439	.069

	Star	Proper Motion (seconds/year)	Parallax (seconds)
α	Bootis (Arcturus)	2.287	0.080
β	Orionis (Rigel)	0.005	.006
α	Canis Minoris (Procyon)	1.242	.312
α	Eridani (Achenar)	0.093	.049
β	Centauri	0.039	.011
α	Aquilae (Altair)	0.659	.204
α	Orionis (Betelgeuse)	0.032	.017
α	Crucis	0.048	.014
α	Tauri (Aldebaran)	0.205	.057
β	Geminorum (Pollux)	0.623	.101
α	Virginis (Spica)	0.051	.014
α	Scorpii (Antares)	0.032	.009
α	Pisces Australis (Fomalhaut)	0.367	.137
α	Cygni (Deneb)	0.004	.005
α	Leonis (Regulus)	0.244	.058
β	Crucis	0.054	.016
α	Geminorum (Castor)	0.201	.076

2. In a particular application, it was decided that a saving in time and cost would result if the chemical analysis for copper in steel with a copper content ranging from 0.02% to 0.20%, could be replaced by a spectrographic method. As a criterion of application, it was arbitrarily decided that the spectrographic and the chemical analyses should agree to within 0.01% of copper, 99% of the time. In a test using 52 samples, the following values for copper content were obtained.

Chemical	Spectrographic	Chemical	Spectrographic	Chemical	Spectrographic
0.092	0.104	0.086	0.097	0.120	0.113
.128	.127	.067	.087	.088	.096
.080	.083	.068	.068	.088	.082
.086	.087	.066	.054	.126	.114
.080	.078	.103	.106	.076	.074
.118	.107	.054	.062	.044	.046
.086	.102	.082	.072	.060	.064
.105	.108	.096	.101	.110	.110
.096	.110	.128	.140	.100	.095
.084	.100	.163	.172	.103	.096
.102	.090	.084	.073	.110	.122
.100	.101	.192	.188	.076	.073
.122	.129	.150	.151	.206	.220
.126	.135	.148	.148	.152	.164
.102	.099	.089	.093	.142	.130
.108	.104	.144	.136	.090	.096
.106	.107	.114	.115	.106	.103
.108	.103				

Determine the correlation coefficient, its probable error, and, on the basis of a normal distribution of measurements and of differences, the correlation coefficient that is demanded in order that the arbitrary criterion should have been satisfied.

3. Given the data below showing metabolism rates, M, taken in a more or less haphazard order, for guinea pigs as a function of the temperature of the surrounding atmosphere, T, as reported by Herrington [1] of the John B. Pierce Laboratory of Hygiene at New Haven, Conn., determine the correlation coefficient, using Pearson's product-moment formula.

T in °C	M in $\dfrac{\text{kcal}}{m^2 \text{ day}}$	T in °C	M in $\dfrac{\text{kcal}}{m^2 \text{ day}}$	T in °C	M in $\dfrac{\text{kcal}}{m^2 \text{ day}}$
35.3	716	27.9	720	21.1	894
34.7	557	27.8	678	21.0	815
34.7	600	27.8	677	20.9	898
34.6	885	27.8	739	20.7	812
34.6	719	27.7	777	20.3	839
34.3	694	27.6	700	20.2	988
33.6	620	27.2	693	20.0	913
32.8	701	26.8	753	19.7	968
32.5	673	26.7	713	18.1	991
32.2	579	26.3	766	17.6	1005
32.0	687	26.1	725	17.5	935
31.9	676	25.7	893	16.7	917
31.4	638	25.4	752	16.7	999
31.2	644	25.3	801	16.4	971
31.2	594	24.8	784	16.4	959
30.9	607	24.2	789	16.4	983
30.9	621	23.7	787	16.4	993
30.7	586	23.2	794	16.3	1023
30.3	561	23.1	891	15.8	1071
30.3	592	23.1	797	15.4	1065
29.8	601	23.1	835	15.1	1050
29.6	703	23.0	855	14.0	1057
29.4	583	22.7	799	13.6	1057
29.4	672	22.7	905	13.5	1104
29.3	628	22.6	804	13.5	1157
29.1	601	22.6	833	13.3	1085
28.8	670	22.5	810	13.3	1047
28.8	605	22.4	742	13.1	1071
28.5	756	22.2	852		
28.2	631	21.6	877		

4. Determine the equations of the lines of regression and the correlation coefficients for the data of problem 3, using the graphical method.

[1] Herrington, L. P., *Am. J. Physiology*, **129**, 123 (1940).

CHAPTER XIII

THE ANALYSIS OF NON-HARMONIC PERIODIC FUNCTIONS

1. Introduction. A periodic function, as used here, is one which is composed in part or in its entirety of a quantity whose magnitude varies in a regular recurring manner. In some cases the periodic variation is sinusoidal, as for the emf of a dynamo. In other cases the variation is in accord with some other law, as that for the magnitude of an eclipsing binary. Some functions contain but one periodicity and are simple. An illustration is the displacement of a particle in simple harmonic motion from its position of equilibrium. No further comment regarding such functions is needed here. Other functions contain more than one periodicity and are complex. Those belonging to this latter group are further subdivided into two types, the harmonic and the non-harmonic.

An illustration of the complex harmonic periodic function is that describing the motion of a particle of a bowed violin string. Such functions may be represented by Fourier series and are subject to Fourier analysis (Chap. V). The frequencies involved are a fundamental and harmonics with frequencies which are whole-number multiples of that fundamental. Illustrations of the non-harmonic periodic function (the descriptive term "complex" is not needed here because there are no simple non-harmonic periodic functions) are (1) the height of a tide at a given place as a function of time, (2) the forced vibrations of a structural member, (3) the frequency of occurrence of sunspots, (4) the solar constant, and (5) the magnitude of a doubly or trebly eclipsing multicomponent star. The analysis of functions of this type forms the subject matter of this chapter. Actually the theory applies as well to complex harmonic periodic functions. In fact, where the harmonics are of rather high orders, i.e., have frequencies many times those of the fundamental and where the range given in the data for the independent variable is less than that needed for the complete representation of an assumed fundamental, the Fourier series method may fail, leaving methods like that advanced here as perhaps the only one possible for an analysis.

Normally there are two parts to the analysis of a non-harmonic periodic function, (1) the search for the periodicities and (2) the determination of their magnitudes. In some cases, e.g., the tides, the periodicities, at least most of them, are known with some precision in advance because of the known causes. The same is true sometimes with regard to structural vibrations. For these cases, the first step of the normal procedure is greatly shortened. For the other cases, for which the normal procedure is generally rather long drawn out, inspection processes will often help in reducing the time required.

Since the procedure for a case involving three or more unknown periodicities is the same as for the case involving only two and differs from it essentially only in being longer, a case involving only two component periodicities has been selected for discussion. Moreover, since nothing in generality is lost and something in completeness is gained by using a function composed of sinusoidal components, the function has been thus further restricted. In what follows, we first discuss the underlying theory, make a search for the periodicities, and then finally determine their amplitudes.

2. General Theory. Let

$$z = f(t) = a + a' \sin\left(\frac{2\pi}{T'} t + \delta'\right) + a'' \sin\left(\frac{2\pi}{T''} t + \delta''\right) + \cdots$$

$$= a + z' + z'' + \cdots \tag{1}$$

describe a function for which values, $z_1, z_2, z_3, \cdots$ are given corresponding to various successive instants of time, $t_1, t_2, t_3, \cdots$ separated from one another by the constant interval, τ. If the function chosen is not sinusoidal, the treatment that follows would still apply unchanged up to a certain point. That point is reached when attention is transferred from periods, for example, to amplitudes and phase lags.

Let the fluctuations in z and the data be such that it is apparent by inspection that one of the periods T' is between $m'\tau$ and $(m' + 1)\tau$ where m' is a whole number. With ϵ' representing a positive unknown fraction less than unity, we may write

$$T' = (m' + \epsilon')\tau \tag{2}$$

Also let

$$T'' = (m'' + \epsilon'')\tau \tag{3}$$

of which m'' and ϵ'', similar to m' and ϵ in meaning, but both unknown, represent the condition so far as the second periodicity is concerned. For the present, let m' and m'' be incommensurable. If the fluctuations are such that a value for m' or m'' is not apparent, the general plan of procedure will remain unchanged. The main difference, as will appear later, is in the amount of labor involved.

With the data tabulated and an approximate value for m', as defined by Eq. 2 or Eq. 3, obtained by inspection or otherwise, the next step in the search for the periodicities consists in arranging the given values of z and certain of their means in the following array

$$
\begin{array}{cccccc}
z_1 & z_2 & z_3 & \cdots & z_{m'} & \\[2mm]
z_{m'+1} & z_{m'+2} & z_{m'+3} & \cdots & z_{2m'} & \\[2mm]
z_{2m'+1} & z_{2m'+2} & z_{2m'+3} & \cdots & z_{3m'} & \\[1mm]
\cdot & \cdot & \cdot & & \cdot & \quad [A] \\
\cdot & \cdot & \cdot & & \cdot & \\
\cdot & \cdot & \cdot & & \cdot & \\[1mm]
\dfrac{z_{km'+1}}{Z'_1} & \dfrac{z_{km'+2}}{Z'_2} & \dfrac{z_{km'+3}}{Z'_3} & \cdots & \dfrac{z_{(k+1)m'}}{Z'_{m'}} &
\end{array}
$$

Let Z'_1, Z'_2, $Z'_3, \cdots$ represent the means for the successive columns. Next one determines σ_z, the standard deviation for the entire group of z values of the array; $\sigma_{Z'}$, that for the means $Z'_1 \cdots Z'_{m'}$; and the ratio $\sigma_{Z'}/\sigma_z$. The value of σ_z does not depend on the details of arrangement in an array.

If $(k + 1)m'/m''$, the number of periods of magnitude T'' involved is very large, the condition that T' and T'' differ appreciably and are incommensurable will insure that the contributions of the z''-term of Eq. 1 to the various Z''s will be approximately equal. All of the variations in the means will then be due to the z'-term, and the $\sigma_{Z'}$ that has been computed will be a function solely of that term of Eq. 1 and the array A.

Consider now the effect on a σ_Z, due to a variation of ϵ. For the discussion that immediately follows, assume that we have at hand the values of the function of z of Eq. 1 at all instants desired rather than at instants differing only by τ. We may therefore consider arrays like that of A above with varying τ's and consequently varying ϵ's. Consider the case of $\epsilon = 0$. It is now evident that, if for one z in a particular column the T-periodicity has given its maximum contribution, every other z in the same column will have received necessarily the same maximum contribution. The evident result is that the σ_Z for that condition will be a maximum. For any slight shift of τ yielding an ϵ other than zero, the σ_Z then computed will be smaller. Only when a σ_Z is known to be a maximum can we be sure that the corresponding $m\tau$ represents a true period for the function.

Generally data are not available for testing with the gradually varying τ assumed possible just above. We must seek the condition for a maximum σ_Z from values for various instants corresponding to a fixed τ. In practice this condition of varying τ is approximated by an artifice.

Occasional appropriate values for z are omitted from the original set, their places in the array are filled by the items of the original set next in order, and the series of values thus obtained are treated in the regular manner but with the understanding that now the period is equal to $(m + \epsilon)\tau$. How this can be done will be illustrated later. It is sufficient to say here that one may thereby effectively determine various σ_Z's corresponding to various ϵ's, to find the ϵ which yields the desired maximum for σ_Z. Strictly, the maximum σ_Z/σ_z, sometimes called the correlation ratio, is desired, for σ_z will vary slightly with the omissions. In practice, a maximum for σ_Z often suffices.

For sinusoidal periodicities only, the values of $(\sigma_{Z'}/\sigma_z)$, $(\sigma_{Z''}/\sigma_z)$, and other similar ratios that may have been obtained for other periodicities present may ordinarily be used to determine the relative amplitudes of these various components and to determine at any stage in the procedure whether any remaining periodicity has been left undiscovered. To show this, one needs to consider in detail how the various σ's and the amplitudes are related.

For the assumed case of incommensurable periods and a sufficiently great number of measurements, we have largely as a result of definitions the following relations for the case of an array of n terms:

$$(\sigma_{Z'})^2 = \frac{1}{m'} \Sigma(Z' - \bar{Z}')^2 = \frac{1}{n} \Sigma(z')^2$$

$$\doteq \frac{1}{T'} \int_0^{T'} a'^2 \sin^2\left(\frac{2\pi}{T'} t + \delta'\right) dt = \frac{a'^2}{2} \quad [4]$$

$$(\sigma_{Z''})^2 = \frac{1}{m''} \Sigma(Z'' - \bar{Z}'')^2 = \frac{1}{n} \Sigma(z'')^2$$

$$\doteq \frac{1}{T''} \int_0^{T''} a''^2 \sin^2\left(\frac{2\pi}{T''} t + \delta''\right) dt = \frac{a''^2}{2} \quad [5]$$

and

$$\sigma_z{}^2 = \frac{1}{n} \Sigma(z - a)^2 = \frac{1}{n} \Sigma(z' + z'' + \cdots)^2$$

$$= \frac{1}{n} \Sigma(z'^2 + 2z'z'' + z''^2 + \cdots) \quad [6]$$

In the above expression, the summation for the term $2z'z''$ will yield zero, since for the signs of the terms being summed the result will be as often negative as positive. Eq. 6, with the aid of Eqs. 4 and 5, may therefore be reduced to

$$\sigma_z{}^2 = \frac{1}{n} \Sigma(z'^2 + z''^2 + \cdots) = \sigma_{Z'}{}^2 + \sigma_{Z''}{}^2 + \cdots \doteq \frac{a'^2}{2} + \frac{a''^2}{2} + \cdots \quad [7]$$

From Eqs. 4, 5, and 7, we obtain finally

$$\frac{a'}{a''} = \frac{\dfrac{\sigma_{Z'}}{\sigma_z}}{\dfrac{\sigma_{Z''}}{\sigma_z}} \qquad\qquad [8]$$

and

$$\left(\frac{\sigma_{Z'}}{\sigma_z}\right)^2 + \left(\frac{\sigma_{Z''}}{\sigma_z}\right)^2 + \cdots = 1 \qquad\qquad [9]$$

Eq. 8 shows that the amplitudes of the various components of z vary as their σ_Z/σ_z's. Eq. 9 shows that the sum of the squares of the various σ_Z/σ_z's must add up to unity. If, then, at any time in an analysis the sum of the values obtained for $(\sigma_Z/\sigma_z)^2$ equals unity, one may be certain that the period analysis is over. Strictly speaking, owing to the approximations involved in the artifice employed and those occurring in Eqs. 4 and 5, one may expect Eqs. 8 and 9 to be only approximately fulfilled. What the expected relations are for certain other types of periodicities is the subject of a problem at the end of the chapter.

An approximate amplitude a may be obtained more directly. From the Z's of an array that yields a maximum σ_Z/σ_z one may take for its value one-half the difference between the greatest and the smallest values algebraically considered. However, the value thus obtained will be exact only if the chosen Z's correspond to a maximum and a minimum for some particular component of the z of Eq. 1, if the number of items is sufficient to insure that the contributions of the other components to the various Z's are strictly equal, and if the corresponding T is just equal to an $m\tau$. Within its limitations, this method of obtaining an amplitude has considerable value.

3. Application of Theory to Determinations of Periods. Data for a function possessing two sinusoidal periodicities such as the z of Eq. 1 are given in Table I and graphed in Fig. 1. Let us apply the theory of the preceding section to this data to obtain values for T' and T'' and then later to evaluate a' and a''.

Inspection of Table I shows positive maxima occurring at roughly regular intervals. In terms of τ, the intervals in succession are 9, 7, 9, 7, 9, 9, 7, 9, 7, and 9. One of the periods, T' say, would seem to be about equal to 8 sec. Let us make this assumption and construct Table II in accord with array A. (In what follows the reading $z = 0$ for $t = 0$ sec has been inadvertently omitted. That such is the case is of no material importance, however.) Should it have been difficult or impossible to obtain an approximate value for T' by inspection, it would be necessary to assume various values for T' and to determine in an exploring way, using perhaps a part only of the data and the method that follows, regions where the periodicities are actually located. Simple inspection has eliminated such exploration.

Computations, made in accord with the preceding section, when applied to the array of Table II, yield the values shown for $\bar{z}$, $\bar{Z}'$, $\sigma_{Z'}$, σ_z, and the ratio $\sigma_{Z'}/\sigma_z$. In determining the σ's, it is well to use the short method of Chapter VII, Eq. 13, namely

$$\sigma_z{}^2 = \frac{\Sigma z^2}{n} - \left(\frac{\Sigma z}{n}\right)^2 \qquad [10]$$

Inspection of Table II shows that maxima tend to shift from columns 2 and 3 to columns 3 and 4 as we progress through the table. It would

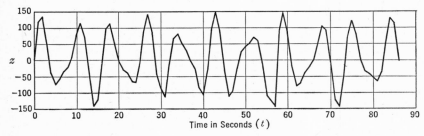

Fig. 1. Graph of the non-harmonic periodic function representing the data of Table I.

seem probable that if the effective value for T' were made equal to 8.1 sec or 8.2 sec, the greatest possible range for the values of Z' might be obtained and possibly the greatest possible values for $\sigma_{Z'}$ and for $\sigma_{Z'}/\sigma_z$.

With the above in mind, let us construct Table III on the assumed basis that $T' = 8.20$ sec. In so doing it is necessary to include the range of 82 readings rather than 80, as was done in Table II. Two readings of the 82 must be eliminated. The basis for selecting the readings to be dropped follows. Starting with the assumption that the first reading is exactly in phase for an assumed cycle covering 8.20 sec, one sees that the phases of the next several readings lead progressively with respect to the readings that would be used were they available for regular intervals 1.02 sec ($= \frac{1}{8} \times 8.20$ sec) long. Nevertheless the readings available are used in succession until it happens that by omission of some one reading the phase difference, thereafter for a time a phase lag, is reduced. Some reflection will show that, where there are n positions in the array and that r numbers from a total of $n + r$ numbers are to be dropped on the basis of a minimum for the sum of the phase differences, the positions of drop in the sequence of $n + r$ numbers are given by the fractions $n/2r + 1$, $3n/2r + 2$, $5n/2r + 3$, etc. Thus for an array of 80 with two numbers to be dropped out of a sequence of 82

TABLE I

VALUES, UNIFORMLY SPACED IN TIME, FOR A NON-HARMONIC FUNCTION
OF THE TYPE SHOWN IN EQ. 1, AND THEIR SQUARES

[The * indicates maximum values.   The arbitrary time interval, τ, elapsing between successive readings is 1.00 sec]

t (sec)	z	z^2	t (sec)	z	z^2	t (sec)	z	z^2
0	0	0	29	− 46	2,116	58	+ 86	7,396
1	+116	13,456	30	− 87	7,569	59	+144*	20,736
2	+133*	17,689	31	−115	13,225	60	+ 86	7,396
3	+ 52	2,704	32	− 16	256	61	− 19	361
4	− 43	1,849	33	+ 65	4,225	62	− 80	6,400
5	− 77	5,929	34	+ 78*	6,084	63	− 72	5,184
6	− 59	3,481	35	+ 50	2,500	64	− 40	1,600
7	− 37	1,369	36	+ 29	841	65	− 21	441
8	− 24	576	37	− 4	16	66	0	0
9	+ 9	81	38	− 30	900	67	+ 51	2,601
10	+ 74	5,476	39	− 87	7,569	68	+104*	10,816
11	+114*	12,996	40	−108	11,664	69	+ 90	8,100
12	+ 68	4,624	41	− 32	1,024	70	− 9	81
13	− 50	2,500	42	+ 90	8,100	71	−121	14,641
14	−143	20,449	43	+150*	22,500	72	−143	20,449
15	−122	14,884	44	+ 90	8,100	73	− 50	2,500
16	− 7	49	45	− 35	1,225	74	+ 73	5,329
17	+ 97	9,409	46	−115	13,225	75	+122*	14,884
18	+110*	12,100	47	− 97	9,409	76	+ 77	5,929
19	+ 51	2,601	48	− 27	729	77	+ 3	9
20	− 9	81	49	+ 24	576	78	− 36	1,296
21	− 33	1,089	50	+ 39	1,521	79	− 44	1,936
22	− 44	1,936	51	+ 50	2,500	80	− 55	3,025
23	− 66	4,356	52	+ 68*	4,624	81	− 67	4,489
24	− 70	4,900	53	+ 56	3,136	82	− 35	1,225
25	− 14	196	54	− 18	324	83	+ 52	2,704
26	+ 85	7,225	55	−112	12,544	84	+129*	16,641
27	+140*	19,600	56	−128	16,384	85	+113	12,769
28	+ 84	7,056	57	− 44	1,936	86	− 2	4

numbers, the numbers to be dropped are the 21st and 62nd.   Table III shows the data of Table I arranged thus on the assumption that $T' = 8.20$ sec.   One sees at once from the positions of the maxima and from the correspondingly increased value for $\sigma_{Z'}/\sigma_z$ that this second guess regarding T' is much better than the first.

Results from treatment similar to the above for additional assumed values for T' of 8.10, 8.30, and 8.50 sec added to those shown in Tables

TABLE II

THE DATA OF TABLE I ARRANGED SIMILAR TO ARRAY A ON THE ASSUMPTION THAT
$T' = 8.00$ SEC

[The numbers at the bottoms of the columns are the mean Z''s. As in Table I, * indicates a positive maximum. The value for $t = 0$ sec has been inadvertently omitted]

+116	+133*	+ 52	− 43	− 77	− 59	− 37	− 24	
+ 9	+ 74	+114*	+ 68	− 50	−143	−122	− 7	
+ 97	+110*	+ 51	− 9	− 33	− 44	− 66	− 70	$\bar{z} = \bar{Z}' = +2.1$
− 14	+ 85	+140*	+ 84	− 46	− 87	−115	− 16	
+ 65	+ 78*	+ 50	+ 29	− 4	− 30	− 87	−108	$\sigma_{Z'} = 64.4$
− 32	+ 90	+150*	+ 90	− 35	−115	− 97	− 21	$\sigma_z = 77.8$
+ 24	+ 39	+ 50	+ 68*	+ 56	− 18	−112	−128	
− 44	+ 86	+114*	+ 86	− 19	− 80	− 72	− 40	$\dfrac{\sigma_{Z'}}{\sigma_z} = 0.828$
− 21	0	+ 51	+104*	+ 90	− 9	−121	−143	
− 50	+ 73	+122	+ 77	+ 3	− 36	− 44	− 55	
+15.0	+76.8	+92.4	+55.4	−11.5	−62.1	−87.3	−61.8	

TABLE III

THE DATA OF TABLE I ARRANGED SIMILAR TO ARRAY A ON THE ASSUMPTION THAT
$T' = 8.20$ SEC

[The numbers at the bottoms of the columns are the mean Z''s. As in Tables I and II, * indicates a positive maximum]

+116	+133*	+ 52	−43	− 77	− 59	− 37	−24	
+ 9	+ 74	+114*	+68	− 50	−143	−122	− 7	
+ 97	+110*	+ 51	− 9	− 44	− 66	− 70	−14	$\bar{z} = \bar{Z}' = +2.2$
+ 85	+140*	+ 84	−46	− 87	−115	− 16	+65	
+ 78*	+ 50	+ 29	− 4	− 30	− 87	−108	−32	$\sigma_{Z'} = 68.9$
+ 90	+150*	+ 90	−35	−115	− 97	− 27	+24	$\sigma_z = 77.6$
+ 39	+ 50	+ 68*	+56	− 18	−112	−128	−44	
+ 86	+144*	+ 86	−19	− 72	− 40	− 21	0	$\dfrac{\sigma_{Z'}}{\sigma_z} = 0.888$
+ 51	+104*	+ 90	− 9	−121	−143	− 50	+73	
+122*	+ 77	+ 3	−36	− 44	− 55	− 67	−35	
+77.3	+103.2	+66.7	−7.7	−65.8	−91.7	−64.6	+0.6	

II and III are given in Table IV. Plotted (Fig. 2), the curve for $\sigma_{Z'}/\sigma_z = f(T)$ shows a maximum at about 8.18 sec. This is the period of the dominant frequency present. It is more difficult but not impossible to estimate the period of the less dominant frequency by inspection.   Looking at Table I, one notes very high values of $f(t)$ at $t = 27$ sec and $t = 43$ sec and only one intervening positive maximum at $t = 34$ sec.   This maximum is much reduced in magnitude and is nearly midway between the other two.   Further, there are two negative maxima in this interval, one each side of the midpoint, and both are intermediate in value.   The simple explanation is that both periodicities had

TABLE IV

CERTAIN VALUES COMPUTED FROM THE DATA OF TABLE I ON THE BASIS OF VARIOUS ASSUMED PERIODICITIES PRESENT

T (sec)	$\bar{z} = \overline{Z}$	$\dfrac{(Z_{max} - Z_{min})}{2}$	σ_z	σ_Z	$\dfrac{\sigma_Z}{\sigma_z}$
8.00	+2.1	89.8	77.8	64.4	0.828
8.10	+1.7	90.9	78.1	68.1	0.872
8.20	+2.2	97.4	77.6	68.9	0.888
8.30	+2.3	81.8	76.6	61.9	0.808
8.50	−0.3	73.0	78.5	52.7	0.671
5.00	+1.8	19.2	77.8	14.1	0.181
5.12	+2.4	33.0	77.7	27.1	0.349
5.19	+2.0	43.2	77.2	34.2	0.443
5.25	+2.6	39.2	78.1	30.0	0.384
5.31	+0.6	37.2	77.9	28.9	0.371
5.38	+2.7	16.0	80.1	13.4	0.167
6.00	+3.0	4.5	78.5	3.1	0.040

separate positive maxima near the 27 and the 43 positions, that, though the 8.18 sec frequency had a positive maximum near the 34 position, the less dominant frequency had a negative maximum at that point, and that three periods of the unknown frequency are approximately equal to two of the known.   We should therefore expect the T'' of the less dominant frequency to be between 5.0 and 5.5 sec.   In accord with the expectancy just deduced, computations based on various assumed values for T'', as shown also in Table IV and Fig. 3, indicate the period of this frequency, despite the failure of one point to conform with the others, to be about 5.19 sec.

The results for an assumed T'' of 6.0 sec (Table IV) at some distance from 5.19 sec show very definitely that that frequency is not present. That the plots of Figs. 2 and 3 should give such definite indications is somewhat a matter of chance. For really satisfactory work, more readings per cycle and a greatly increased number of cycles are desired.

Comparison of $(\sigma_{Z'}/\sigma_z)$ with $(\sigma_{Z''}/\sigma_z)$ on the bases of Eqs. 8 and 9 indicates (1) that the amplitude for the dominant frequency is twice

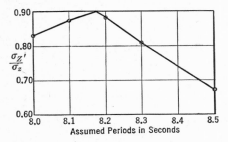

FIG. 2. Values computed, using the data of Table I and Fig. 1, for $\sigma_{Z'}/\sigma_z$ for various assumed periods in the neighborhood of 8.2 sec.

that for the less dominant frequency and (2) that no additional frequency having an appreciable amplitude is present. Except for the fact that these periodicities are sinusoidal, these conclusions could not be deduced without further consideration (see problem 2).

That the peaks of Figs. 2 and 3 are not more definitely resolved than they are is a consequence of the relative smallness of the number of terms given in Table I. Were the number doubled the resolution would be effectively doubled. The effect is the same as in the resolution of

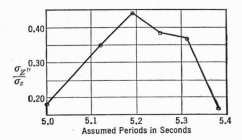

FIG. 3. Values computed, using the data of Table I and Fig. 1, for $\sigma_{Z''}/\sigma_z$ for various assumed periods in the neighborhood of 5.2 sec.

spectral lines by a grating; the greater the number of grating lines, other things the same, the greater is the resolution.

An alternate procedure for determining T''' consists (1) in subtracting from the data of Table I values for an assumed periodicity of 8.18 sec whose amplitude is 97.4 and whose phase is zero for $t = 43$ sec, and (2) in treating the results thus obtained in the manner that the original data have been treated. This entails more work than the inspection method and normally would be used only in case the latter fails.

4. Determining the Amplitude and Phase Constants. It is advisable, in view of the results already gained by inspection, to attempt its application further. Looking over Table I once more, it is found that an absolute positive maximum value for z occurs at position 43. Further, the values of z for positions 42 and 44 are equal at least to within one part in 90. This suggests, despite, if not more strongly because of, the readings for positions 58, 59, and 60, that

$$a' + a'' \doteq 150 \qquad [11]$$

and that, if t were taken as zero at position 43, then

$$\left[(\delta')' = (\delta'')' = \frac{\pi}{2} \right]_{43 \text{ sec}} \qquad [12]$$

Eq. 11 combined with the conclusion reached above that a'/a'' equals approximately 2, leads to the conclusion that a' and a'' may have the values 100 and 50 respectively. It is a simple matter to transfer to a time origin corresponding to that used in constructing Table I. Doing so, we find that

$$[\delta' = -2°]_{t=0} \qquad [13]$$

$$[\delta'' = -2°]_{t=0} \qquad [14]$$

From the inspectional analysis we therefore conclude as an approximate expression

$$z \doteq 100 \sin \left(\frac{2\pi}{8.18 \text{ sec}} t - 2° \right) + 50 \sin \left(\frac{2\pi}{5.19 \text{ sec}} t - 2° \right) \qquad [15]$$

Let us compare Eq. 15 with what is obtained by a much more extended determination of the four constants a', a'', δ', and δ'' by what we ordinarily consider the "straightforward" mathematical method, which follows. We shall make the same assumption as above, namely, that a is zero. Although Table IV by its average values for $\bar{z}$ seems to indicate that a may be of the order of $+1.5$, this may well be a consequence of the small number of terms.

For the evaluation of the constants on the proposed basis, it is necessary to rewrite Eq. 1 in the following form

$$z = a + (a' \sin \delta') \cos \frac{2\pi}{T'} t + (a' \cos \delta') \sin \frac{2\pi}{T'} t$$

$$+ (a'' \sin \delta'') \cos \frac{2\pi}{T''} t + (a'' \cos \delta'') \sin \frac{2\pi}{T''} t \qquad [16]$$

In this form the constants to be determined are a, $a'\sin\delta'$, $a'\cos\delta'$, $a''\sin\delta''$, and $a''\cos\delta''$. Selecting five points from Table I, and inserting the appropriate values for z and t, together with the determined values for T' and T'', in Eq. 16 leads to five simultaneous linear equations connecting the desired constants. Values for them may be determined by standard methods.

The authors, assuming a of Eq. 5 to be zero, have carried through such computations. The points selected corresponded to t equal to 7, 18, 34, and 36 sec. In theory any four points could be chosen. These were chosen on the basis that for these, position z varied but slowly with t. The resultant computed equation is

$$z = 85.0 \sin\left(\frac{2\pi}{T'}\, t + 250°\right) + 47.9 \sin\left(\frac{2\pi}{T''}\, t + 167°\right) \qquad [17]$$

The constants of Eq. 17 do not check well (1) with the conclusion, drawn in connection with Table IV and Eq. 8, that the amplitude of the first component is twice that of the second, (2) with the original data of Table I which shows at 43 sec that the sum of the two amplitudes must be equal at least to 150, nor (3) with the original equation used in the construction of Table I, namely

$$z = 100.0 \sin\frac{2\pi}{T'}\, t + 50.0 \sin\frac{2\pi}{T''}\, t \qquad [18]$$

Eq. 15 arrived at by the inspection method fits much more nearly with the construction equation, Eq. 18, than does Eq. 17, which was arrived at by straightforward mathematical procedure. That the latter method should fail can be explained on the basis of propagation of precision indexes (Chap. IX). It perhaps suffices here to say that certain procedures, starting with given quantities with moderate given precision indexes, tend toward highly precise results for certain other computed quantities when carried through in a so-called forward direction, and that those same procedures will tend toward greater uncertainty of results if the direction is reversed and the former initially given quantities are now the quantities sought in the reversed procedure. Evaluating a', a'', δ', and δ'' in terms of given z and T' and T'' is such a backward procedure when contrasted with the forward procedure of finding z, given those constants.

Failing the benefits of an inspection or other method, the best procedure for finding the best equation of the type of Eq. 1 would seem to be that of (1) accepting an equation such as Eq. 17 as preliminary, (2) plotting the resulting curve of deviations, (3) computing the resulting variations for this curve due to separate small variations of T', T'', a', a'', δ', and δ'', and (4) adjusting the values of these constants to yield a minimum standard deviation in accord with Gaussian theory.

Even with the benefits of assumed possible inspectional method, adjustments in accord with the preceding paragraph may be necessary.

5. Summary.   Certain problems involve variations of two or more components each having a periodicity of its own unrelated to that of the other.   When only the added effects of these periodicities can be measured, there is need of a procedure for their separate determinations.

Granted a disturbance of the type

$$z = a + a' \sin\left(\frac{2\pi}{T'} t + \delta'\right) + a'' \sin\left(\frac{2\pi}{T''} t + \delta''\right) + \cdots \qquad [1]$$

and data for z for a long series of equally spaced instants of time, τ, one first inspects the tabulated data to determine an approximate period for one periodicity.   If an approximate period is not obtainable thus, one must be assumed.

With a definite assumption of period as $m'\tau$ where m' is a whole number, the data are arrayed as follows:

$$
\begin{array}{cccccc}
z_1 & z_2 & z_3 & & & z_{m'} \\[2mm]
z_{m'+1} & z_{m'+2} & z_{m'+3} & \cdots & & z_{2m'} \\[2mm]
z_{2m'+1} & z_{2m'+2} & z_{2m'+3} & \cdots & & z_{3m'} \\
\cdot & \cdot & \cdot & & & \cdot \\
\cdot & \cdot & \cdot & & & \cdot \\
\cdot & \cdot & \cdot & & & \cdot \\[2mm]
Z'_1 & Z'_2 & Z'_3 & \cdots & & Z'_m
\end{array} \qquad [A]
$$

of which the Z''s represent the averages of the corresponding columns. For this array the ratio of two standard deviations is sought, namely $\sigma_{Z'}/\sigma_z$. If this ratio is zero or approximately zero, $m'\tau$ is not a period present in the data nor is it approximately such period. If, however, this ratio differs from zero considerably, a period near $m'\tau$ is present. It then becomes necessary to array the data corresponding to periods of $(m' \pm \epsilon')\tau$ of which ϵ' is a proper fraction. The procedure for this, involving the elimination of certain of the z's according to an ordered plan, is described in the text. The ratios $\sigma_{Z'}/\sigma_z$ for several such arrays are separately determined. The value of $(m' \pm \epsilon')\tau$ corresponding to a maximum for this ratio is a frequency sought. Other frequencies are similarly determined by seeking maxima of the ratio in other regions of assumed frequencies.

In case the periodicities are sinusoidal the ratios σ_Z/σ_z are in proportion to their amplitudes and the sum of their squares is unity. Procedures for determining actual amplitudes and phase relations for the component periodicities are discussed.

PROBLEMS

1. Taking from the data of Table I those which are necessary separately for 13 and 14 cycles, compute two values for $\sigma_{Z''}/\sigma_z$ corresponding to $T'' = 5.31$ sec. What is your conclusion?

2. When two periodic functions of the straight-side saw tooth type with different frequencies and amplitudes are combined, what are the expected relations corresponding to those of Eqs. 8 and 9? What generalization may be made?

APPENDIX 1

BRIEF DISCUSSION OF DETERMINANT METHODS

Introduction. Throughout this text determinants are used (1) in the solution of simultaneous equations and (2) in the determination of the equations of curves of selected types that pass through selected points. To the authors they represent much time saved and simplified, generalized procedures. Recognizing, however, that many users of this text will not have the necessary preparation, simple though it is, we here present without discussion of underlying theory the simple procedures for carrying out the two processes indicated above.

The Solution of Simultaneous Equations. Consider the determinant solution for the following three equations.

$$3x + 2y - z = 19 \qquad [1]$$

$$2x - 6y - z = 7 \qquad [2]$$

$$5x - 4y + 3z = 1 \qquad [3]$$

In determinant form they are

$$x = \frac{\begin{vmatrix} 19 & 2 & -1 \\ 7 & -6 & -1 \\ 1 & -4 & 3 \end{vmatrix}}{\begin{vmatrix} 3 & 2 & -1 \\ 2 & -6 & -1 \\ 5 & -4 & 3 \end{vmatrix}} \qquad [4]$$

$$y = \frac{\begin{vmatrix} 3 & 19 & -1 \\ 2 & 7 & -1 \\ 5 & 1 & 3 \end{vmatrix}}{\begin{vmatrix} 3 & 2 & -1 \\ 2 & -6 & -1 \\ 5 & -4 & 3 \end{vmatrix}} \qquad [5]$$

$$z = \frac{\begin{vmatrix} 3 & 2 & 19 \\ 2 & -6 & 7 \\ 5 & -4 & 1 \end{vmatrix}}{\begin{vmatrix} 3 & 2 & -1 \\ 2 & -6 & -1 \\ 5 & -4 & 3 \end{vmatrix}} \qquad [6]$$

The denominators are the same and consist of a determinant composed of the coefficients of x, y, and z in Eqs. 1, 2, and 3 arrayed in the order appearing there. The numerator determinant for x differs only in that the coefficients of x in Eqs. 1, 2, and 3 are replaced by the numerics on the right of the equality signs. The numerators for y and z are similarly determined. In case there are four or more unknowns, expressions similar to the above may be written for their values. Each unknown will be represented by the ratio of two determinants. For the convenient evaluation of these determinants, there are several rules which we shall discuss in general terms previous to obtaining the numerical values ordinarily desired for the three unknowns.

The Evaluation of Determinants. Let us consider in succession the generalized procedures for evaluating determinants of the (1) second, (2) third, and (3) higher orders.

The standard form for the second order determinant and its algebraic equivalents are shown in the following equations:

$$\begin{vmatrix} a_1 & a_2 \\ b_1 & b_2 \end{vmatrix} = a_1b_2 - a_2b_1 \tag{7}$$

The standard form for a third order determinant is

$$\begin{vmatrix} a_1 & a_2 & a_3 \\ b_1 & b_2 & b_3 \\ c_1 & c_2 & c_3 \end{vmatrix} \tag{A}$$

There are two convenient methods to evaluate it.

According to one method, the operator either draws, or sees drawn in his mind's eye, lines as indicated in the following form:

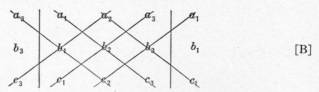

$$\tag{B}$$

In the evaluation the determinant is equated to the sum of the products of items connected by the lines. In this equating one takes as positives the products of terms connected by the lines sloping generally downward to the right and as negative the products of terms connected by the lines sloping generally downward to the left. Thus we have

$$\begin{vmatrix} a_1 & a_2 & a_3 \\ b_1 & b_2 & b_3 \\ c_1 & c_2 & c_3 \end{vmatrix} = a_1b_2c_3 + a_2b_3c_1 + a_3b_1c_2 - a_1b_3c_2 - a_2b_1c_3 - a_3b_2c_1 \tag{8}$$

As a general characteristic of the terms of the algebraic equivalent of the determinant, it is seen that each row and column is represented in every such term.

The second method is based on the breaking up of the determinant into second-order determinants as follows:

$$\begin{vmatrix} a_1 & a_2 & a_3 \\ b_1 & b_2 & b_3 \\ c_1 & c_2 & c_3 \end{vmatrix} = a_1 \begin{vmatrix} b_2 & b_3 \\ c_2 & c_3 \end{vmatrix} - a_2 \begin{vmatrix} b_1 & b_3 \\ c_1 & c_3 \end{vmatrix} + a_3 \begin{vmatrix} b_1 & b_2 \\ c_1 & c_2 \end{vmatrix} \qquad [9]$$

Expansion of these second-order determinants leads at once to the expression given above. These smaller determinants in order are called minors of the terms a_1, a_2, and a_3. Note that, in the expansion of the main determinant in terms of minors, the signs are alternately positive and negative and that the first sign is positive. For the one who makes considerable use of determinants, the first method is commonly used when a determinant of the third order is to be evaluated.

Consider next the evaluation of a determinant of the fourth or higher order. The method of Array B cannot be used. Instead we use that given above as the second method for the third order determinant. Thus we have

$$\begin{vmatrix} a_1 & a_2 & a_3 & a_4 \\ b_1 & b_2 & b_3 & b_4 \\ c_1 & c_2 & c_3 & c_4 \\ d_1 & d_2 & d_3 & d_4 \end{vmatrix} = a_1 \begin{vmatrix} b_2 & b_3 & b_4 \\ c_2 & c_3 & c_4 \\ d_2 & d_3 & d_4 \end{vmatrix} - a_2 \begin{vmatrix} b_1 & b_3 & b_4 \\ c_1 & c_3 & c_4 \\ d_1 & d_3 & d_4 \end{vmatrix} + a_3 \begin{vmatrix} b_1 & b_2 & b_4 \\ c_1 & c_2 & c_4 \\ d_1 & d_2 & d_4 \end{vmatrix} - a_4 \begin{vmatrix} b_1 & b_2 & b_3 \\ c_1 & c_2 & c_3 \\ d_1 & d_2 & d_3 \end{vmatrix} \qquad [10]$$

of which the third order determinants are to be evaluated as above. Note the alternate changing of signs. Writing $|a_1b_2c_3d_4|$ for the main determinant and A_1, A_2, A_3, and A_4 as the minors to the elements a_1, a_2, a_3, and a_4, we have as an abbreviated form

$$|a_1b_2c_3d_4| = a_1A_1 - a_2A_2 + a_3A_3 - a_4A_4 \qquad [11]$$

According to another method of breaking up, we may write

$$|a_1b_2c_3d_4| = a_1A_1 - b_1B_1 + c_1C_1 - d_1D_1 \qquad [12]$$

There are six other methods in fact. Based for instance on the second column, we write

$$|a_1b_2c_3d_4| = - a_2A_2 + b_2B_2 - c_2C_2 + d_2D_2 \qquad [13]$$

The sign of any term depends on the location in the determinant of the item preceding the minor. These are shown in the following array:

$$\begin{vmatrix} + & - & + & - \\ - & + & - & + \\ + & - & + & - \\ - & + & - & + \end{vmatrix} \qquad [C]$$

Rules for the Simplification of Determinants. The time required to evaluate a determinant is often much lessened by the application of certain rules which we shall state without giving proof. They are:

(1) If, from a row or column of a determinant, a common factor may be removed, that determinant may be equated to the product of that factor and the determinant with that factor eliminated from the row or column in question. Thus

$$\begin{vmatrix} 3 & 2 & -1 \\ 2 & -6 & -1 \\ 5 & -4 & 3 \end{vmatrix} = 2 \begin{vmatrix} 3 & 1 & -1 \\ 2 & -3 & -1 \\ 5 & -2 & 3 \end{vmatrix} \qquad [14]$$

(2) The elements of one row or column may all be multiplied by a constant and added to or subtracted from the corresponding elements of another row or column without changing the value of the determinant. Thus

$$\begin{vmatrix} 3 & 1 & -1 \\ 2 & -3 & -1 \\ 5 & -2 & 3 \end{vmatrix} = \begin{vmatrix} 3 & 1 & -1 \\ -1 & -4 & 0 \\ 5 & -2 & 3 \end{vmatrix} = \begin{vmatrix} 3 & 1 & -1 \\ -1 & -4 & 0 \\ 14 & 1 & 0 \end{vmatrix} \qquad [15]$$

The first row was first subtracted from the second and then multiplied by 3 and added to the last row. The advantage for the evaluation has been the introduction of zeros.

(3) If the elements of a row or a column of a determinant are all zeros with one exception, the determinant may be equated to the product of that element and its minor with the appropriate sign derived from array C. Thus we have

$$\begin{vmatrix} 3 & 1 & -1 \\ -1 & -4 & 0 \\ 14 & 1 & 0 \end{vmatrix} = -1 \begin{vmatrix} -1 & -4 \\ 14 & 1 \end{vmatrix} = \begin{vmatrix} 1 & 4 \\ 14 & 1 \end{vmatrix} \qquad [16]$$

the last step following rule 1. Evaluated in accord with Eq. 7, the last determinant yields -55. Accordingly the original determinant of Eq. 14 and the denominators of Eqs. 4, 5, and 6 are equal to -110.

(4) If two rows or two columns of a determinant are equal or the elements of one are in direct proportion to those of the other, the value of the determinant is zero. Thus

$$\begin{vmatrix} 6 & 4 & 2 \\ 8 & 4 & 3 \\ 9 & 6 & 3 \end{vmatrix} = \begin{vmatrix} 6 & 4 & 2 \\ 8 & 4 & 3 \\ 0 & 0 & 0 \end{vmatrix} = 0 \qquad [17]$$

a consequence in fact of rule 2 and of the general characteristic of the terms to which a determinant may be equated as noted above in connection with Eq. 8.

Applying the general and special rules for the evaluation of the determinants of Eqs. 4, 5, and 6, one obtains

$$x = \frac{-440}{-110} = 4 \qquad [18]$$

$$y = \frac{-110}{-110} = 1 \qquad [19]$$

$$z = \frac{550}{-110} = -5 \qquad [20]$$

Were all sets of simultaneous equations which are to be solved of no higher order than three and were the coefficients always simple whole numbers, it is doubtful that the time-saving feature of determinants would be of much value. When, however, the order is higher than three and the coefficients are not simple, there is no question but that the determinant method is advisable.

There are additional special rules which have been developed and proved. We shall not have need for them, however.

Equations of Specific Curves by the Determinant Method. The determinant procedure for the determination of the equation of a specific curve is the same whatever the general form may be. For the straight line of the form

$$y + a + bx = 0 \qquad [21]$$

passing through points $(3,5)$ and $(6,2)$, for instance, the equation is

$$\begin{vmatrix} y & 1 & x \\ 5 & 1 & 3 \\ 2 & 1 & 6 \end{vmatrix} = 0 \qquad [22]$$

Reduced to an algebraic form in conformity with the procedures and rules outlined above, this yields

$$y - 8 + x = 0 \qquad [23]$$

For the third-degree equation of the form

$$y + a + bx + cx^2 + dx^3 = 0 \qquad [24]$$

passing through four points (corresponding to the four arbitrary constants) namely $(0,2)$, $(2,5)$, $(4,10)$, and $(6,12)$, the equation is

$$\begin{vmatrix} y & 1 & x & x^2 & x^3 \\ 2 & 1 & 0 & 0 & 0 \\ 5 & 1 & 2 & 4 & 8 \\ 10 & 1 & 4 & 16 & 64 \\ 12 & 1 & 6 & 36 & 216 \end{vmatrix} = 0 \qquad [25]$$

The determination of the algebraic form is left to the reader.

For an equation of the form

$$y^2 + ay + b + cx^2 + dx = 0 \qquad [26]$$

passing through the points listed above for Eqs. 24 and 25 the equation is similarly

$$\begin{vmatrix} y^2 & y & 1 & x & x^2 \\ 4 & 2 & 1 & 0 & 0 \\ 25 & 5 & 1 & 2 & 4 \\ 100 & 10 & 1 & 4 & 16 \\ 144 & 12 & 1 & 6 & 36 \end{vmatrix} = 0 \qquad [27]$$

The determination of the algebraic form is left to the reader.

The occurrence of a column each element of which is unity may be slightly disturbing at first. Its presence is understood when it is seen that these determinants are composed entirely of the coefficients of the undetermined constants and of the constant arbitrarily taken as unity and that the so-called constant term of Eq. 26 for instance may be viewed as bx^0 or by^0 or a combination and that x^0 and y^0 are unity.

Often in the determination of equations, the operator may select certain convenient points for his purpose. So doing, the necessary computations may be greatly abbreviated. If additionally certain simplifying changes of variables may be employed, an additional reduction in computational effort sometimes results. Illustrating these procedures, we shall consider the data of Table I wherein is presented the time-temperature relation for the constantly stirred liquid of a calorimeter to which heat was supplied electrically at a constant rate.

TABLE I

DATA SHOWING THE TIME-TEMPERATURE RELATION FOR THE LIQUID OF A CALORIMETER SUPPLIED WITH HEAT AT A CONSTANT RATE

t in min	T in °C	t in min	T in °C
0	20.95	9	34.65
1	22.60	10	36.10
2	24.20	11	37.50
3	25.75	12	38.90
4	27.30	13	40.30
5	28.80	14	41.70
6	30.30	15	43.05
7	31.75	16	44.40
8	33.20		

Let the purpose be that of determining values of dT/dt for various temperatures such as 25° C, 30° C, 35° C and 40° C. We first seek $T = f(t)$ and for the relation let us assume

$$T = T_0 + at + bt^2 \qquad [28]$$

Making use of the selected-points method, which is described fully in Chapter III of the text, we select points corresponding to 2 min, 8 min, and 14 min as fairly representative of three roughly equal groups into which the data may be divided. The determinant equation, disregarding the units of measurement, that results is

$$\begin{vmatrix} T & 1 & t & t^2 \\ 24.20 & 1 & 2 & 4 \\ 33.20 & 1 & 8 & 64 \\ 41.70 & 1 & 14 & 196 \end{vmatrix} = 0 \tag{29}$$

This may be solved directly, but let us introduce certain new simplifying, dimensionless variables, e.g.

$$y = \frac{T - 33.20^\circ \text{ C}}{1 \text{ C}^\circ} \tag{30}$$

and

$$x = \frac{t - 8 \text{ min}}{6 \text{ min}} \tag{31}$$

Rewritten, Eq. 29 becomes

$$\begin{vmatrix} y & 1 & x & x^2 \\ -9.00 & 1 & -1 & 1 \\ .00 & 1 & 0 & 0 \\ 8.50 & 1 & 1 & 1 \end{vmatrix} = 0 \tag{32}$$

This simplifies at once, in view of rule 3 above, to

$$\begin{vmatrix} y & x & x^2 \\ -9.00 & -1 & 1 \\ 8.50 & 1 & 1 \end{vmatrix} = 0 \tag{33}$$

which at once reduces to

$$y = 8.75x - 0.25x^2 \tag{34}$$

Verification shows that no computational error has been made. How well the equation fits the data as a whole may be determined easily. Differentiation leads to

$$\frac{dy}{dx} = 8.75 - 0.50x \tag{35}$$

For dT/dt, the quantity desired, we have

$$\frac{dT}{dt} = \frac{dy}{dx}\frac{dx}{dt}\frac{dT}{dy} \tag{36}$$

Substitution, for the condition that $t = 5$ min, leads to a desired result, namely

$$\left(\frac{dT}{dt}\right)_{5\text{ min}} = (8.75 + 0.25)\frac{1}{6\text{ min}}\ 1\ \text{C}° = 1.50\ \frac{\text{C}°}{\text{min}} \qquad [37]$$

Other values for dT/dt follow quickly. Obviously with slight practice, one will see that the writing down of Eqs. 29 and 32 is needless. Possibly also he will be able to obtain Eq. 34 from Eq. 33, if written at all, by inspection. It is evident, however, that the selection and the change-of-variables procedures may simplify computations greatly.

PROBLEMS

1. Solve the following equations for x, y, and z.

$2x + 3y + z = 0$
$x + y + 2z = 5$
$x - z = 2$

2. Solve the following equations:

$w + x + y + z = 6$
$w + y = 2$
$x + y + z = 4$
$w + z = 1$

3. Find equations for straight lines passing through points

(a) $(3,0)$ and $(2,9)$;
(b) $(0,4)$ and $(6,0)$;
(c) $(-2,3)$ and $(3,-4)$.

4. Find equations for a line of type $y = a + bx + cx^2$ through

(a) $(0,0)$, $(4,6)$, and $(12,6)$;
(b) $(-3,0)$, $(2,-6)$, and $(7,-10)$;
(c) $(-3,0)$, $(2,-6)$, and $(7,2)$.

5. Find equations for a circle passing through the points

(a) $(0,0)$, $(2,2)$, and $(4,8)$;
(b) $(-4,3)$, $(3,-4)$, and $(4,3)$.

6. Find the equation of the conic passing through the points $(0,0)$, $(2,2)$, $(4,8)$, $(2,12)$, and $(-2,8)$.

7. (a) Express Eq. 25 in its normal algebraic form. (b) Express Eq. 27 in its normal algebraic form.

8. Using the data of Table I, but selecting values corresponding to 3, 8, and 13 min, determine values for dT/dt corresponding to $t = 5$ min, 10 min, 15 min. Check the value for 5 min with that given in the text.

9. Using the data of Table I, determine an equation of the form of $T = T_0 + at + bt^2 + ct^3$ to fit the data. Also determine dT/dt for $t = 5$ min.

APPENDIX 2

TABLES

TABLE I [1]

THE PROBABILITY COEFFICIENT y_{hx} FOR THE NORMAL DISTRIBUTION CURVE

$$y_{hx} = \frac{1}{\sqrt{\pi}}\, e^{-h^2x^2} \text{ AS A FUNCTION OF } hx$$

Frequently in tables values of $2y_{hx}$ are given in place of y_{hx}

To obtain values of $y_{x/\sigma}$ as a function of x/σ, determine in order for each given x/σ, a corresponding hx ($= x/\sqrt{2}\sigma$), a y_{hx} as given by the table, and $y_{x/\sigma}$ ($= h\sigma y_{hx}$ $= y_{hx}/\sqrt{2}$). To obtain values of $y_{x/p}$ as a function of x/p, determine in order for each given x/p a corresponding hx ($= 0.477\,x/p$), a y_{hx} as given by the table, and a $y_{x/p}$ ($= hp\,y_{hx} = 0.477\,y_{hx}$). To obtain values of y_x as a function of x, one must have a value for h, σ, or p. Given h, determine, for each given x, a corresponding hx, a y_{hx} as given by the table, and a y_x ($= hy_{hx}$).

hx	.00	.01	.02	.03	.04	.05	.06	.07	.08	.09	Diff.
0.0	0.5642	0.5641	0.5640	0.5637	0.5633	0.5628	0.5622	0.5614	0.5606	0.5596	0.0006
0.1	.5586	.5574	.5561	.5547	.5532	.5516	.5499	.5481	.5462	.5442	.0017
0.2	.5421	.5398	.5375	.5351	.5326	.5300	.5273	.5245	.5216	.5187	.0026
0.3	.5156	.5125	.5093	.5060	.5026	.4991	.4956	.4920	.4883	.4846	.0035
0.4	.4808	.4769	.4730	.4689	.4649	.4608	.4566	.4524	.4481	.4438	.0041
0.5	.4394	.4350	.4305	.4260	.4215	.4169	.4123	.4077	.4030	.3983	.0046
0.6	.3936	.3889	.3841	.3794	.3746	.3698	.3650	.3601	.3553	.3505	.0048
0.7	.3456	.3408	.3360	.3311	.3263	.3215	.3166	.3118	.3070	.3023	.0048
0.8	.2975	.2927	.2880	.2833	.2786	.2739	.2693	.2647	.2601	.2555	.0047
0.9	.2510	.2465	.2420	.2376	.2332	.2288	.2245	.2202	.2159	.2117	.0043
1.0	.2076	.2034	.1993	.1953	.1913	.1873	.1834	.1796	.1757	.1720	.0039
1.1	.1682	.1646	.1609	.1574	.1538	.1503	.1469	.1435	.1402	.1369	.0035
1.2	.1337	.1305	.1274	.1243	.1212	.1183	.1153	.1124	.1096	.1068	.0030
1.3	.1041	.1014	.0988	.0962	.0937	.0912	.0887	.0864	.0840	.0817	.0025
1.4	.0795	.0773	.0751	.0730	.0709	.0689	.0669	.0650	.0631	.0613	.0020
1.5	.0595	.0577	.0560	.0543	.0527	.0511	.0495	.0480	.0465	.0450	.0016
1.6	.0436	.0422	.0409	.0396	.0383	.0371	.0359	.0347	.0335	.0324	.0012
1.7	.0314	.0303	.0293	.0283	.0273	.0264	.0255	.0246	.0237	.0229	.0009
1.8	.0221	.0213	.0206	.0198	.0191	.0184	.0177	.0171	.0165	.0159	.0007
1.9	.0153	.0147	.0141	.0136	.0131	.0126	.0121	.0116	.0112	.0108	.0005

hx	0.0	0.1	0.2	0.3	0.4	0.5	0.6	0.7	0.8	0.9	Diff.
2.0	.0103	.0069	.0045	.0028	.0018	.0011	.0007	.0004	.0002	.0001	.0010

[1] This table is based on *Tables of Probability Functions*, Vol. 1, Federal Works Agency, Work Projects Administration for the City of New York, 1941, sponsored by the National Bureau of Standards.

TABLE II [1]

Values of the Probability Integral $P_{hx}\left[= \dfrac{2}{\sqrt{\pi}}\int_0^{hx} e^{-h^2x^2}\,d(hx)\right]$

as a Function of hx

Frequently in tables, this integral is designated by P_t. *The $P_{x/\sigma}$ corresponding to a given x/σ limit is the P_{hx} of the table which corresponds to the hx ($= x/\sqrt{2}\,\sigma$) for the given x/σ limit. The $P_{x/p}$ corresponding to a given x/p limit is the P_{hx} of the table which corresponds to the hx ($= 0.477\,x/p$) for the given x/p limit. The P_x corresponding to a given x-limit* is obtainable only if the appropriate value for h, σ, or p is known. Given h, it may be read from the table as the P_{hx} corresponding to the hx for the given x-limit.

hx	.00	.01	.02	.03	.04	.05	.06	.07	.08	.09	Diff.
0.0	0.0000	0.0113	0.0226	0.0338	0.0451	0.0564	0.0676	0.0789	0.0901	0.1013	0.0112
0.1	.1125	.1236	.1348	.1459	.1569	.1680	.1790	.1900	.2009	.2118	.0110
0.2	.2227	.2335	.2443	.2550	.2657	.2763	.2869	.2974	.3079	.3183	.0106
0.3	.3286	.3389	.3491	.3593	.3694	.3794	.3893	.3992	.4090	.4187	.0100
0.4	.4284	.4380	.4475	.4569	.4662	.4755	.4847	.4937	.5027	.5117	.0092
0.5	.5205	.5292	.5379	.5465	.5549	.5633	.5716	.5798	.5879	.5959	.0083
0.6	.6039	.6117	.6194	.6270	.6346	.6420	.6494	.6566	.6638	.6708	.0074
0.7	.6778	.6847	.6914	.6981	.7047	.7112	.7175	.7238	.7300	.7361	.0064
0.8	.7421	.7480	.7538	.7595	.7651	.7707	.7761	.7814	.7867	.7918	.0055
0.9	.7969	.8019	.8068	.8116	.8163	.8209	.8254	.8299	.8342	.8385	.0046
1.0	.8427	.8468	.8508	.8548	.8586	.8624	.8661	.8698	.8733	.8768	.0038
1.1	.8802	.8835	.8868	.8900	.8931	.8961	.8991	.9020	.9048	.9076	.0030
1.2	.9103	.9130	.9155	.9181	.9205	.9229	.9252	.9275	.9297	.9319	.0024
1.3	.9340	.9361	.9381	.9400	.9419	.9438	.9456	.9473	.9490	.9507	.0018
1.4	.9523	.9539	.9554	.9569	.9583	.9597	.9611	.9624	.9637	.9649	.0014
1.5	.9661	.9673	.9684	.9695	.9706	.9716	.9726	.9736	.9745	.9755	.0010
1.6	.9763	.9772	.9780	.9788	.9796	.9804	.9811	.9818	.9825	.9832	.0007
1.7	.9838	.9844	.9850	.9856	.9861	.9867	.9872	.9877	.9882	.9886	.0005
1.8	.9891	.9895	.9899	.9903	.9907	.9911	.9915	.9918	.9922	.9925	.0004
1.9	.9928	.9931	.9934	.9937	.9939	.9942	.9944	.9947	.9949	.9951	.0003

hx	0.0	0.1	0.2	0.3	0.4	0.5	0.6	0.7	0.8	0.9	
2.0	.9953	.9970	.9981	.9989	.9993	.9996	.9998	.9999	.9999	.99995	

[1] This table is based on *Tables of Probability Functions*, Vol. 1, Federal Works Agency, Work Projects Administration for the City of New York, 1941, sponsored by the National Bureau of Standards.

TABLE III

CHAUVENET'S CRITERION. LIMITING VALUES OF hx, x/σ, AND x/p CORRESPONDING
TO VARIOUS NUMBERS OF ITEMS, n, FOR THE EXCLUSION OF AN ITEM FROM A SET
ON THE BASIS THAT, IN COMPARISON WITH THE OTHER ITEMS, IT EXERTS TOO GREAT
AN INFLUENCE ON COMPUTED VALUES

n	hx	x/σ	x/p	n	hx	x/σ	x/p
5	1.16	1.73	2.44	20	1.58	2.35	3.32
6	1.22	1.81	2.57	22	1.61	2.39	3.38
7	1.27	1.88	2.68	24	1.63	2.42	3.43
8	1.32	1.95	2.76	26	1.66	2.46	3.47
9	1.35	2.01	2.84	30	1.69	2.51	3.55
10	1.39	2.05	2.91	40	1.77	2.62	3.70
12	1.44	2.13	3.02	50	1.82	2.70	3.82
14	1.49	2.20	3.12	100	1.98	2.94	4.16
16	1.52	2.26	3.20	200	2.14	3.17	4.48
18	1.56	2.31	3.26	500	2.33	3.45	4.88

TABLE IV[1]

SHOWING VALUES OF χ^2 CORRESPONDING TO LISTED VALUES OF P_{χ^2} AND n', WHERE n' IS THE NUMBER OF GROUPS INTO WHICH THE DATA ARE DIVIDED LESS THE NUMBER OF IMPOSED CONDITIONS

n'	$P_{\chi^2}=0.99$	0.98	0.95	0.90	0.80	0.70	0.50	0.30	0.20	0.10	0.05	0.02	0.01
1	0.000157	0.00628	0.00393	0.0158	0.0642	0.148	0.455	1.074	1.642	2.706	3.841	5.412	6.635
2	0.0201	0.0404	0.103	0.211	0.446	0.713	1.386	2.408	3.219	4.605	5.991	7.824	9.210
3	0.115	0.185	0.352	0.584	1.005	1.424	2.366	3.665	4.642	6.251	7.815	9.837	11.345
4	0.297	0.429	0.711	1.064	1.649	2.195	3.357	4.878	5.989	7.779	9.488	11.668	13.277
5	0.554	0.752	1.145	1.610	2.343	3.000	4.351	6.064	7.289	9.236	11.070	13.388	15.086
6	0.872	1.134	1.635	2.204	3.070	3.828	5.348	7.231	8.558	10.645	12.592	15.033	16.812
7	1.239	1.564	2.167	2.833	3.822	4.671	6.346	8.383	9.803	12.017	14.067	16.622	18.475
8	1.646	2.032	2.733	3.490	4.594	5.527	7.344	9.524	11.030	13.362	15.507	18.168	20.090
9	2.088	2.532	3.325	4.168	5.380	6.393	8.343	10.656	12.242	14.684	16.919	19.679	21.666
10	2.558	3.059	3.940	4.865	6.179	7.267	9.342	11.781	13.442	15.987	18.307	21.161	23.209
11	3.053	3.609	4.575	5.578	6.989	8.148	10.341	12.899	14.631	17.275	19.675	22.618	24.725
12	3.571	4.178	5.226	6.304	7.807	9.034	11.340	14.011	15.812	18.549	21.026	24.054	26.217
13	4.107	4.765	5.892	7.042	8.634	9.926	12.340	15.119	16.985	19.812	22.362	25.472	27.688
14	4.660	5.368	6.571	7.790	9.467	10.821	13.339	16.222	18.151	21.064	23.685	26.873	29.141
15	5.229	5.985	7.261	8.547	10.307	11.721	14.339	17.322	19.311	22.307	24.996	28.259	30.578
16	5.812	6.614	7.962	9.312	11.152	12.624	15.338	18.418	20.465	23.542	26.296	29.633	32.000
17	6.408	7.255	8.672	10.085	12.002	13.531	16.338	19.511	21.615	24.769	27.587	30.995	33.409
18	7.015	7.906	9.390	10.865	12.857	14.440	17.338	20.601	22.760	25.989	28.869	32.346	34.805
19	7.633	8.567	10.117	11.651	13.716	15.352	18.338	21.689	23.900	27.204	30.144	33.687	36.191
20	8.260	9.237	10.851	12.443	14.578	16.266	19.337	22.775	25.038	28.412	31.410	35.020	37.566
21	8.897	9.915	11.591	13.240	15.445	17.182	20.337	23.858	26.171	29.615	32.671	36.343	38.932
22	9.542	10.600	12.338	14.041	16.314	18.101	21.337	24.939	27.301	30.813	33.924	37.659	40.289
23	10.196	11.293	13.091	14.848	17.187	19.021	22.337	26.018	28.429	32.007	35.172	38.968	41.638
24	10.856	11.992	13.848	15.659	18.062	19.943	23.337	27.096	29.553	33.196	36.415	40.270	42.980
25	11.524	12.697	14.611	16.473	18.940	20.867	24.337	28.172	30.675	34.382	37.652	41.566	44.314
26	12.198	13.409	15.379	17.292	19.820	21.792	25.336	29.246	31.795	35.563	38.885	42.856	45.642
27	12.879	14.125	16.151	18.114	20.703	22.719	26.336	30.319	32.912	36.741	40.113	44.140	46.963
28	13.565	14.847	16.928	18.939	21.588	23.647	27.336	31.391	34.027	37.916	41.337	45.419	48.278
29	14.256	15.574	17.708	19.768	22.475	24.577	28.336	32.461	35.139	39.087	42.557	46.693	49.588
30	14.953	16.306	18.493	20.599	23.364	25.508	29.336	33.530	36.250	40.256	43.773	47.962	50.892

For larger values of n, the expression $\sqrt{2\chi^2} - \sqrt{2n-1}$ may be used as a normal deviate with unit variance.

[1] From R. A. Fisher, *Statistical Methods for Research Workers*, London, Oliver & Boyd, 1938.

TABLE V [1]

SHOWING VALUES OF CORRELATION COEFFICIENT r CORRESPONDING TO VARIOUS VALUES OF FISHER'S z-FUNCTION

z	.01	.02	.03	.04	.05	.06	.07	.08	.09	.10
0.0	0.0100	0.0200	0.0300	0.0400	0.0500	0.0599	0.0699	0.0798	0.0898	0.0997
0.1	.1096	.1194	.1293	.1391	.1489	.1586	.1684	.1781	.1877	.1974
0.2	.2070	.2165	.2260	.2355	.2449	.2543	.2636	.2729	.2821	.2913
0.3	.3004	.3095	.3185	.3275	.3364	.3452	.3540	.3627	.3714	.3800
0.4	.3885	.3969	.4053	.4136	.4219	.4301	.4382	.4462	.4542	.4621
0.5	.4699	.4777	.4854	.4930	.5005	.5080	.5154	.5227	.5299	.5370
0.6	.5441	.5511	.5580	.5649	.5717	.5784	.5850	.5915	.5980	.6044
0.7	.6107	.6169	.6231	.6291	.6351	.6411	.6469	.6527	.6584	.6640
0.8	.6696	.6751	.6805	.6858	.6911	.6963	.7014	.7064	.7114	.7163
0.9	.7211	.7259	.7306	.7352	.7398	.7443	.7487	.7531	.7574	.7616
1.0	.7658	.7699	.7739	.7779	.7818	.7857	.7895	.7932	.7969	.8005
1.1	.8041	.8076	.8110	.8144	.8178	.8210	.8243	.8275	.8306	.8337
1.2	.8367	.8397	.8426	.8455	.8483	.8511	.8538	.8565	.8591	.8617
1.3	.8643	.8668	.8692	.8717	.8741	.8764	.8787	.8810	.8832	.8854
1.4	.8875	.8896	.8917	.8937	.8957	.8977	.8996	.9015	.9033	.9051
1.5	.9069	.9087	.9104	.9121	.9138	.9154	.9170	.9186	.9201	.9217
1.6	.9232	.9246	.9261	.9275	.9289	.9302	.9316	.9329	.9341	.9354
1.7	.9366	.9379	.9391	.9402	.9414	.9425	.9436	.9447	.9458	.94681
1.8	.94783	.94884	.94983	.95080	.95175	.95268	.95359	.95449	.95537	.95624
1.9	.95709	.95792	.95873	.95953	.96032	.96109	.96185	.96259	.96331	.96403
2.0	.96473	.96541	.96609	.96675	.96739	.96803	.96865	.96926	.96986	.97045
2.1	.97103	.97159	.97215	.97269	.97323	.97375	.97426	.97477	.97526	.97574
2.2	.97622	.97668	.97714	.97759	.97803	.97846	.97888	.97929	.97970	.98010
2.3	.98049	.98087	.98124	.98161	.98197	.98233	.98267	.98301	.98335	.98367
2.4	.98399	.98431	.98462	.98492	.98522	.98551	.98579	.98607	.98635	.98661
2.5	.98688	.98714	.98739	.98764	.98788	.98812	.98835	.98858	.98881	.98903
2.6	.98924	.98945	.98966	.98987	.99007	.99026	.99045	.99064	.99083	.99101
2.7	.99118	.99136	.99153	.99170	.99186	.99202	.99218	.99233	.99248	.99263
2.8	.99278	.99292	.99306	.99320	.99333	.99346	.99359	.99372	.99384	.99396
2.9	.99408	.99420	.99431	.99443	.99454	.99464	.99475	.99485	.99495	.99505

For greater accuracy, and for values beyond the table,

$$r = (e^{2z} - 1) \div (e^{2z} + 1)$$

$$z = \tfrac{1}{2}\{\log (1 + r) - \log (1 - r)\}$$

[1] From R. A. Fisher, *Statistical Methods for Research Workers*, London, Oliver & Boyd, 1938.

TABLE VI

SHOWING THE MAKEUP OF THE CONSTANTS OF THE LEAST-SQUARES EQUATION OF
THE TYPE $y = a + bx + cx^2 + dx^3$ FOR EQUATIONS OF VARYING DEGREES WHEN
THE ABBREVIATED METHOD OF BAILY [1] AND OF COX AND MATUSCHAK [2] IS USED

This method is applicable only when succeeding values of x have a common difference and are equally weighted. The independent variable, changed if necessary, must have a zero value at the midpoint of the series with succeeding values differing by unity if the number of terms is odd and by two if even. Values for the various k's, as computed by Cox and Matuschak, are to be found in Tables VII and VIII of this appendix.

Degree of Equation	Parameters			
	a	b	c	d
1	$k_1\Sigma y$	$k_2\Sigma xy$		
2	$k_3\Sigma y - k_4\Sigma x^2 y$	$k_2\Sigma xy$	$k_5\Sigma x^2 y - k_4\Sigma y$	
3	$k_3\Sigma y - k_4\Sigma x^2 y$	$k_6\Sigma xy - k_7\Sigma x^3 y$	$k_5\Sigma x^2 y - k_4\Sigma y$	$k_8\Sigma x^3 y - k_7\Sigma xy$

[1] Baily, J. L., *Ann. Math. Statistics*, **2**, 355 (1931).
[2] Cox, G. J., and Matuschak, M. C., *J. Phys. Chem.*, **45**, 362 (1941).

TABLE VII

VALUES OF THE CONSTANTS, k_n, ENTERING LEAST-SQUARES SOLUTIONS USING THE ABBREVIATED METHOD OF BAILY AND COX AND MATUSCHAK, WHEN THE NUMBER OF TERMS, n, IS ODD

The numbers in ( ) show the negative powers of 10 by which the adjacent numbers must be multiplied in order to obtain appropriate k_n's.

To illustrate, k_2 for $n = 13$ is $54,945,055 \times 10^{-10}$.

[See Table VI]

n	k_1	k_2	k_3	k_4	k_5	k_6	k_7	k_8
3	3333 3333 (8)	5000 0000 (8)	1000 0000 (7)	1000 0000 (7)	1500 0000 (7)	9027 7778 (8)	2361 1111 (8)	6944 4444 (9)
5	2000 0000	1000 0000	4857 1429 (8)	1428 5714 (8)	7142 8571 (9)	2625 6614	3240 7407 (9)	4629 6296 (10)
7	1428 5714	3571 4286 (9)	3333 3333	4761 9048 (9)	1190 4762 (10)	1143 3782	8277 2166 (10)	7014 5903 (11)
9	1111 1111 (9)	1666 6667	2554 1126	2164 5022	3246 7532	6037 9435 (9)	2881 3779	1618 7516
11	9090 9091	9090 9091 (10)	2074 5921	1165 5012	1165 5012			
13	7692 3077	5494 5055	1748 2517	6993 0070 (10)	4995 0050 (11)	3584 6098	1214 0637	4856 2549 (12)
15	6666 6667	3571 4286	1511 3122	4524 8869	2424 0465	2304 5899	5830 6799 (11)	1745 7125
17	5882 3529	2450 9803	1331 2693	3095 9752	1289 9897	1570 2041	3081 6420	7166 6093 (13)
19	5263 1579	1754 3860	1189 7391	2211 4109	7371 3696 (12)	1118 3168	1752 5617	3257 5497
21	4761 9048	1298 7013	1075 5149	1634 5211	4457 7848	8248 5070 (10)	1056 2015	1605 1694
23	4347 8261	9881 4229 (11)	9813 6646 (9)	1242 2360	2823 2637	6259 0791	6672 0719 (12)	8445 6606 (14)
25	4000 0000	7692 3077	9024 1546	9661 8357 (11)	1858 0453	4862 3545	4382 3595	4692 0337
27	3703 7037	6105 0061	8352 4904	7662 8352	1263 1047	3852 7423	2974 5336	2728 9299
29	3448 2759	4926 1084	7774 0700	6179 7058	8828 1512 (13)	3104 7316	2076 4076	1650 5625
31	3225 8065	4032 2581	7270 7048	5056 1230	6320 1537	2538 6983	1485 0296	1032 7049
33	3030 3030	3342 2460	6828 6552	4189 3590	4620 6166	2102 4471	1084 7991	6655 2091 (15)
35	2857 1429	2801 1204	6437 3464	3510 0035	3441 1799	1760 7811	8073 4407 (13)	4402 0942
37	2702 7027	2370 7918	6088 5061	2970 0030	2605 2658	1489 3734	6108 7522	2979 8791
39	2564 1026	2024 2915	5775 5692	2535 3684	2001 6066	1271 0408	4691 0081	2059 2661
41	2439 0244	1742 1603	5493 2589	2181 5961	1558 2829	1093 4097	3650 4910	1449 7581
43	2325 5814	1510 1178	5237 2849	1890 7166	1227 7380	9474 1490 (11)	2875 1015	1037 9428
45	2222 2222	1317 5231	5004 1234	1649 3485	9778 7461 (14)	8263 1159	2289 2527	7545 3288 (16)
47	2127 6596	1156 3367	4790 8525	1447 3875	7866 2362	7250 1033	1841 0171	5561 9852
49	2040 8163	1020 4082	4595 0295	1277 1066	6385 5329	6396 2170	1494 1103	4152 6134
51	1960 7843	9049 7738 (12)	4414 5960	1132 5285	5227 0545	5671 3855	1222 7830	3136 9497

TABLE VIII

VALUES OF THE CONSTANTS, k_n, ENTERING LEAST-SQUARES SOLUTIONS, USING THE ABBREVIATED METHOD OF BAILY AND COX AND MATUSCHAK, WHEN THE NUMBER OF TERMS, n, IS EVEN

[See preceding table for the meanings of numbers in ( ).   See also Table VI.]

n	k_1	k_2	k_3	k_4	k_5	k_6	k_7	k_8
4	2500 0000 (8)	5000 0000 (9)	6406 2500 (8)	7812 5000 (9)	1562 5000 (9)	6336 8056 (8)	7118 0556 (9)	8680 5556 (10)
6	1666 6667	1428 5714	3945 3125	1953 1250	1674 1071 (10)	1126 7499 (9)	4870 7562 (10)	2411 2654 (11)
8	1250 0000	5952 3810 (10)	2890 6250	7812 5000 (10)	3720 2381 (11)	4196 3534	9732 7441 (11)	2630 4714 (12)
10	1000 0000	3030 3030	2289 0625	3906 2500	1183 7121	2040 1329	2964 3389	5058 5988 (13)
12	8333 3333 (9)	1748 2517	1897 3214	2232 1429	4682 8172 (12)	1149 4485	1146 6157	1348 9597
14	7142 8571	1098 9011	1621 0938	1395 0893	2146 2912	7125 6741 (10)	5186 5517 (12)	4463 4695 (14)
16	6250 0000	7352 9412 (11)	1415 5506	9300 5952 (11)	1094 1877	4725 9999	2622 0143	1722 7426
18	5555 5556	5159 9587	1256 5104	6510 4167	6046 8266 (13)	3296 7149	1440 7871	7465 2181 (15)
20	5000 0000	3759 3985	1129 7349	4734 8485	3560 0365	2391 7243	8448 3844 (13)	3540 8149
22	4545 4545	2823 2637	1026 2784	3551 1364	2205 6748	1790 5616	5218 8071	1805 8156
24	4166 6667	2173 9130	9402 3164 (9)	2731 6434	1425 2052	1375 4794	3364 5791	9775 0702 (16)
26	3846 1538	1709 4017	8675 3091	2146 2912	9539 0720 (14)	1079 5940	2248 0302	5561 6779
28	3571 4286	1368 3634	8052 8846	1717 0330	6578 6704	8629 5508 (11)	1548 2276	3301 1249
30	3333 3333	1112 3471	7513 9509	1395 0893	4655 4704	7006 8080	1094 4042	2031 9424
32	3125 0000	9164 2229 (12)	7042 7390	1148 8971	3369 1996	5767 1532	7913 1009 (14)	1290 8811
34	2941 1765	7639 4194	6627 2213	9574 1423 (12)	2486 7902	4803 7846	5836 2361	8431 4304 (17)
36	2777 7778	6435 0064	6258 0624	8062 4358	1867 7458	4043 7597	4380 6481	5643 7105
38	2631 5789	5471 0581	5927 9058	6853 0703	1424 7547	3436 0952	3339 8722	3861 1239
40	2500 0000	4690 4315	5630 8741	5874 0602	1102 0751	2944 4203	2582 2837	2693 8074
42	2380 9524	4051 5355	5362 2160	5073 0520	8632 5332 (15)	2542 3116	2021 9092	1912 8753
44	2272 7273	3523 6081	5118 0477	4411 3495	6839 3016	2210 2564	1601 3580	1380 2431
46	2173 9130	3083 5646	4895 1643	3859 9309	5475 0792	1933 6316	1281 5606	1010 5351
48	2083 3333	2713 8515	4690 8968	3396 7392	4424 7580	1701 3314	1035 4426	7497 7742 (18)
50	2000 0000	2400 9604	4503 0048	3004 8077	3607 2121	1504 8177	8439 3542 (15)	5631 4922

TABLE IX

SUMS OF INTEGERS $\sum\limits_{m=1}^{n} m$ AND OF SQUARES OF INTEGERS $\sum\limits_{m=1}^{n} m^2$

FOR USE IN LEAST-SQUARES SOLUTIONS

n	$\sum\limits_{m=1}^{n} m$	$\sum\limits_{m=1}^{n} m^2$	n	$\sum\limits_{m=1}^{n} m$	$\sum\limits_{m=1}^{n} m^2$
1	1	1	26	351	6,201
2	3	5	27	378	6,930
3	6	14	28	406	7,714
4	10	30	29	435	8,555
5	15	55	30	465	9,455
6	21	91	31	496	10,416
7	28	140	32	528	11,440
8	36	204	33	561	12,529
9	45	285	34	595	13,685
10	55	385	35	630	14,910
11	66	506	36	666	16,206
12	78	650	37	703	17,575
13	91	819	38	741	19,019
14	105	1,015	39	780	20,540
15	120	1,240	40	820	22,140
16	136	1,496	41	861	23,821
17	153	1,785	42	903	25,585
18	171	2,109	43	946	27,434
19	190	2,470	44	990	29,370
20	210	2,870	45	1,035	31,395
21	231	3,311	46	1,081	33,511
22	253	3,795	47	1,128	35,720
23	276	4,324	48	1,176	38,024
24	300	4,900	49	1,225	40,425
25	325	5,525	50	1,275	42,925

TABLE X

Logarithms to the Base *e*

These two pages give the natural (hyperbolic, or Napierian) logarithms of numbers between 1 and 10, correct to four places. Moving the decimal point *n* places to the right (or left) in the number is equivalent to adding *n* times 2.3026 (or *n* times 3.6974) to the logarithm.

1	2.3026	1	0.6974–3
2	4.6052	2	0.3948–5
3	6.9078	3	0.0922–7
4	9.2103	4	0.7897–10
5	11.5129	5	0.4871–12
6	13.8155	6	0.1845–14
7	16.1181	7	0.8819–17
8	18.4207	8	0.5793–19
9	20.7233	9	0.2767–21

	0	1	2	3	4	5	6	7	8	9	10	Tenths of the Tabular Difference 1 2 3 4 5
1.0	0.0000	0100	0198	0296	0392	0488	0583	0677	0770	0862	0.0953	10 19 29 38 48
1.1	0953	1044	1133	1222	1310	1398	1484	1570	1655	1740	1823	9 17 26 35 44
1.2	1823	1906	1989	2070	2151	2231	2311	2390	2469	2546	2624	8 16 24 32 40
1.3	2624	2700	2776	2852	2927	3001	3075	3148	3221	3293	3365	7 15 22 30 37
1.4	3365	3436	3507	3577	3646	3716	3784	3853	3920	3988	4055	7 14 21 28 34
1.5	4055	4121	4187	4253	4318	4383	4447	4511	4574	4637	4700	6 13 19 26 32
1.6	4700	4762	4824	4886	4947	5008	5068	5128	5188	5247	5306	6 12 18 24 30
1.7	5306	5365	5423	5481	5539	5596	5653	5710	5766	5822	5878	6 11 17 23 29
1.8	5878	5933	5988	6043	6098	6152	6206	6259	6313	6366	6419	5 11 16 22 27
1.9	6419	6471	6523	6575	6627	6678	6729	6780	6831	6881	0.6931	5 10 15 21 26
2.0	0.6931	6981	7031	7080	7129	7178	7227	7275	7324	7372	7419	5 10 15 20 24
2.1	7419	7467	7514	7561	7608	7655	7701	7747	7793	7839	7885	5 9 14 19 23
2.2	7885	7930	7975	8020	8065	8109	8154	8198	8242	8286	8329	4 9 13 18 22
2.3	8329	8372	8416	8459	8502	8544	8587	8629	8671	8713	8755	4 9 13 17 21
2.4	8755	8796	8838	8879	8920	8961	9002	9042	9083	9123	9163	4 8 12 16 20
2.5	9163	9203	9243	9282	9322	9361	9400	9439	9478	9517	9555	4 8 12 16 20
2.6	9555	9594	9632	9670	9708	9746	9783	9821	9858	9895	0.9933	4 8 11 15 19
2.7	0.9933	9969	∫0006	0043	0080	0116	0152	0188	0225	0260	1.0296	4 7 11 15 18
2.8	1.0296	0332	0367	0403	0438	0473	0508	0543	0578	0613	0647	4 7 11 14 18
2.9	0647	0682	0716	0750	0784	0818	0852	0886	0919	0953	1.0986	3 7 10 14 17
3.0	1.0986	1019	1053	1086	1119	1151	1184	1217	1249	1282	1314	3 7 10 13 16
3.1	1314	1346	1378	1410	1442	1474	1506	1537	1569	1600	1632	3 6 10 13 16
3.2	1632	1663	1694	1725	1756	1787	1817	1848	1878	1909	1939	3 6 9 12 15
3.3	1939	1969	2000	2030	2060	2090	2119	2149	2179	2208	2238	3 6 9 12 15
3.4	2238	2267	2296	2326	2355	2384	2413	2442	2470	2499	2528	3 6 9 12 14
3.5	2528	2556	2585	2613	2641	2669	2698	2726	2754	2782	2809	3 6 8 11 14
3.6	2809	2837	2865	2892	2920	2947	2975	3002	3029	3056	3083	3 5 8 11 14
3.7	3083	3110	3137	3164	3191	3218	3244	3271	3297	3324	3350	3 5 8 11 13
3.8	3350	3376	3403	3429	3455	3481	3507	3533	3558	3584	3610	3 5 8 10 13
3.9	3610	3635	3661	3686	3712	3737	3762	3788	3813	3838	1.3863	3 5 8 10 13
4.0	1.3863	3888	3913	3938	3962	3987	4012	4036	4061	4085	4110	2 5 7 10 12
4.1	4110	4134	4159	4183	4207	4231	4255	4279	4303	4327	4351	2 5 7 10 12
4.2	4351	4375	4398	4422	4446	4469	4493	4516	4540	4563	4586	2 5 7 9 12
4.3	4586	4609	4633	4656	4679	4702	4725	4748	4770	4793	4816	2 5 7 9 11
4.4	4816	4839	4861	4884	4907	4929	4951	4974	4996	5019	5041	2 4 7 9 11
4.5	5041	5063	5085	5107	5129	5151	5173	5195	5217	5239	5261	2 4 7 9 11
4.6	5261	5282	5304	5326	5347	5369	5390	5412	5433	5454	5476	2 4 6 9 11
4.7	5476	5497	5518	5539	5560	5581	5602	5623	5644	5665	5686	2 4 6 8 11
4.8	5686	5707	5728	5748	5769	5790	5810	5831	5851	5872	5892	2 4 6 8 10
4.9	5892	5913	5933	5953	5974	5994	6014	6034	6054	6074	1.6094	2 4 6 8 10

TABLE X

Log_e (Base $e = 2.718284$)

	0	1	2	3	4	5	6	7	8	9	10	Tenths of the Tabular Difference 1 2 3 4 5
5.0	1.6094	6114	6134	6154	6174	6194	6214	6233	6253	6273	6292	2 4 6 8 10
5.1	6292	6312	6332	6351	6371	6390	6409	6429	6448	6467	6487	2 4 6 8 10
5.2	6487	6506	6525	6544	6563	6582	6601	6620	6639	6658	6677	2 4 6 8 10
5.3	6677	6696	6715	6734	6752	6771	6790	6808	6827	6845	6864	2 4 6 7 9
5.4	6864	6882	6901	6919	6938	6956	6974	6993	7011	7029	7047	2 4 6 7 9
5.5	7047	7066	7084	7102	7120	7138	7156	7174	7192	7210	7228	2 4 5 7 9
5.6	7228	7246	7263	7281	7299	7317	7334	7352	7370	7387	7405	2 4 5 7 9
5.7	7405	7422	7440	7457	7475	7492	7509	7527	7544	7561	7579	2 3 5 7 9
5.8	7579	7596	7613	7630	7647	7664	7681	7699	7716	7733	7750	2 3 5 7 9
5.9	7750	7766	7783	7800	7817	7834	7851	7867	7884	7901	1.7918	2 3 5 7 8
6.0	1.7918	7934	7951	7967	7984	8001	8017	8034	8050	8066	8083	2 3 5 7 8
6.1	8083	8099	8116	8132	8148	8165	8181	8197	8213	8229	8245	2 3 5 7 8
6.2	8245	8262	8278	8294	8310	8326	8342	8358	8374	8390	8405	2 3 5 6 8
6.3	8405	8421	8437	8453	8469	8485	8500	8516	8532	8547	8563	2 3 5 6 8
6.4	8563	8579	8594	8610	8625	8641	8656	8672	8687	8703	8718	2 3 5 6 8
6.5	8718	8733	8749	8764	8779	8795	8810	8825	8840	8856	8871	2 3 5 6 8
6.6	8871	8886	8901	8916	8931	8946	8961	8976	8991	9006	9021	2 3 5 6 8
6.7	9021	9036	9051	9066	9081	9095	9110	9125	9140	9155	9169	1 3 4 6 7
6.8	9169	9184	9199	9213	9228	9242	9257	9272	9286	9301	9315	1 3 4 6 7
6.9	9315	9330	9344	9359	9373	9387	9402	9416	9430	9445	1.9459	1 3 4 6 7
7.0	1.9459	9473	9488	9502	9516	9530	9544	9559	9573	9587	9601	1 3 4 6 7
7.1	9601	9615	9629	9643	9657	9671	9685	9699	9713	9727	9741	1 3 4 6 7
7.2	9741	9755	9769	9782	9796	9810	9824	9838	9851	9865	1.9879	1 3 4 6 7
7.3	1.9879	9892	9906	9920	9933	9947	9961	9974	9988	0001	2.0015	1 3 4 5 7
7.4	2.0015	0028	0042	0055	0069	0082	0096	0109	0122	0136	0149	1 3 4 5 7
7.5	0149	0162	0176	0189	0202	0215	0229	0242	0255	0268	0281	1 3 4 5 7
7.6	0281	0295	0308	0321	0334	0347	0360	0373	0386	0399	0412	1 3 4 5 7
7.7	0412	0425	0438	0451	0464	0477	0490	0503	0516	0528	0541	1 3 4 5 6
7.8	0541	0554	0567	0580	0592	0605	0618	0631	0643	0656	0669	1 3 4 5 6
7.9	0669	0681	0694	0707	0719	0732	0744	0757	0769	0782	2.0794	1 3 4 5 6
8.0	2.0794	0807	0819	0832	0844	0857	0869	0882	0894	0906	0919	1 2 4 5 6
8.1	0919	0931	0943	0956	0968	0980	0992	1005	1017	1029	1041	1 2 4 5 6
8.2	1041	1054	1066	1078	1090	1102	1114	1126	1138	1150	1163	1 2 4 5 6
8.3	1163	1175	1187	1199	1211	1223	1235	1247	1258	1270	1282	1 2 4 5 6
8.4	1282	1294	1306	1318	1330	1342	1353	1365	1377	1389	1401	1 2 4 5 6
8.5	1401	1412	1424	1436	1448	1459	1471	1483	1494	1506	1518	1 2 4 5 6
8.6	1518	1529	1541	1552	1564	1576	1587	1599	1610	1622	1633	1 2 3 5 6
8.7	1633	1645	1656	1668	1679	1691	1702	1713	1725	1736	1748	1 2 3 5 6
8.8	1748	1759	1770	1782	1793	1804	1815	1827	1838	1849	1861	1 2 3 5 6
8.9	1861	1872	1883	1894	1905	1917	1928	1939	1950	1961	2.1972	1 2 3 4 6
9.0	2.1972	1983	1994	2006	2017	2028	2039	2050	2061	2072	2083	1 2 3 4 6
9.1	2083	2094	2105	2116	2127	2138	2148	2159	2170	2181	2192	1 2 3 4 5
9.2	2192	2203	2214	2225	2235	2246	2257	2268	2279	2289	2300	1 2 3 4 5
9.3	2300	2311	2322	2332	2343	2354	2364	2375	2386	2396	2407	1 2 3 4 5
9.4	2407	2418	2428	2439	2450	2460	2471	2481	2492	2502	2513	1 2 3 4 5
9.5	2513	2523	2534	2544	2555	2565	2576	2586	2597	2607	2618	1 2 3 4 5
9.6	2618	2628	2638	2649	2659	2670	2680	2690	2701	2711	2721	1 2 3 4 5
9.7	2721	2732	2742	2752	2762	2773	2783	2793	2803	2814	2824	1 2 3 4 5
9.8	2824	2834	2844	2854	2865	2875	2885	2895	2905	2915	2925	1 2 3 4 5
9.9	2925	2935	2946	2956	2966	2976	2986	2996	3006	3016	2.3026	1 2 3 4 5

TABLE XI

LOGARITHMS TO THE BASE 10

	0	1	2	3	4	5	6	7	8	9	10
1.00	0.0000	0004	0009	0013	0017	0022	0026	0030	0035	0039	0043
1.01	0043	0048	0052	0056	0060	0065	0069	0073	0077	0082	0086
1.02	0086	0090	0095	0099	0103	0107	0111	0116	0120	0124	0128
1.03	0128	0133	0137	0141	0145	0149	0154	0158	0162	0166	0170
1.04	0170	0175	0179	0183	0187	0191	0195	0199	0204	0208	0212
1.05	0212	0216	0220	0224	0228	0233	0237	0241	0245	0249	0253
1.06	0253	0257	0261	0265	0269	0273	0278	0282	0286	0290	0294
1.07	0294	0298	0302	0306	0310	0314	0318	0322	0326	0330	0334
1.08	0334	0338	0342	0346	0350	0354	0358	0362	0366	0370	0374
1.09	0374	0378	0382	0386	0390	0394	0398	0402	0406	0410	0414
1.10	0.0414	0418	0422	0426	0430	0434	0438	0441	0445	0449	0453
1.11	0453	0457	0461	0465	0469	0473	0477	0481	0484	0488	0492
1.12	0492	0496	0500	0504	0508	0512	0515	0519	0523	0527	0531
1.13	0531	0535	0538	0542	0546	0550	0554	0558	0561	0565	0569
1.14	0569	0573	0577	0580	0584	0588	0592	0596	0599	0603	0607
1.15	0607	0611	0615	0618	0622	0626	0630	0633	0637	0641	0645
1.16	0645	0648	0652	0656	0660	0663	0667	0671	0674	0678	0682
1.17	0682	0686	0689	0693	0697	0700	0704	0708	0711	0715	0719
1.18	0719	0722	0726	0730	0734	0737	0741	0745	0748	0752	0755
1.19	0755	0759	0763	0766	0770	0774	0777	0781	0785	0788	0792
1.20	0.0792	0795	0799	0803	0806	0810	0813	0817	0821	0824	0828
1.21	0828	0831	0835	0839	0842	0846	0849	0853	0856	0860	0864
1.22	0864	0867	0871	0874	0878	0881	0885	0888	0892	0896	0899
1.23	0899	0903	0906	0910	0913	0917	0920	0924	0927	0931	0934
1.24	0934	0938	0941	0945	0948	0952	0955	0959	0962	0966	0969
1.25	0969	0973	0976	0980	0983	0986	0990	0993	0997	1000	1004
1.26	1004	1007	1011	1014	1017	1021	1024	1028	1031	1035	1038
1.27	1038	1041	1045	1048	1052	1055	1059	1062	1065	1069	1072
1.28	1072	1075	1079	1082	1086	1089	1092	1096	1099	1103	1106
1.29	1106	1109	1113	1116	1119	1123	1126	1129	1133	1136	1139
1.30	0.1139	1143	1146	1149	1153	1156	1159	1163	1166	1169	1173
1.31	1173	1176	1179	1183	1186	1189	1193	1196	1199	1202	1206
1.32	1206	1209	1212	1216	1219	1222	1225	1229	1232	1235	1239
1.33	1239	1242	1245	1248	1252	1255	1258	1261	1265	1268	1271
1.34	1271	1274	1278	1281	1284	1287	1290	1294	1297	1300	1303
1.35	1303	1307	1310	1313	1316	1319	1323	1326	1329	1332	1335
1.36	1335	1339	1342	1345	1348	1351	1355	1358	1361	1364	1367
1.37	1367	1370	1374	1377	1380	1383	1386	1389	1392	1396	1399
1.38	1399	1402	1405	1408	1411	1414	1418	1421	1424	1427	1430
1.39	1430	1433	1436	1440	1443	1446	1449	1452	1455	1458	1461
1.40	0.1461	1464	1467	1471	1474	1477	1480	1483	1486	1489	1492
1.41	1492	1495	1498	1501	1504	1508	1511	1514	1517	1520	1523
1.42	1523	1526	1529	1532	1535	1538	1541	1544	1547	1550	1553
1.43	1553	1556	1559	1562	1565	1569	1572	1575	1578	1581	1584
1.44	1584	1587	1590	1593	1596	1599	1602	1605	1608	1611	1614
1.45	1614	1617	1620	1623	1626	1629	1632	1635	1638	1641	1644
1.46	1644	1647	1649	1652	1655	1658	1661	1664	1667	1670	1673
1.47	1673	1676	1679	1682	1685	1688	1691	1694	1697	1700	1703
1.48	1703	1706	1708	1711	1714	1717	1720	1723	1726	1729	1732
1.49	1732	1735	1738	1741	1744	1746	1749	1752	1755	1758	1761

TABLE XI

Logarithms to the Base 10

	0	1	2	3	4	5	6	7	8	9	10
1.50	0.1761	1764	1767	1770	1772	1775	1778	1781	1784	1787	1790
1.51	1790	1793	1796	1798	1801	1804	1807	1810	1813	1816	1818
1.52	1818	1821	1824	1827	1830	1833	1836	1838	1841	1844	1847
1.53	1847	1850	1853	1855	1858	1861	1864	1867	1870	1872	1875
1.54	1875	1878	1881	1884	1886	1889	1892	1895	1898	1901	1903
1.55	1903	1906	1909	1912	1915	1917	1920	1923	1926	1928	1931
1.56	1931	1934	1937	1940	1942	1945	1948	1951	1953	1956	1959
1.57	1959	1962	1965	1967	1970	1973	1976	1978	1981	1984	1987
1.58	1987	1989	1992	1995	1998	2000	2003	2006	2009	2011	2014
1.59	2014	2017	2019	2022	2025	2028	2030	2033	2036	2038	2041
1.60	0.2041	2044	2047	2049	2052	2055	2057	2060	2063	2066	2068
1.61	2068	2071	2074	2076	2079	2082	2084	2087	2090	2092	2095
1.62	2095	2098	2101	2103	2106	2109	2111	2114	2117	2119	2122
1.63	2122	2125	2127	2130	2133	2135	2138	2140	2143	2146	2148
1.64	2148	2151	2154	2156	2159	2162	2164	2167	2170	2172	2175
1.65	2175	2177	2180	2183	2185	2188	2191	2193	2196	2198	2201
1.66	2201	2204	2206	2209	2212	2214	2217	2219	2222	2225	2227
1.67	2227	2230	2232	2235	2238	2240	2243	2245	2248	2251	2253
1.68	2253	2256	2258	2261	2263	2266	2269	2271	2274	2276	2279
1.69	2279	2281	2284	2287	2289	2292	2294	2297	2299	2302	2304
1.70	0.2304	2307	2310	2312	2315	2317	2320	2322	2325	2327	2330
1.71	2330	2333	2335	2338	2340	2343	2345	2348	2350	2353	2355
1.72	2355	2358	2360	2363	2365	2368	2370	2373	2375	2378	2380
1.73	2380	2383	2385	2388	2390	2393	2395	2398	2400	2403	2405
1.74	2405	2408	2410	2413	2415	2418	2420	2423	2425	2428	2430
1.75	2430	2433	2435	2438	2440	2443	2445	2448	2450	2453	2455
1.76	2455	2458	2460	2463	2465	2467	2470	2472	2475	2477	2480
1.77	2480	2482	2485	2487	2490	2492	2494	2497	2499	2502	2504
1.78	2504	2507	2509	2512	2514	2516	2519	2521	2524	2526	2529
1.79	2529	2531	2533	2536	2538	2541	2543	2545	2548	2550	2553
1.80	0.2553	2555	2558	2560	2562	2565	2567	2570	2572	2574	2577
1.81	2577	2579	2582	2584	2586	2589	2591	2594	2596	2598	2601
1.82	2601	2603	2605	2608	2610	2613	2615	2617	2620	2622	2625
1.83	2625	2627	2629	2632	2634	2636	2639	2641	2643	2646	2648
1.84	2648	2651	2653	2655	2658	2660	2662	2665	2667	2669	2672
1.85	2672	2674	2676	2679	2681	2683	2686	2688	2690	2693	2695
1.86	2695	2697	2700	2702	2704	2707	2709	2711	2714	2716	2718
1.87	2718	2721	2723	2725	2728	2730	2732	2735	2737	2739	2742
1.88	2742	2744	2746	2749	2751	2753	2755	2758	2760	2762	2765
1.89	2765	2767	2769	2772	2774	2776	2778	2781	2783	2785	2788
1.90	0.2788	2790	2792	2794	2797	2799	2801	2804	2806	2808	2810
1.91	2810	2813	2815	2817	2819	2822	2824	2826	2828	2831	2833
1.92	2833	2835	2838	2840	2842	2844	2847	2849	2851	2853	2856
1.93	2856	2858	2860	2862	2865	2867	2869	2871	2874	2876	2878
1.94	2878	2880	2882	2885	2887	2889	2891	2894	2896	2898	2900
1.95	2900	2903	2905	2907	2909	2911	2914	2916	2918	2920	2923
1.96	2923	2925	2927	2929	2931	2934	2936	2938	2940	2942	2945
1.97	2945	2947	2949	2951	2953	2956	2958	2960	2962	2964	2967
1.98	2967	2969	2971	2973	2975	2978	2980	2982	2984	2986	2989
1.99	2989	2991	2993	2995	2997	2999	3002	3004	3006	3008	3010

TABLE XI

Logarithms to the Base 10

These two pages give the common logarithms of numbers between 1 and 10, correct to four places. Moving the decimal point n places to the right (or left) in the number is equivalent to adding n (or $-n$) to the logarithm. Thus, log 0.017453 = 0.2419 − 2 [= $\bar{2}$.2419].

To facilitate interpolation, the tenths of the tabular differences are given at the end of each line, so that the differences themselves need not be considered. In using these aids, first find the nearest tabular entry, and then add (to move to the right) or subtract (to move to the left), as the case may require.

	0	1	2	3	4	5	6	7	8	9	10	Tenths of the Tabular Difference 1 2 3 4 5
1.0	0.0000	0043	0086	0128	0170	0212	0253	0294	0334	0374	0414	
1.1	0414	0453	0492	0531	0569	0607	0645	0682	0719	0755	0792	
1.2	0792	0828	0864	0899	0934	0969	1004	1038	1072	1106	1139	
1.3	1139	1173	1206	1239	1271	1303	1335	1367	1399	1430	1461	To avoid Interpolation in the first ten lines, use the special table on the preceding page.
1.4	1461	1492	1523	1553	1584	1614	1644	1673	1703	1732	1761	
1.5	1761	1790	1818	1847	1875	1903	1931	1959	1987	2014	2041	
1.6	2041	2068	2095	2122	2148	2175	2201	2227	2253	2279	2304	
1.7	2304	2330	2355	2380	2405	2430	2455	2480	2504	2529	2553	
1.8	2553	2577	2601	2625	2648	2672	2695	2718	2742	2765	2788	
1.9	2788	2810	2833	2856	2878	2900	2923	2945	2967	2989	3010	
2.0	0.3010	3032	3054	3075	3096	3118	3139	3160	3181	3201	3222	2 4 6 8 11
2.1	3222	3243	3263	3284	3304	3324	3345	3365	3385	3404	3424	2 4 6 8 10
2.2	3424	3444	3464	3483	3502	3522	3541	3560	3579	3598	3617	2 4 6 8 10
2.3	3617	3636	3655	3674	3692	3711	3729	3747	3766	3784	3802	2 4 5 7 9
2.4	3802	3820	3838	3856	3874	3892	3909	3927	3945	3962	3979	2 4 5 7 9
2.5	3979	3997	4014	4031	4048	4065	4082	4099	4116	4133	4150	2 3 5 7 9
2.6	4150	4166	4183	4200	4216	4232	4249	4265	4281	4298	4314	2 3 5 7 8
2.7	4314	4330	4346	4362	4378	4393	4409	4425	4440	4456	4472	2 3 5 6 8
2.8	4472	4487	4502	4518	4533	4548	4564	4579	4594	4609	4624	2 3 5 6 8
2.9	4624	4639	4654	4669	4683	4698	4713	4728	4742	4757	4771	1 3 4 6 7
3.0	0.4771	4786	4800	4814	4829	4843	4857	4871	4886	4900	4914	1 3 4 6 7
3.1	4914	4928	4942	4955	4969	4983	4997	5011	5024	5038	5051	1 3 4 6 7
3.2	5051	5065	5079	5092	5105	5119	5132	5145	5159	5172	5185	1 3 4 5 7
3.3	5185	5198	5211	5224	5237	5250	5263	5276	5289	5302	5315	1 3 4 5 6
3.4	5315	5328	5340	5353	5366	5378	5391	5403	5416	5428	5441	1 3 4 5 6
3.5	5441	5453	5465	5478	5490	5502	5514	5527	5539	5551	5563	1 2 4 5 6
3.6	5563	5575	5587	5599	5611	5623	5635	5647	5658	5670	5682	1 2 4 5 6
3.7	5682	5694	5705	5717	5729	5740	5752	5763	5775	5786	5798	1 2 3 5 6
3.8	5798	5809	5821	5832	5843	5855	5866	5877	5888	5899	5911	1 2 3 5 6
3.9	5911	5922	5933	5944	5955	5966	5977	5988	5999	6010	6021	1 2 3 4 6
4.0	0.6021	6031	6042	6053	6064	6075	6085	6096	6107	6117	6128	1 2 3 4 5
4.1	6128	6138	6149	6160	6170	6180	6191	6201	6212	6222	6232	1 2 3 4 5
4.2	6232	6243	6253	6263	6274	6284	6294	6304	6314	6325	6335	1 2 3 4 5
4.3	6335	6345	6355	6365	6375	6385	6395	6405	6415	6425	6435	1 2 3 4 5
4.4	6435	6444	6454	6464	6474	6484	6493	6503	6513	6522	6532	1 2 3 4 5
4.5	6532	6542	6551	6561	6571	6580	6590	6599	6609	6618	6628	1 2 3 4 5
4.6	6628	6637	6646	6656	6665	6675	6684	6693	6702	6712	6721	1 2 3 4 5
4.7	6721	6730	6739	6749	6758	6767	6776	6785	6794	6803	6812	1 2 3 4 5
4.8	6812	6821	6830	6839	6848	6857	6866	6875	6884	6893	6902	1 2 3 4 4
4.9	6902	6911	6920	6928	6937	6946	6955	6964	6972	6981	6990	1 2 3 4 4

TABLE XI

Logarithms to the Base 10

	0	**1**	**2**	**3**	**4**	**5**	**6**	**7**	**8**	**9**	**10**	**Tenths of the Tabular Difference**				
												1	**2**	**3**	**4**	**5**
5.0	0.6990	6998	7007	7016	7024	7033	7042	7050	7059	7067	7076	1	2	3	3	4
5.1	7076	7084	7093	7101	7110	7118	7126	7135	7143	7152	7160	1	2	3	3	4
5.2	7160	7168	7177	7185	7193	7202	7210	7218	7226	7235	7243	1	2	2	3	4
5.3	7243	7251	7259	7267	7275	7284	7292	7300	7308	7316	7324	1	2	2	3	4
5.4	7324	7332	7340	7348	7356	7364	7372	7380	7388	7396	7404	1	2	2	3	4
5.5	7404	7412	7419	7427	7435	7443	7451	7459	7466	7474	7482	1	2	2	3	4
5.6	7482	7490	7497	7505	7513	7520	7528	7536	7543	7551	7559	1	2	2	3	4
5.7	7559	7566	7574	7582	7589	7597	7604	7612	7619	7627	7634	1	2	2	3	4
5.8	7634	7642	7649	7657	7664	7672	7679	7686	7694	7701	7709	1	1	2	3	4
5.9	7709	7716	7723	7731	7738	7745	7752	7760	7767	7774	7782	1	1	2	3	4
6.0	0.7782	7789	7796	7803	7810	7818	7825	7832	7839	7846	7853	1	1	2	3	4
6.1	7853	7860	7868	7875	7882	7889	7896	7903	7910	7917	7924	1	1	2	3	4
6.2	7924	7931	7938	7945	7952	7959	7966	7973	7980	7987	7993	1	1	2	3	3
6.3	7993	8000	8007	8014	8021	8028	8035	8041	8048	8055	8062	1	1	2	3	3
6.4	8062	8069	8075	8082	8089	8096	8102	8109	8116	8122	8129	1	1	2	3	3
6.5	8129	8136	8142	8149	8156	8162	8169	8176	8182	8189	8195	1	1	2	3	3
6.6	8195	8202	8209	8215	8222	8228	8235	8241	8248	8254	8261	1	1	2	3	3
6.7	8261	8267	8274	8280	8287	8293	8299	8306	8312	8319	8325	1	1	2	3	3
6.8	8325	8331	8338	8344	8351	8357	8363	8370	8376	8382	8388	1	1	2	3	3
6.9	8388	8395	8401	8407	8414	8420	8426	8432	8439	8445	8451	1	1	2	3	3
7.0	0.8451	8457	8463	8470	8476	8482	8488	8494	8500	8506	8513	1	1	2	2	3
7.1	8513	8519	8525	8531	8537	8543	8549	8555	8561	8567	8573	1	1	2	2	3
7.2	8573	8579	8585	8591	8597	8603	8609	8615	8621	8627	8633	1	1	2	2	3
7.3	8633	8639	8645	8651	8657	8663	8669	8675	8681	8686	8692	1	1	2	2	3
7.4	8692	8698	8704	8710	8716	8722	8727	8733	8739	8745	8751	1	1	2	2	3
7.5	8751	8756	8762	8768	8774	8779	8785	8791	8797	8802	8808	1	1	2	2	3
7.6	8808	8814	8820	8825	8831	8837	8842	8848	8854	8859	8865	1	1	2	2	3
7.7	8865	8871	8876	8882	8887	8893	8899	8904	8910	8915	8921	1	1	2	2	3
7.8	8921	8927	8932	8938	8943	8949	8954	8960	8965	8971	8976	1	1	2	2	3
7.9	8976	8982	8987	8993	8998	9004	9009	9015	9020	9025	9031	1	1	2	2	3
8.0	0.9031	9036	9042	9047	9053	9058	9063	9069	9074	9079	9085	1	1	2	2	3
8.1	9085	9090	9096	9101	9106	9112	9117	9122	9128	9133	9138	1	1	2	2	3
8.2	9138	9143	9149	9154	9159	9165	9170	9175	9180	9186	9191	1	1	2	2	3
8.3	9191	9196	9201	9206	9212	9217	9222	9227	9232	9238	9243	1	1	2	2	3
8.4	9243	9248	9253	9258	9263	9269	9274	9279	9284	9289	9294	1	1	2	2	3
8.5	9294	9299	9304	9309	9315	9320	9325	9330	9335	9340	9345	1	1	2	2	3
8.6	9345	9350	9355	9360	9365	9370	9375	9380	9385	9390	9395	1	1	2	2	3
8.7	9395	9400	9405	9410	9415	9420	9425	9430	9435	9440	9445	0	1	1	2	2
8.8	9445	9450	9455	9460	9465	9469	9474	9479	9484	9489	9494	0	1	1	2	2
8.9	9494	9499	9504	9509	9513	9518	9523	9528	9533	9538	9542	0	1	1	2	2
9.0	0.9542	9547	9552	9557	9562	9566	9571	9576	9581	9586	9590	0	1	1	2	2
9.1	9590	9595	9600	9605	9609	9614	9619	9624	9628	9633	9638	0	1	1	2	2
9.2	9638	9643	9647	9652	9657	9661	9666	9671	9675	9680	9685	0	1	1	2	2
9.3	9685	9689	9694	9699	9703	9708	9713	9717	9722	9727	9731	0	1	1	2	2
9.4	9731	9736	9741	9745	9750	9754	9759	9763	9768	9773	9777	0	1	1	2	2
9.5	9777	9782	9786	9791	9795	9800	9805	9809	9814	9818	9823	0	1	1	2	2
9.6	9823	9827	9832	9836	9841	9845	9850	9854	9859	9863	9868	0	1	1	2	2
9.7	9868	9872	9877	9881	9886	9890	9894	9899	9903	9908	9912	0	1	1	2	2
9.8	9912	9917	9921	9926	9930	9934	9939	9943	9948	9952	9956	0	1	1	2	2
9.9	9956	9961	9965	9969	9974	9978	9983	9987	9991	9996		0	1	1	2	2

TABLE XII

Square Roots of Numbers

N	0	1	2	3	4	5	6	7	8	9	Avg. diff.
1.0	1.000	1.005	1.010	1.015	1.020	1.025	1.030	1.034	1.039	1.044	5
1	1.049	1.054	1.058	1.063	1.068	1.072	1.077	1.082	1.086	1.091	
2	1.095	1.100	1.105	1.109	1.114	1.118	1.122	1.127	1.131	1.136	4
3	1.140	1.145	1.149	1.153	1.158	1.162	1.166	1.170	1.175	1.179	
4	1.183	1.187	1.192	1.196	1.200	1.204	1.208	1.212	1.217	1.221	
1.5	1.225	1.229	1.233	1.237	1.241	1.245	1.249	1.253	1.257	1.261	
6	1.265	1.269	1.273	1.277	1.281	1.285	1.288	1.292	1.296	1.300	
7	1.304	1.308	1.311	1.315	1.319	1.323	1.327	1.330	1.334	1.338	
8	1.342	1.345	1.349	1.353	1.356	1.360	1.364	1.367	1.371	1.375	
9	1.378	1.382	1.386	1.389	1.393	1.396	1.400	1.404	1.407	1.411	
2.0	1.414	1.418	1.421	1.425	1.428	1.432	1.435	1.439	1.442	1.446	
1	1.449	1.453	1.456	1.459	1.463	1.466	1.470	1.473	1.476	1.480	3
2	1.483	1.487	1.490	1.493	1.497	1.500	1.503	1.507	1.510	1.513	
3	1.517	1.520	1.523	1.526	1.530	1.533	1.536	1.539	1.543	1.546	
4	1.549	1.552	1.556	1.559	1.562	1.565	1.568	1.572	1.575	1.578	
2.5	1.581	1.584	1.587	1.591	1.594	1.597	1.600	1.603	1.606	1.609	
6	1.612	1.616	1.619	1.622	1.625	1.628	1.631	1.634	1.637	1.640	
7	1.643	1.646	1.649	1.652	1.655	1.658	1.661	1.664	1.667	1.670	
8	1.673	1.676	1.679	1.682	1.685	1.688	1.691	1.694	1.697	1.700	
9	1.703	1.706	1.709	1.712	1.715	1.718	1.720	1.723	1.726	1.729	
3.0	1.732	1.735	1.738	1.741	1.744	1.746	1.749	1.752	1.755	1.758	
1	1.761	1.764	1.766	1.769	1.772	1.775	1.778	1.780	1.783	1.786	
2	1.789	1.792	1.794	1.797	1.800	1.803	1.806	1.808	1.811	1.814	
3	1.817	1.819	1.822	1.825	1.828	1.830	1.833	1.836	1.838	1.841	
4	1.844	1.847	1.849	1.852	1.855	1.857	1.860	1.863	1.865	1.868	
3.5	1.871	1.873	1.876	1.879	1.881	1.884	1.887	1.889	1.892	1.895	
6	1.897	1.900	1.903	1.905	1.908	1.910	1.913	1.916	1.918	1.921	
7	1.924	1.926	1.929	1.931	1.934	1.936	1.939	1.942	1.944	1.947	
8	1.949	1.952	1.954	1.957	1.960	1.962	1.965	1.967	1.970	1.972	
9	1.975	1.977	1.980	1.982	1.985	1.987	1.990	1.992	1.995	1.997	
4.0	2.000	2.002	2.005	2.007	2.010	2.012	2.015	2.017	2.020	2.022	2
1	2.025	2.027	2.030	2.032	2.035	2.037	2.040	2.042	2.045	2.047	
2	2.049	2.052	2.054	2.057	2.059	2.062	2.064	2.066	2.069	2.071	
3	2.074	2.076	2.078	2.081	2.083	2.086	2.088	2.090	2.093	2.095	
4	2.098	2.100	2.102	2.105	2.107	2.110	2.112	2.114	2.117	2.119	
4.5	2.121	2.124	2.126	2.128	2.131	2.133	2.135	2.138	2.140	2.142	
6	2.145	2.147	2.149	2.152	2.154	2.156	2.159	2.161	2.163	2.166	
7	2.168	2.170	2.173	2.175	2.177	2.179	2.182	2.184	2.186	2.189	
8	2.191	2.193	2.195	2.198	2.200	2.202	2.205	2.207	2.209	2.211	
9	2.214	2.216	2.218	2.220	2.223	2.225	2.227	2.229	2.232	2.234	

$$\sqrt{\pi} = 1.77245+ \qquad 1/\sqrt{\pi} = 0.56419 \qquad \sqrt{\pi/2} = 1.25331 \qquad \sqrt{e} = 1.64872$$

Explanation of Table of Square Roots

This table gives the values of $\sqrt{N}$ for values of N from 1 to 100, correct to four figures. (Interpolated values may be in error by 1 in the fourth figure.)

To find the square root of a number N outside the range from 1 to 100, divide the digits of the number into blocks of two (beginning with the decimal point), and note that moving the decimal point **two** places in N is equivalent to moving it **one** place in the square root of N. For example:

$$\sqrt{2.718} = 1.648; \quad \sqrt{271.8} = 16.48; \quad \sqrt{0.0002718} = 0.01648;$$
$$\sqrt{27.18} = 5.213; \quad \sqrt{2718} = 52.13; \quad \sqrt{0.002718} = 0.05213.$$

TABLE XII

Square Roots

N	0	1	2	3	4	5	6	7	8	9	Avg. diff.
5.0	2.236	2.238	2.241	2.243	2.245	2.247	2.249	2.252	2.254	2.256	2
1	2.258	2.261	2.263	2.265	2.267	2.269	2.272	2.274	2.276	2.278	
2	2.280	2.283	2.285	2.287	2.289	2.291	2.293	2.296	2.298	2.300	
3	2.302	2.304	2.307	2.309	2.311	2.313	2.315	2.317	2.319	2.322	
4	2.324	2.326	2.328	2.330	2.332	2.335	2.337	2.339	2.341	2.343	
5.5	2.345	2.347	2.349	2.352	2.354	2.356	2.358	2.360	2.362	2.364	
6	2.366	2.369	2.371	2.373	2.375	2.377	2.379	2.381	2.383	2.385	
7	2.387	2.390	2.392	2.394	2.396	2.398	2.400	2.402	2.404	2.406	
8	2.408	2.410	2.412	2.415	2.417	2.419	2.421	2.423	2.425	2.427	
9	2.429	2.431	2.433	2.435	2.437	2.439	2.441	2.443	2.445	2.447	
6.0	2.449	2.452	2.454	2.456	2.458	2.460	2.462	2.464	2.466	2.468	
1	2.470	2.472	2.474	2.476	2.478	2.480	2.482	2.484	2.486	2.488	
2	2.490	2.492	2.494	2.496	2.498	2.500	2.502	2.504	2.506	2.508	
3	2.510	2.512	2.514	2.516	2.518	2.520	2.522	2.524	2.526	2.528	
4	2.530	2.532	2.534	2.536	2.538	2.540	2.542	2.544	2.546	2.548	
6.5	2.550	2.551	2.553	2.555	2.557	2.559	2.561	2.563	2.565	2.567	
6	2.569	2.571	2.573	2.575	2.577	2.579	2.581	2.583	2.585	2.587	
7	2.588	2.590	2.592	2.594	2.596	2.598	2.600	2.602	2.604	2.606	
8	2.608	2.610	2.612	2.613	2.615	2.617	2.619	2.621	2.623	2.625	
9	2.627	2.629	2.631	2.632	2.634	2.636	2.638	2.640	2.642	2.644	
7.0	2.646	2.648	2.650	2.651	2.653	2.655	2.657	2.659	2.661	2.663	
1	2.665	2.666	2.668	2.670	2.672	2.674	2.676	2.678	2.680	2.681	
2	2.683	2.685	2.687	2.689	2.691	2.693	2.694	2.696	2.698	2.700	
3	2.702	2.704	2.706	2.707	2.709	2.711	2.713	2.715	2.717	2.718	
4	2.720	2.722	2.724	2.726	2.728	2.729	2.731	2.733	2.735	2.737	
7.5	2.739	2.740	2.742	2.744	2.746	2.748	2.750	2.751	2.753	2.755	
6	2.757	2.759	2.760	2.762	2.764	2.766	2.768	2.769	2.771	2.773	
7	2.775	2.777	2.778	2.780	2.782	2.784	2.786	2.787	2.789	2.791	
8	2.793	2.795	2.796	2.798	2.800	2.802	2.804	2.805	2.807	2.809	
9	2.811	2.812	2.814	2.816	2.818	2.820	2.821	2.823	2.825	2.827	
8.0	2.828	2.830	2.832	2.834	2.835	2.837	2.839	2.841	2.843	2.844	
1	2.846	2.848	2.850	2.851	2.853	2.855	2.857	2.858	2.860	2.862	
2	2.864	2.865	2.867	2.869	2.871	2.872	2.874	2.876	2.877	2.879	
3	2.881	2.883	2.884	2.886	2.888	2.890	2.891	2.893	2.895	2.897	
4	2.898	2.900	2.902	2.903	2.905	2.907	2.909	2.910	2.912	2.914	
8.5	2.915	2.917	2.919	2.921	2.922	2.924	2.926	2.927	2.929	2.931	
6	2.933	2.934	2.936	2.938	2.939	2.941	2.943	2.944	2.946	2.948	
7	2.950	2.951	2.953	2.955	2.956	2.958	2.960	2.961	2.963	2.965	
8	2.966	2.968	2.970	2.972	2.973	2.975	2.977	2.978	2.980	2.982	
9	2.983	2.985	2.987	2.988	2.990	2.992	2.993	2.995	2.997	2.998	
9.0	3.000	3.002	3.003	3.005	3.007	3.008	3.010	3.012	3.013	3.015	
1	3.017	3.018	3.020	3.022	3.023	3.025	3.027	3.028	3.030	3.032	
2	3.033	3.035	3.036	3.038	3.040	3.041	3.043	3.045	3.046	3.048	
3	3.050	3.051	3.053	3.055	3.056	3.058	3.059	3.061	3.063	3.064	
4	3.066	3.068	3.069	3.071	3.072	3.074	3.076	3.077	3.079	3.081	
9.5	3.082	3.084	3.085	3.087	3.089	3.090	3.092	3.094	3.095	3.097	
6	3.098	3.100	3.102	3.103	3.105	3.106	3.108	3.110	3.111	3.113	
7	3.114	3.116	3.118	3.119	3.121	3.122	3.124	3.126	3.127	3.129	
8	3.130	3.132	3.134	3.135	3.137	3.138	3.140	3.142	3.143	3.145	
9	3.146	3.148	3.150	3.151	3.153	3.154	3.156	3.158	3.159	3.161	

Moving the decimal point TWO places in N requires moving it ONE place in body of table.

TABLE XII

Square Roots

N	0	1	2	3	4	5	6	7	8	9	Avg. diff.
10.	3.162	3.178	3.194	3.209	3.225	3.240	3.256	3.271	3.286	3.302	16
1.	3.317	3.332	3.347	3.362	3.376	3.391	3.406	3.421	3.435	3.450	15
2.	3.464	3.479	3.493	3.507	3.521	3.536	3.550	3.564	3.578	3.592	14
3.	3.606	3.619	3.633	3.647	3.661	3.674	3.688	3.701	3.715	3.728	
4.	3.742	3.755	3.768	3.782	3.795	3.808	3.821	3.834	3.847	3.860	13
15.	3.873	3.886	3.899	3.912	3.924	3.937	3.950	3.962	3.975	3.987	
6.	4.000	4.012	4.025	4.037	4.050	4.062	4.074	4.087	4.099	4.111	12
7.	4.123	4.135	4.147	4.159	4.171	4.183	4.195	4.207	4.219	4.231	
8.	4.243	4.254	4.266	4.278	4.290	4.301	4.313	4.324	4.336	4.347	
9.	4.359	4.370	4.382	4.393	4.405	4.416	4.427	4.438	4.450	4.461	11
20.	4.472	4.483	4.494	4.506	4.517	4.528	4.539	4.550	4.561	4.572	
1.	4.583	4.593	4.604	4.615	4.626	4.637	4.648	4.658	4.669	4.680	
2.	4.690	4.701	4.712	4.722	4.733	4.743	4.754	4.764	4.775	4.785	
3.	4.796	4.806	4.817	4.827	4.837	4.848	4.858	4.868	4.879	4.889	10
4.	4.899	4.909	4.919	4.930	4.940	4.950	4.960	4.970	4.980	4.990	
25.	5.000	5.010	5.020	5.030	5.040	5.050	5.060	5.070	5.079	5.089	
6.	5.099	5.109	5.119	5.128	5.138	5.148	5.158	5.167	5.177	5.187	
7.	5.196	5.206	5.215	5.225	5.235	5.244	5.254	5.263	5.273	5.282	
8.	5.292	5.301	5.310	5.320	5.329	5.339	5.348	5.357	5.367	5.376	9
9.	5.385	5.394	5.404	5.413	5.422	5.431	5.441	5.450	5.459	5.468	
30.	5.477	5.486	5.495	5.505	5.514	5.523	5.532	5.541	5.550	5.559	
1.	5.568	5.577	5.586	5.595	5.604	5.612	5.621	5.630	5.639	5.648	
2.	5.657	5.666	5.675	5.683	5.692	5.701	5.710	5.718	5.727	5.736	
3.	5.745	5.753	5.762	5.771	5.779	5.788	5.797	5.805	5.814	5.822	
4.	5.831	5.840	5.848	5.857	5.865	5.874	5.882	5.891	5.899	5.908	8
35.	5.916	5.925	5.933	5.941	5.950	5.958	5.967	5.975	5.983	5.992	
6.	6.000	6.008	6.017	6.025	6.033	6.042	6.050	6.058	6.066	6.075	
7.	6.083	6.091	6.099	6.107	6.116	6.124	6.132	6.140	6.148	6.156	
8.	6.164	6.173	6.181	6.189	6.197	6.205	6.213	6.221	6.229	6.237	
9.	6.245	6.253	6.261	6.269	6.277	6.285	6.293	6.301	6.309	6.317	
40.	6.325	6.332	6.340	6.348	6.356	6.364	6.372	6.380	6.387	6.395	
1.	6.403	6.411	6.419	6.427	6.434	6.442	6.450	6.458	6.465	6.473	
2.	6.481	6.488	6.496	6.504	6.512	6.519	6.527	6.535	6.542	6.550	
3.	6.557	6.565	6.573	6.580	6.588	6.595	6.603	6.611	6.618	6.626	
4.	6.633	6.641	6.648	6.656	6.663	6.671	6.678	6.686	6.693	6.701	
45.	6.708	6.716	6.723	6.731	6.738	6.745	6.753	6.760	6.768	6.775	
6.	6.782	6.790	6.797	6.804	6.812	6.819	6.826	6.834	6.841	6.848	
7.	6.856	6.863	6.870	6.877	6.885	6.892	6.899	6.907	6.914	6.921	
8.	6.928	6.935	6.943	6.950	6.957	6.964	6.971	6.979	6.986	6.993	
9.	7.000	7.007	7.014	7.021	7.029	7.036	7.043	7.050	7.057	7.064	

Square Roots of Certain Fractions

N	$\sqrt{N}$	N	$\sqrt{N}$	N	$\sqrt{N}$	N	$\sqrt{N}$	N	$\sqrt{N}$	N	$\sqrt{N}$
$\frac{1}{2}$	0.7071	$\frac{3}{5}$	0.7746	$\frac{4}{7}$	0.7559	$\frac{1}{9}$	0.3333	$\frac{5}{12}$	0.6455	$\frac{9}{16}$	0.7500
$\frac{1}{3}$	0.5774	$\frac{4}{5}$	0.8944	$\frac{5}{7}$	0.8452	$\frac{2}{9}$	0.4714	$\frac{7}{12}$	0.7638	$\frac{11}{16}$	0.8292
$\frac{2}{3}$	0.8165	$\frac{1}{6}$	0.4082	$\frac{6}{7}$	0.9258	$\frac{4}{9}$	0.6667	$\frac{11}{12}$	0.9574	$\frac{13}{16}$	0.9014
$\frac{1}{4}$	0.5000	$\frac{5}{6}$	0.9129	$\frac{1}{8}$	0.3536	$\frac{5}{9}$	0.7454	$\frac{1}{16}$	0.2500	$\frac{15}{16}$	0.9682
$\frac{3}{4}$	0.8660	$\frac{1}{7}$	0.3780	$\frac{3}{8}$	0.6124	$\frac{7}{9}$	0.8819	$\frac{3}{16}$	0.4330	$\frac{1}{32}$	0.1768
$\frac{1}{5}$	0.4472	$\frac{2}{7}$	0.5345	$\frac{5}{8}$	0.7906	$\frac{8}{9}$	0.9428	$\frac{5}{16}$	0.5590	$\frac{1}{64}$	0.1250
$\frac{2}{5}$	0.6325	$\frac{3}{7}$	0.6547	$\frac{7}{8}$	0.9354	$\frac{1}{12}$	0.2887	$\frac{7}{16}$	0.6614	$\frac{1}{50}$	0.1414

TABLE XII

SQUARE ROOTS

N	0	1	2	3	4	5	6	7	8	9	Avg. diff.
50.	7.071	7.078	7.085	7.092	7.099	7.106	7.113	7.120	7.127	7.134	7
1.	7.141	7.148	7.155	7.162	7.169	7.176	7.183	7.190	7.197	7.204	
2.	7.211	7.218	7.225	7.232	7.239	7.246	7.253	7.259	7.266	7.273	
3.	7.280	7.287	7.294	7.301	7.308	7.314	7.321	7.328	7.335	7.342	
4.	7.348	7.355	7.362	7.369	7.376	7.382	7.389	7.396	7.403	7.409	
55.	7.416	7.423	7.430	7.436	7.443	7.450	7.457	7.463	7.470	7.477	
6.	7.483	7.490	7.497	7.503	7.510	7.517	7.523	7.530	7.537	7.543	
7.	7.550	7.556	7.563	7.570	7.576	7.583	7.589	7.596	7.603	7.609	
8.	7.616	7.622	7.629	7.635	7.642	7.649	7.655	7.662	7.668	7.675	
9.	7.681	7.688	7.694	7.701	7.707	7.714	7.720	7.727	7.733	7.740	6
60.	7.746	7.752	7.759	7.765	7.772	7.778	7.785	7.791	7.797	7.804	
1.	7.810	7.817	7.823	7.829	7.836	7.842	7.849	7.855	7.861	7.868	
2.	7.874	7.880	7.887	7.893	7.899	7.906	7.912	7.918	7.925	7.931	
3.	7.937	7.944	7.950	7.956	7.962	7.969	7.975	7.981	7.987	7.994	
4.	8.000	8.006	8.012	8.019	8.025	8.031	8.037	8.044	8.050	8.056	
65.	8.062	8.068	8.075	8.081	8.087	8.093	8.099	8.106	8.112	8.118	
6.	8.124	8.130	8.136	8.142	8.149	8.155	8.161	8.167	8.173	8.179	
7.	8.185	8.191	8.198	8.204	8.210	8.216	8.222	8.228	8.234	8.240	
8.	8.246	8.252	8.258	8.264	8.270	8.276	8.283	8.289	8.295	8.301	
9.	8.307	8.313	8.319	8.325	8.331	8.337	8.343	8.349	8.355	8.361	
70.	8.367	8.373	8.379	8.385	8.390	8.396	8.402	8.408	8.414	8.420	
1.	8.426	8.432	8.438	8.444	8.450	8.456	8.462	8.468	8.473	8.479	
2.	8.485	8.491	8.497	8.503	8.509	8.515	8.521	8.526	8.532	8.538	
3.	8.544	8.550	8.556	8.562	8.567	8.573	8.579	8.585	8.591	8.597	
4.	8.602	8.608	8.614	8.620	8.626	8.631	8.637	8.643	8.649	8.654	
75.	8.660	8.666	8.672	8.678	8.683	8.689	8.695	8.701	8.706	8.712	
6.	8.718	8.724	8.729	8.735	8.741	8.746	8.752	8.758	8.764	8.769	
7.	8.775	8.781	8.786	8.792	8.798	8.803	8.809	8.815	8.820	8.826	
8.	8.832	8.837	8.843	8.849	8.854	8.860	8.866	8.871	8.877	8.883	
9.	8.888	8.894	8.899	8.905	8.911	8.916	8.922	8.927	8.933	8.939	
80.	8.944	8.950	8.955	8.961	8.967	8.972	8.978	8.983	8.989	8.994	
1.	9.000	9.006	9.011	9.017	9.022	9.028	9.033	9.039	9.044	9.050	
2.	9.055	9.061	9.066	9.072	9.077	9.083	9.088	9.094	9.099	9.105	5
3.	9.110	9.116	9.121	9.127	9.132	9.138	9.143	9.149	9.154	9.160	
4.	9.165	9.171	9.176	9.182	9.187	9.192	9.198	9.203	9.209	9.214	
85.	9.220	9.225	9.230	9.236	9.241	9.247	9.252	9.257	9.263	9.268	
6.	9.274	9.279	9.284	9.290	9.295	9.301	9.306	9.311	9.317	9.322	
7.	9.327	9.333	9.338	9.343	9.349	9.354	9.359	9.365	9.370	9.375	
8.	9.381	9.386	9.391	9.397	9.402	9.407	9.413	9.418	9.423	9.429	
9.	9.434	9.439	9.445	9.450	9.455	9.460	9.466	9.471	9.476	9.482	
90.	9.487	9.492	9.497	9.503	9.508	9.513	9.518	9.524	9.529	9.534	
1.	9.539	9.545	9.550	9.555	9.560	9.566	9.571	9.576	9.581	9.586	
2.	9.592	9.597	9.602	9.607	9.612	9.618	9.623	9.628	9.633	9.638	
3.	9.644	9.649	9.654	9.659	9.664	9.670	9.675	9.680	9.685	9.690	
4.	9.695	9.701	9.706	9.711	9.716	9.721	9.726	9.731	9.737	9.742	
95.	9.747	9.752	9.757	9.762	9.767	9.772	9.778	9.783	9.788	9.793	
6.	9.798	9.803	9.808	9.813	9.818	9.823	9.829	9.834	9.839	9.844	
7.	9.849	9.854	9.859	9.864	9.869	9.874	9.879	9.884	9.889	9.894	
8.	9.899	9.905	9.910	9.915	9.920	9.925	9.930	9.935	9.940	9.945	
9.	9.950	9.955	9.960	9.965	9.970	9.975	9.980	9.985	9.990	9.995	

$$\sqrt{\pi} = 1.77245+ \qquad 1/\sqrt{\pi} = 0.56419 \qquad \sqrt{\pi/2} = 1.25331 \qquad \sqrt{e} = 1.64872$$

NOTE. This table was taken, by permission, from Marks' Mechanical Engineers' Handbook, published by McGraw-Hill Book Co. This arrangement was reproduced directly from Pierce's *A Short Table of Integrals*, published by Ginn & Co., with permission.

TABLE XIII
Trigonometric Functions

Radians	Degrees	Sines	Cosines	Tangents	Cotangents		
.0000	0	.0000	1.0000	.0000	∞	90	1.5708
.0175	1	.0175	.9998	.0175	57.29	89	1.5533
.0349	2	.0349	.9994	.0349	28.64	88	1.5359
.0524	3	.0523	.9986	.0524	19.08	87	1.5184
.0698	4	.0698	.9976	.0699	14.30	86	1.5010
.0873	5	.0872	.9962	.0875	11.430	85	1.4835
.1047	6	.1045	.9945	.1051	9.514	84	1.4661
.1222	7	.1219	.9925	.1228	8.144	83	1.4486
.1396	8	.1392	.9903	.1405	7.115	82	1.4312
.1571	9	.1564	.9877	.1584	6.314	81	1.4137
.1745	10	.1736	.9848	.1763	5.671	80	1.3963
.1920	11	.1908	.9816	.1944	5.145	79	1.3788
.2094	12	.2079	.9781	.2126	4.705	78	1.3614
.2269	13	.2250	.9744	.2309	4.332	77	1.3439
.2443	14	.2419	.9703	.2493	4.011	76	1.3265
.2618	15	.2588	.9659	.2679	3.732	75	1.3090
.2793	16	.2756	.9613	.2867	3.487	74	1.2915
.2967	17	.2924	.9563	.3057	3.271	73	1.2741
.3142	18	.3090	.9511	.3249	3.078	72	1.2566
.3316	19	.3256	.9455	.3443	2.904	71	1.2392
.3491	20	.3420	.9397	.3640	2.748	70	1.2217
.3665	21	.3584	.9336	.3839	2.605	69	1.2043
.3840	22	.3746	.9272	.4040	2.475	68	1.1868
.4014	23	.3907	.9205	.4245	2.356	67	1.1694
.4189	24	.4067	.9135	.4452	2.246	66	1.1519
.4363	25	.4226	.9063	.4663	2.144	65	1.1345
.4538	26	.4384	.8988	.4877	2.050	64	1.1170
.4712	27	.4540	.8910	.5095	1.963	63	1.0996
.4887	28	.4695	.8829	.5317	1.881	62	1.0821
.5061	29	.4848	.8746	.5543	1.804	61	1.0647
.5236	30	.5000	.8660	.5774	1.732	60	1.0472
.5411	31	.5150	.8572	.6009	1.664	59	1.0297
.5585	32	.5299	.8480	.6249	1.600	58	1.0123
.5760	33	.5446	.8387	.6494	1.540	57	0.9948
.5934	34	.5592	.8290	.6745	1.483	56	0.9774
.6109	35	.5736	.8192	.7002	1.428	55	0.9599
.6283	36	.5878	.8090	.7265	1.376	54	0.9425
.6458	37	.6018	.7986	.7536	1.327	53	0.9250
.6632	38	.6157	.7880	.7813	1.280	52	0.9076
.6807	39	.6293	.7771	.8098	1.235	51	0.8901
.6981	40	.6428	.7660	.8391	1.192	50	0.8727
.7156	41	.6561	.7547	.8693	1.150	49	0.8552
.7330	42	.6691	.7431	.9004	1.111	48	0.8378
.7505	43	.6820	.7314	.9325	1.072	47	0.8203
.7679	44	.6947	.7193	.9657	1.036	46	0.8029
.7854	45	.7071	.7071	1.0000	1.000	45	0.7854
		Cosines	Sines	Cotangents	Tangents	Degrees	Radians

BIBLIOGRAPHY

The fields of interest for this bibliography are here listed as

1. Tabular, Graphical and Mathematical Representation of Data.
2. Graphical and Tabular Differentiation and Integration.
3. Fourier Series Analysis.
4. Normal Frequency Distribution and Precision Indexes.
5. Adjustment of Conditioned Data.
6. Least Squares Equations.
7. Correlation.
8. Non-Harmonic Analysis.

The fields of particular interest in the books and articles listed are indicated in the column headed "Fields" by numbers to correspond to the fields tabulated above. Generally references dated earlier than 1900 have been ignored. Also, except for a very few cases where the book or article includes fields 3 and 7 with other fields, references to fields 3 and 7 have not been included because of their relatively large numbers. Further, this bibliography has been limited to material in English and is admittedly incomplete.

REFERENCE	FIELD
Am. Soc. Test. Materials, *1933 A.S.T.M. manual on presentation of data*, 2nd print., Philadelphia, A.S.T.M. (1937).	1, 4
Baily, J. L., *Ann. Math. Statistics*, **2**, 355 (1931).	6
Birge, R. T., *Phys. Rev.*, **40**, 207, 228 (1932).	4, 6
Am. Phys. Teacher, **7**, 351 (1939).	4
Rev. Modern Phys., **1**, 1 (1929).	5
Phys. Rev., **13**, 360 (1919).	1, 4, 6
Birge, R. T., and Shea, J. D., *Univ. Calif. Pub. Math.*, **2**, 67 (1927).	6
Bond, W. N., *Phil. Mag.*, **10**, 994 (1930), **12**, 632 (1931).	5
Probability and Random Errors, London, Arnold (1935).	4
Brunt, David, *The Combination of Observations*, Cambridge, England, University Press (1923).	3, 4, 5, 6, 7
Comstock, G. C., *Method of Least Squares*, Boston, Ginn & Co. (1903).	4, 6
Condon, E. U., *Univ. Calif. Pub. Math.*, **2**, 55 (1927).	6
Cox, G. C., and Matuschak, Margaret, *J. Phys. Chem.*, **45**, 362 (1941).	6
Crumpler, T. B., and Yoe, J. H., *Chemical Computations and Errors*, New York, John Wiley & Sons, Inc. (1940).	1, 4, 6
Darwin, C. G., *Proc. Phys. Soc.*, **52**, 202 (1940).	5
Deming, W. E., and Birge, R. T., *Rev. Modern Phys.*, **6**, 119 (1934).	4

REFERENCE	FIELD
DuMond, J. W. M., *Phys. Rev.*, **56**, 153 (1939).	5
Dunnington, F. G., *Rev. Modern Phys.*, **11**, 65 (1939).	5
Federal Works Agency, *Tables of Probability Function*, Vol. 1, Works Project Administration for the City of New York (1941).	4
Fisher, R. A., *Statistical Methods for Research Workers*, 7th Ed., Edinburgh, Oliver & Boyd (1938).	4, 7
Fry, T. C., *Probability and Its Engineering Uses*, New York, D. Van Nostrand Co., Inc. (1928).	4, 7
Goodwin, A. M., *Precision of Measurements and Graphical Methods*, New York, McGraw-Hill Book Co. (1920).	1, 4
Leland, O. M., *Practical Least Squares*, New York, McGraw-Hill Book Co. (1921).	4, 5, 6
Lipka, J., *Graphical and Mechanical Computation*, New York, John Wiley & Sons, Inc. (1918).	2, 3
Marshall, W. C., *Graphical Methods*, New York, McGraw-Hill Book Co. (1921).	2
Mellor, J. W., *Higher Mathematics for Students of Chemistry and Physics*, London, Longmans Green & Co. (1919).	3, 4
Merriman, M., *The Method of Least Squares*, 8th Ed., New York, John Wiley & Sons, Inc. (1911).	4, 5, 6
Mills, F. C., *Statistical Methods Applied to Economics and Business*, Rev. Ed., New York, Henry Holt & Co. (1938).	1, 4, 6, 7
Palmer, A. D., *The Theory of Measurements*, New York, McGraw-Hill Book Co. (1912).	4, 5, 6
Pearson, K., *Trans. Am. Math. Soc.*, **31**, 133 (1929).	
Rossini, F. D., and Deming, W. E., *J. Wash. Acad. Sci.*, **29**, 416 (1939).	4, 5
Running, T. R., *Empirical Formulas*, New York, John Wiley & Sons, Inc. (1917).	1, 6
Stevens, J. S., *Theory of Measurements*, New York, D. Van Nostrand Co.	
Tuttle, L., and Satterly, J., *The Theory of Measurements*, London, Longmans Green & Co. (1925).	1, 2, 4, 6, 7
Weld, L. G., *Theory of Errors and Least Squares*, New York, Macmillan Co. (1916).	4, 6
Wensel, H. T., and Tuckerman, L. B., *Rev. Sci. Instruments*, **9**, 237 (1938).	6
Whittaker, E. T., and Robinson, G., *Calculus of Observation*, London, Blackie & Son (1924).	1, 3, 4, 6, 7, 8
Woodward, R. S., *Probability and Theory of Errors*, New York, John Wiley & Sons, Inc. (1906).	4

INDEX

ANSWERS TO PROBLEMS

Chapter I, p. 26

5. 0.43, 0.69.   **6.** 0.460, 0.348.   **7.** 0.147.

Chapter III, p. 83

1. $y = 1.0003e^{-0.1815t \text{ per day}}$, 0.1815 day^{-1}, 3.82 days.

3. $\rho/\rho_0 = (T/T_0)^{1.200}$.

Chapter IV, p. 105

2. 12.3, 9.9, 8.3.

Chapter V, p. 145

1. $y = \dfrac{4}{3}\pi^2 + \sum \dfrac{4}{m^2}\cos m\theta - \sum \dfrac{4\pi}{m}\sin m\theta.$

2. $y = \dfrac{4}{3}\pi^2 + \sum \dfrac{4}{m}\sqrt{\dfrac{1}{m^2} + \pi^2}\cos(m\theta + \tan^{-1} m\pi).$

3. $y = \dfrac{E}{2} + \dfrac{2E}{m\pi}\Sigma \sin m\theta;$ m, odd only.

4. $y = \dfrac{2E}{3} + \dfrac{3E}{2\pi}\left(\sin\dfrac{2\pi}{T}t + \dfrac{1}{2}\sin\dfrac{4\pi}{T}t + \dfrac{1}{4}\sin\dfrac{8\pi}{T}t + \dfrac{1}{5}\sin\dfrac{10\pi}{T}t + \cdots\right)$

$- \dfrac{\sqrt{3}E}{2\pi}\left(\cos\dfrac{2\pi}{T}t - \dfrac{1}{2}\cos\dfrac{4\pi}{T}t + \dfrac{1}{4}\cos\dfrac{8\pi}{T}t - \dfrac{1}{5}\cos\dfrac{10\pi}{T}t + \cdots\right).$

5. $y = \dfrac{4}{\pi}\left(\dfrac{\sin\theta}{1^2} - \dfrac{\sin 3\theta}{3^2} + \dfrac{\sin 5\theta}{5^2} - \cdots\right).$

6. $y = \dfrac{3\pi}{8} + \dfrac{2}{1^2}\left(1 - \dfrac{1}{\pi}\right)\cos\theta - \dfrac{2}{2^2}\dfrac{2}{\pi}\cos 2\theta - \dfrac{2}{3^2}\left(2 + \dfrac{1}{\pi}\right)\cos 3\theta$

$+ \dfrac{2}{5^2}\left(3 - \dfrac{1}{\pi}\right)\cos 5\theta + \dfrac{2}{6^2}\dfrac{2}{\pi}\cos 6\theta - \dfrac{2}{7^2}\left(4 + \dfrac{1}{\pi}\right)\cos 7\theta - \cdots.$

7. $y = \dfrac{4}{\sqrt{3}\pi}\sum \dfrac{1}{m^2}\left[2\sin\dfrac{m\pi}{4}\sin m\theta + \left(2\cos\dfrac{m\pi}{4} - 1\right)\cos m\theta\right];$ m, odd only.

9. $6.37\sin(5\theta - 145.9°).$

Chapter VI, p. 165

5. 43×10^{-6}, 7.1×10^{-6}.   **7.** 0.162, 0.0327.

8. $9 \times 10^{-5}A$, $7.9 \times 10^3 A^{-1}$, 99.0%.

343

Chapter VII, p. 187

1. $0.00008_8'$, $0.00104'$, $0.00131'$, $0.00185'$.   **2.** 0.098 sec, 0.116 sec, 0.144 sec, 0.204 sec.   **6.** 52.49 °F, 0.9 F°, 1.4 F°, 1.9 F°, 5.5%, $51.58° \text{F} < T < 53.40° \text{F}$. **7.** 30% to 40%, depending on details of procedure.

Chapter VIII, p. 203

1. 9.98 ± 0.04 gm.   **3.** (α_v and α_p) $273.150 \pm 0.005°$ K, (α_v) $273.154 \pm 0.008°$ K, (α_p) $273.143 \pm 0.004°$ K.

Chapter IX, p. 214

1. 0.06 mm.   **3.** 0.4%, 3.0%, 1.0%, 2.5%.   **5.** 0.5K°, 2.2K°, 6.5K°. **7.** 273.45 ± 0.06 mm, 0.05107 ± 0.00007 mm^2, 219.1 ± 0.3 mm^2, 19.23 ± 0.03 gm/cm^3.   **8.** Assume the two $80°45'30''$ readings to be independent, 1.66693 ± 0.00005.   **9.** 0.1946 ± 0.0003, 0.01458 ± 0.00006.

Chapter X, p. 236

1. 100.7 ft, 500.3 ft, 151.1 ft, 79.9 ft, 1.4 ft.   **2.** $60°9.6'$, $60°0.4'$, $59°50.0'$. **3.** 0.061 mm, 0.221 mm, 0.249 mm.   **4.** 0.2720 cal/(gm C°), 0.1918 cal/(gm C°), 1.418.   **5.** $8,030 \pm 110$ cal, $15,300 \pm 250$ cal.

Chapter XI, p. 266

1. 6.47×10^{-27} erg sec.   **2.** $\alpha_v = 36,606.73 \times 10^{-7}$ $K°^{-1} + 133.72 \times 10^{-7}$ $p/(\text{m–Hg K°})$, $273.174 \pm .002°$ K.   **6.** $a = 1.00643$ cal/(gm C°), $b = -495.5 \times 10^{-6}$ cal/(gm C°^{2}), $c = +8.371 \times 10^{-6}$ cal/(gm C°^{3}), $d = -0.03398 \times 10^{-6}$ cal/(gm C°^{4}).

7. $\log \dfrac{K_p}{1A} = -6.58 + 374 \dfrac{100 \text{ K°}}{T}$, $\Delta H = -R \dfrac{86,100 \text{ K°}}{T}$.

9. $78°42'$, $19°55'$.

Chapter XII, p. 291

1. 93%.   **2.** 97%, less than 1%, 99.5%.   **3.** 91%.